The Story of Herefordshire's Hospitals

The Story of Herefordshire's Hospitals

by

Charles Renton

Logaston Press

LOGASTON PRESS
Little Logaston, Logaston,
Woonton, Almeley, Herefordshire HR3 6QH

First published by Logaston Press 1999
Copyright © Charles Renton 1999

ISBN 1 873827 21 0

Set in Times by Logaston Press
and printed in Great Britain by
The Cromwell Press, Trowbridge

Contents

		page
	Acknowledgments	vi
	Preface	vii
1	A Hospital Service for Herefordshire	1
2	The Hereford General Infirmary from Inception to the Twentieth Century	21
3	Herefordshire General Hospital from 1900 to the advent of the N.H.S.	59
4	Bromyard Cottage Hospital	101
5	Ross Dispensary and Cottage Hospital	109
6	Ledbury Cottage Hospital	125
7	Victoria Cottage Hospital, Kington	137
8	Leominster Cottage Hospital	153
9	The Victoria Eye and Ear Hospital	169
10	Madhouse to Mental Hospital— Hereford Lunatic Asylums	183
11	The Struggle Against Infectious Diseases	199
12	The County Hospital	219
13	One Family 1948 - 1959	237
14	Epilogue	251
	Appendix	254
	Index	255

ACKNOWLEDGMENTS

I am grateful to Miss Sue Hubbard at the County Record Office in Hereford, and to Mr Robin Hill at the Hereford City Library and their staff who not only provided information about the hospitals and county, but made helpful suggestions when I was struggling. Similarly I have received generous help from the staff at the county libraries at Kington, Leominster, Ross, the Bromyard and District Local History Society, the Barrett Browning Institute at Ledbury and the Leominster Folk Museum.

I have had full co-operation from the Health Service Management, allowing me access to records and hospitals. Wherever I went throughout Herefordshire I have met with interest and enthusiasm from countless individuals, too many to mention by name, who went to endless trouble to provide the relevant information.

However, there are some who must be thanked for allowing reproduction of some of the illustrations contained within this book, namely the Derek Foxton Collection (pp.11 from *Edwardian Hereford*, 43 (bottom) from *Hereford Then and Now* Vol.2, 201, 202, 213 from *Hereford, Then and Now* Vol.3); the Herefordshire Light Infantry Regimental Museum (p.12); Mr David Whitehead (p.15, from *Yesterday's Town*); Mr D.R. Guttery and the British Institute of Radiology (pp.55, 56); Mrs Elaine Jones (p.72 (top)); Mr Basil Butcher (p.72 (bottom)); Mrs Sue Farr (p.80); Miss Tessa Ruthven (p.87); Barry Stephenson (p.102, from *Bromyard, The Day Before Yesterday*); Phyllis Williams (p.104 from *Bromyard, The Day Before Yesterday*, p.205 from *Bromyard; Minster, Manor and Town*); Mr Fred Druce (pp.110, 117, from *Remembrances of Things Past*); Mr Martin Morris (p.111, from the *Book of Ross-on-Wye*); Mr Tom Rigby and Mr Alan Sutton (p.120 from *Ross-on-Wye*, old photograph series); Mr Bill Masefield (p.135); National Monuments Record (English Heritage) (p.139) (Crown copyright material is reproduced by permission of English Heritage acting under licence from the Controller of Her Majesty's Stationery Office); Mr Alexander Haines (p.157); Leominster Folk Museum (pp.164, 165); H.P. Bulmers (p.178); Mr Colin Boylett of Green Gables, Kingswood (p.209 (both)));

Finally I would like to thank my editor Mr Andy Johnson for his advice and discipline in preventing me straying too far from the main themes.

PREFACE

For the purpose of this story, financial details are given in pounds shillings and pence, which were used at the time. There were 20 shillings in the pound and 12 pence to the shilling. A guinea was 21 shillings. Large sums are given to the nearest pound.

The titles of some of the medical staff vary. Surgeons in this country have traditionally been addressed as 'Mr' following their early participation in the Company of Barber Surgeons. The early surgeons in Herefordshire were also in general practice and were sometimes referred to as 'Dr'. The Physicians were usually addressed as 'Dr'.

The Appendix spells out the details of qualifications credited to each member of the medical staff in the tables included in the text.

CHAPTER 1

A Hospital Service for Herefordshire

At the Dissolution of the Monasteries during the reign of Henry VIII, the rudi-
mentary treatment offered by the religious houses disappeared. The mayor,
aldermen and commonality of the city of London petitioned the king to
replace these houses. In response he established five chartered hospitals in
London, including now famous names such as St Bartholomew's and St
Thomas's. In the eighteenth century they provided care of very poor quality.

The first voluntary hospital in England was the Westminster Hospital in
London which opened in 1720. The first provincial hospital was Winchester
County Hospital founded in 1736, whilst Bristol Royal Infirmary was founded
in 1737, Worcester Royal Infirmary in 1746 and the Royal Salop Infirmary in
1747. Even with these hospitals, most of the sick or injured were looked after
at home by relatives or friends.

The very poorest, known as 'paupers' received some support through the poor
laws. Under the Poor Law of 1601 each parish had been made responsible for its
poor, either by providing individual financial help or setting up workhouses.
Small parishes could not afford their own workhouse, and in Hereford five city
parishes agreed to establish a common workhouse which in the late eighteenth
century was situated outside Eign Gate and was run by All Saints Church.

The more fortunate and respectable destitute, helpless and aged infirm
received help through almshouses. These were pious and charitable institutions,
either being founded by donations as a result of appeals by the Church, or by
bequests from wealthy individuals interested in helping less fortunate citizens.
Although they looked after some sick people this was not their prime function.
Hereford contained 11 almshouses with a total provision for 72 men and
women. The most famous was Coningsby Hospital, in Widemarsh Street,

founded by Sir John Coningsby in 1614 and containing 12 houses for old soldiers and for serving-men who had spent at least seven years with one family.

The provision for specific medical advice was varied. Most people would initially turn to their family, especially elderly grandparents, aunts or uncles who might well suggest 'folk remedies'. They might also consult knowledgeable friends or the clergy whom they hoped had special knowledge. There were few medical books suitable for lay people, though, in November 1784, the *Hereford Journal* advertised a new medical work, *The Domestic Physician or Guardian of Health*. This described in great detail the symptoms of every disorder known to mankind, together with their gradual progress and the methods of cure. It was claimed to be particularly useful for private families, though equally essential to doctors.

In the eighteenth century a plentiful source of advice was contained in advertisements carried by the *Hereford Journal*, which each week allocated over a quarter of a page for this purpose. There was no law against anyone, including doctors, advertising remedies, advice and services, and anyone could pretend to be a doctor or expert.

'Dr Radcliffe's Famous Purging Elixir from Messrs Dicey and Co., no.10 Bow Churchyard, London' was advertised, claiming for itself 'multitudinous virtues. It is a purgative of agreeable bitter, but no unpleasant taste. It requires no confinement or alteration of diet. It cleans the blood from all humours contracted by hard drinking, surfeits, colds, measles, or smallpox, and destroys worms in children and adults. It gives immediate ease in the colic, and cures the dropsy, scurvy, and eruptions of every sort. It is also found serviceable in the black or yellow jaundice, and all disorders proceeding from the impurities of the blood. It is particularly useful in female complaints, helps indigestion and creates an appetite. No person, or family, especially voyagers, ought to be unprovided with it.'

The unfortunately named Messrs. Dicey and Co could offer you the choice of another 20 splendid concoctions if the above remedy did not work; fortunately most of these were harmless. However, some examples were more genuine such as 'Glasses' Magnesia ... A powerful corrector of acid in the stomach and bowel.'

There was regular advice about cures for cancer that did not involve the surgeon's knife and those for venereal disease which avoided treatment using mercury, which was of doubtful efficacy, and had a bad reputation for side effects.

In the *Hereford Journal* in June 1789, Mr John Powell, a surgeon in Brecon, offered to extract a cataract from the eye and restore sight for a minimum fee of £5. A cataract is an opacity in the lens of the eye causing visual impairment or blindness, and his treatment was an accepted procedure, called couching, consisting of displacing the opaque lens by inserting a needle into the eye, resulting in improved but imperfect vision.

It must have been difficult if not impossible to separate knowledgeable advice from that of charlatans. Some orthodox advice came from the local chemist and druggist who had often begun life as a grocer and rarely made the drugs they sold. More professional advice came from an apothecary who by the eighteenth century was like a tradesmen who had served an apprenticeship. He would be examined by the Society of Apothecaries and if suitable awarded the qualification of Licentiate of the Society of Apothecaries (L.S.A.). They dispensed medicines, often provided medical advice and some practised surgery. They were allowed to charge for medicines, but not for advice, unsurprisingly resulting in the dispensing of plenty of medication. They were the poor man's doctor.

Surgeons, who used manual means of treatment, such as an open operation, manipulation or splinting, had a poor reputation. They were initially governed by the Company of Barber Surgeons, a livery company, formed in 1540 by Act of Parliament, and so were under the control of the Mayor and Aldermen of the City of London. In 1745 the surgeons broke away to form their own independent Company of Surgeons, at a time when their training consisted of a seven year apprenticeship followed by an examination. However, over the next 55 years the new Company of Surgeons failed to provide a lead in surgical education and relaxed the duration of apprenticeship, resulting in declining influence and status. In 1800 the Royal College of Surgeons was formed by Royal Charter and surgical education improved. The basic degree of M.R.C.S. was granted after apprenticeship and examination while in 1843 the higher degree of F.R.C.S. was offered after satisfactory training and examination.

Only the very wealthy could afford a fully trained physician, who provided advice and prescribed drugs. The Royal College of Physicians had been founded in 1518 to regulate the practice of medicine within a seven mile radius of London, but opportunities to become a physician were sparse, initially as the Universities of Oxford and Cambridge held a complete and rigid monopoly. In addition, the training they offered lasted for up to 14 years, and even then only provided an intellectual and theoretical knowledge of medicine, not really suitable for its practice. The best physicians studied at the continental universities, particularly Leiden, though by 1800 Edinburgh had gained a reputation for practical teaching. The universities granted an M.D. by examination.

In 1783 only one out of ten practising doctors were physicians and four-fifths were apothecary surgeons. But at least there was now an awakened interest in the theory and practise of medicine and there was increasing understanding of anatomy and physiology, the structure and function of the body and of pathology, the study of disease. The pioneers were surgical giants like John Hunter, from St George's Hospital in London. By the end of the eighteenth century there was clinical teaching in medicine, surgery and midwifery. In spite of this, practical progress was slow particularly in surgery, and the hospitals that did exist often had a bad reputation due to a high mortality rate caused by overcrowding and infection.

This was also a time of increasing concern for the poor and sick. John Bellars, a Quaker, put forward 12 proposals for hospital provision and challenged the Royal College of Physicians and the Company of Surgeons to draw up advice on how to avoid common errors. It stimulated much discussion but produced no constructive advice.

It was also a period of increasing wealth amongst the nobility and gentry which made major philanthropic enterprises practicable. But launching a charity to found a voluntary hospital required a determined leader who could inspire the enthusiasm of the local community—in most cases this proved either to be a clergyman, aware of the problems from his visits to the poor and

sick, or a doctor. They tapped the conscience of the wealthy, as well as encouraging their paternalism as benefactors (annual subscribers or lump sum donors) who were provided with tickets of recommendation allowing them to sponsor patients for admission to hospital or outpatient treatment. Doctors involved with hospitals in turn gained prestige, were able to use their skills in helping the sick and had the chance to meet prosperous supporters which would help bolster their private practices. They also participated in administering the hospitals and in teaching students. For the patients the treatment in hospitals may have been limited and the care basic, but the diet, bedding, warmth and general nursing were often much better than at home.

Rev. Dr Thomas Talbot

At the Mayor of Hereford's feast on 3rd October 1774, each guest was presented with a printed appeal from the Rev. Dr Thomas Talbot, Rector of Ullingswick. It was addressed to the nobility, gentry, and clergy of Herefordshire and he called upon their representatives in parliament or any other gentlemen of rank and property to take the lead in subscribing towards an infirmary in Hereford.

Rev. Dr Talbot had come to Ullingswick in 1739. By 1763 he had decided to take action to alleviate the plight of the poor and sick in his agricultural parish eight miles north-east of Hereford, and issued his first appeal for money to provide a hospital, but this met with minimal response. A similar appeal a year later was also unsuccessful, although it received the support of the bishop of Hereford.

His subsequent appeal in 1774 was long and ponderous, taking up a whole page in the *Hereford Journal*. Indeed it was thought to have been written by Dr Samuel Johnson whom he had known at Oxford. He pointed out the hardship of the hard working poor in Herefordshire, made worse by the recent rise in the cost of living that had not been matched by an increase in wages—the average price of the necessities of life had almost doubled in the previous 20 years. He entreated the rich and prosperous to reflect on the deplorable conditions of so many of their fellow creatures and fellow Christians and stressed their obligation to the sick and poor. His appeal also laid out the advantages of an infirmary, which he rather exaggerated, claiming that it offered immediate relief, removed anxiety from the patient and the relatives, and provided a complete cure in 90 per cent of cases.

He pointed out that a skilled surgeon or physician was not available in every parish and when they lived some distance away they could not be expected to attend every poor patient. An infirmary would be attended by honorary surgeons and physicians who would give their services free and the concentration of patient care would help the instruction of students and increase medical knowledge.

The address ended on a high spiritual note. 'I humbly take my leave with earnest prayer, that the Great Patron of the poor and afflicted may open your hearts to consider their distress, and that he may reward every person who shall contribute to their relief, with health, prosperity and peace in this life, and with honour, glory, and immortality in that where the inhabitants shall not say, I am sick.'

The immediate response to Dr Talbot's appeal was once again poor, but within a week he took the lead himself and donated the huge sum of £500. Despite this, during the first two months the appeal gained only five annual subscribers and five benefactors donating a lump sum. These included Viscount

Bateman of Shobdon, Sir George Cornewall of Moccas, Thomas Foley of Stoke Edith and John Scudamore of Kentchurch, indicating support from the gentry. In February 1775 the readers of the *Hereford Journal* were informed that well wishers should send their subscriptions and donations to Mr Joseph Perrin in Castle Street.

By the end of March 1775, almost six months after the initiative was launched, annual subscriptions promised had reached £617 and donations totalled £3,301. On 29th March a meeting of all supporters and well wishers was called at the Swan and Falcon Inn, in Broad Street, Hereford. The meeting set up a committee consisting of all annual subscribers of 2 guineas or more and all benefactors of £20 or more, who were to be known as governors, together with the physicians and surgeons of the city. Their brief was to consider how best to institute a public infirmary, in or near the city for the relief of sick and diseased persons. Any five would form a quorum and the committee set to work with vigour, holding meetings in various inns. One of their first acts was to call on the county's clergy to promote this charitable undertaking in their parishes. An appeal was also made to the nobility, gentry and clergy of the counties of Monmouth, Brecon and Radnor to join the project. These did not receive a great response, but several subscribers and benefactors with Hereford connections came from London and Bristol.

By August annual subscriptions of £778 and donations of £4,008 had been promised. The money was to be invested in public funds, which would be in the names of trustees, initially two landowners, Sir George Cornewall, a JP and Deputy Lieutenant, and Thomas Foley. Mr Joseph Perrin was confirmed as treasurer.

A general meeting resolved that the infirmary should be be called the Hereford General Infirmary—'General' indicating that patients from outside the county would be accepted, and 'Infirmary' reflecting the then perceived function of hospitals to care for the infirm. The General Infirmary was the first voluntary hospital to be formed in Herefordshire, and only the 22nd provincial hospital to open in England, preceding any hospital in Birmingham or Wales.

From the late 1850s the voluntary hospital movement spread into the rural areas with the building of small cottage hospitals. Treatment at the Hereford General Infirmary had gradually become more effective while the availability of anaesthesia had made operations more acceptable. However the journey to Hereford from the market towns was often slow and uncomfortable resulting in delays in treatment and the occasional unnecessary death. Of the five market towns only Bromyard didn't have rail links before their cottage hospital opened, but most of the poorer people anyway travelled by cart along rough roads. Many patients were also inappropriately treated at home because they were reluctant to travel out of their district to Hereford where it would be difficult for their relatives and friends to visit them regularly. The advantages of local hospitals was clear.

Bromyard Cottage Hospital was opened in 1869 in the old toll house near St Peter's Churchyard. It was expanded 20 years later, but had to close during the First World War due to lack of support. Ross Cottage Hospital and Dispensary opened in 1872 in the Old Dispensary in New Street. A new hospital was built in Gloucester Road seven years later. Ledbury Cottage Hospital opened in 1873 in the old Railway Inn in Homend Street. Eighteen years later Michael Biddulph built a new hospital for the town almost opposite the earlier one. The Victoria Cottage Hospital at Kington opened in 1888 having been built in memory of Queen Victoria's Jubilee. Leominster Cottage Hospital was established by the Friendly Societies and opened in 1899 in a purpose-built hospital in South Street.

The other voluntary hospital was the Eye and Ear Hospital in Hereford. It opened in 1882 as the Herefordshire and South Wales Eye and Ear Institution in Commercial Road, supported by a few private subscribers. Before long it was changed to a well supported charitable institution due to the considerable efforts of the Mayor of Hereford, M.J.G. Scobie. It was replaced in 1889 by a new purpose-built hospital in Eign Street, called the Victoria Eye and Ear Hospital, also in memory of Queen Victoria's Jubilee. This was a specialised hospital which served a wide area including Herefordshire, the surrounding counties and much of south Wales.

Over the years there were regular improvements to the buildings at all the voluntary hospitals as electricity was installed, heating systems were modernised and telephone facilities provided. Accommodation was increased for both patients and staff. Medical advances required repeated improvements to operating theatres and the installation of X-ray facilities.

All the voluntary hospitals were subject to a set of Rules which described their function, how they were to be governed and the responsibilities of their officers. There were minor variations in the Rules between hospitals and the Rules themselves were modified over the years. Those who made annual subscriptions or gave donations to a hospital became its governors, and thence eligible to be elected to serve on committees of management.

For example, under the initial Rules of the Hereford Infirmary, for every guinea subscribed, the subscriber received a ticket of recommendation to sponsor one in-patient and one out-patient a year. A benefactor giving £20 was allowed the privileges of a subscriber of 2 guineas a year and a benefactor of

£50 the privileges of a subscriber of 5 guineas a year. From time to time the governors would modify the number of tickets of recommendation and their duration available to their supporters. By increasing these privileges, especially for small subscribers, they hoped to enlarge their income by gaining more supporters. As an example, in 1857 the Rules of the General Hospital were changed to allow subscribers who contributed £1 10s p.a. to recommend one inpatient and two outpatients per year, while subscribers of one guinea could recommend two outpatients.

The governors at the general infirmary were to hold annual general meetings, quarterly meetings and additional special meetings for specific purposes such as making appointments. These meetings were to be advertised in the local papers. Weekly board meetings, consisting of elected governors and the medical staff. The resident apothecary would supervise the daily running and be responsible for admitting patients. Each potential patient had to attend punctually at 10a.m., bring their ticket of recommendation as provided by a subscriber or donor, be clean and free from vermin and bring two shirts or shifts, with any other necessary change of clothing. The board would then decide if the patient was a 'Real Object of Charity', as defined by the Rules, and if accepted as suitable for admission would be admitted that day between 11 a.m. and 1 p.m. Patients were admitted on no other day except in the case of a sudden emergency.

The function of the infirmary was rigidly restricted to the treatment of acute illness or accidents in the hard working or industrious poor who could be effectively helped within one or two months. Those who could afford to pay for treatment were excluded and paupers were only occasionally admitted if the parish or friends contributed 2s 6d a week towards maintenance.

Patients with illnesses which hospital treatment was unlikely to improve were also excluded, such as the chronic sick, the incurable or dying. Cancer not suitable for surgery, chronic leg ulcers, consumption (loss of weight often due to tuberculosis), dropsy (heart failure) in its late stages, epilepsy and mental illness also came into this category. Midwifery was excluded and children under seven years of age were not eligible for treatment, except in cases of fractured bones or where an operative procedure was necessary. Any patient with suspected infectious disease, such as smallpox or the itch (scabies) was refused admission. No person was to be admitted as an in-patient if, because of the nearness of their home or other circumstances, they could be treated as an out-patient.

In the latter part of the nineteenth century private paying patients were accepted by the cottage hospitals. The General followed after the turn of the century. Midwifery cases were only finally allowed in some of the hospitals in the twentieth century.

There is no detailed information from Hereford until 1873 about what types of conditions were actually treated. However, by studying cases treated at other provincial hospitals during the last half of the eighteenth century, a reasonable deduction can be made that conditions included asthma, dropsy (heart failure), palsy from strokes, flux and bloody flux (diarrhoea), abdominal colic, cancer, rheumatism, sciatica, consumption (wasting of the body often due to tuberculosis), and eye disorders.

Effective drugs available included opiates for control of pain and sedation, digitalis (from the foxglove) for heart failure and quinine for fevers. In addition there would be available a mass of speculative mixtures. Bleeding the patient with leeches was popular. Scarification was regularly used to make multiple small cuts in the skin with a spring loaded scarificator to release fluid from under the skin as in swollen legs due to the dropsy or in abscesses.

There was always a selection of injuries such as lacerations, burns, fractures, dislocations, and head injuries. In a rural area, farm injuries were common. Wounds would be dressed, fractures set, and dislocations reduced. The skull was trephined (bore holes made) for depressed fractures and to relieve blood clots pressing on the brain. Abscesses were drained. Cysts and superficial tumours were removed. Cataracts were treated by couching. Occasionally a breast was amputated for cancer. Major surgery was limited due to a lack of knowledge, particularly of anatomy, the great pain and shock caused by the lack of any anaesthetic, complications due to infection and the high risk of death. Major amputations of arms and legs were uncommon and carried out mainly for life-threatening infected open fractures.

A scarifier, 'opened' so showing the blades, used to make multiple small cuts in patients' skin

The only internal operation performed at this time was the removal of bladder stones. However one of the first national surveys in 1820 resulted in a letter from Mr Samuel Cam, honorary surgeon at the General Infirmary, indicating there had not been a single patient in the Hereford General Infirmary out of 16,248 patients to date with such stones. The incident of bladder stones is known to have varied throughout England.

Until about 1900 these hospitals were mainly financed by charitable giving. Annual subscribers were the main contributors but they provided a decreasing proportion of income as time went on. Small donations were used to help cover running costs, while large donations and legacies were invested to produce long term income, or to cover one-off deficits, or to finance improvements to the hospital. The clergy were very supportive and from the beginning church collections contributed to the income. For many years a Hospital Sunday, often associated with a street parade, raised additional funds for the hospitals.

It was also at the turn of the century that the General Infirmary changed its name to the General Hospital.

The beginning of the twentieth century was a time of increasing local fundraising. Every conceivable social, artistic and sporting activity was used and organised by individuals, ladies guilds, committees and groups of every sort. Being in agricultural areas the cottage hospitals were well provided with everything that was edible — chickens, turkeys, pheasants, rabbits, calves heads and feet, tripe, eggs, vegetables and fruit of all sorts, puddings cakes and sweets. Most hospitals also had a Ladies' Linen League made up of ladies who contributed a yearly subscription which provided linen for the hospital.

The cottage hospitals charged their patients a nominal small sum for maintenance on the grounds that many were wage earners who could afford the charge and it helped to instil a sense of responsibility. The sums varied over the years from 3s 6d to 5s a week for an adult and from 2s to 2s 6d a week for a child. The very poor were not charged.

From the latter part of the nineteenth century a new

Mr George Cresswell,
founder of the Cresswell Penny Fund

source of income appeared for the cottage hospitals. Firms established contributory schemes where their employees contributed a weekly sum to the hospital in return for services when required. In 1903 a letter was sent by a Mr. Bowers, of Bowers & Co., builders, to the governors of the General Hospital suggesting a similar weekly scheme for his employees. This letter proved to the stimulus for a large contributory scheme organised by the General. Mr George Cresswell, governor and secretary to the General Hospital, organised and managed this scheme and it became known as the Cresswell Penny Fund. The intention was to collect a penny a month from working class households in Herefordshire, and in return the fund would provide them with hospital care when it was required. The county was divided into 138 districts, each with a lady secretary who organised the collections and provided tickets of recommendation for inpatient and outpatient attendance. In the five market towns the collections were shared with the cottage hospitals.

But in 1905 Mr Cresswell resigned following a clash with the medical staff of the General. The house surgeon, Mr Eric Lindsay, had denigrated patients referred from the fund because of their social status. When Mr Lindsay's appointment was completed, his friend, Mr Meyrick James, applied for the post, but as a result of the above incident, Mr Cresswell supported another candidate. Dr Chapman, a physician, took exception to this and was said to have stated 'that rather than Mr Cresswell thrusting down their throat his

A party in the grounds of the General Infirmary for the district secretaries of the Cresswell Penny Fund in 1910. Lord Biddulph, Sir Archer Croft and the dean of Hereford are in the centre of the group

nominee, he and his penny fund should go.' It was a sad ending for a pioneer, but the fund remained.

Occasional parties were held for fund's district secretaries to thank them and maintain morale. Initially the scheme produced £100 a month, but contributions slowly fell and in 1926 Colonel Sleeman, a governor who had previously organised appeals on behalf of the General Hospital, was asked to advise on different systems of contributory schemes. He sought information from 150 hospitals and proposed a new scheme. Called The Herefordshire General Hospital Contributory Scheme, it incorporated the Cresswell Penny Fund, and applied only to those whose incomes were below £260 p.a. Wage earners over 19 years of age, or a man and his wife living together with or without children under 16 years of age and other relatives living with and dependent on the contributor would pay 3d per week. Each child between 16 and 19 years of age living with the contributor would cost another 1d per week. There was a reduced rate for those who paid annually in advance. A committee and 54 district secretaries ran the scheme using the same system as the Cresswell Penny Fund to contact families and collect the money. Within two years 10,000 members had been enrolled at which point its management was transferred to the House Committee. By 1930 contributions totalled £5,103 rising to £8,069 in 1939.

Col. Mackay Scobie on parade in the centre of the picture,
with Col. Sleeman on the left

However, as the Cresswell Penny Fund had never raised significant sums for the cottage hospitals and they were apprehensive about losing local patients to the General Hospital, only the Victoria Cottage Hospital in Kington temporarily took up the offer to join the new 'Sleeman' scheme. Later this hospital ran a contributory scheme of its own, and Ledbury Cottage Hospital benefitted from a local independent scheme.

From 1900 an increasing proportion of income came from a mixture of private patients, the selling of services to local authorities and from contributory schemes. Unlike the General Hospital the cottage hospitals were only able to sell limited services to the local authorities, mainly tonsillectomies. Even so, by 1948 and the advent of the N.H.S. less than a fifth of the hospitals' income came from charitable sources.

Medical staff appointed to the hospitals were usually already in practice in the district and were called honorary staff as they gave their services free to charitable patients, although they were allowed to charge private patients. They were subject to the Rules and were required to attend their patients regularly, appear at outpatient clinics and be available to treat emergencies. The honorary medical staff at the General Infirmary were elected by the governors and were permanent appointments, while those in the cottage hospitals consisted of most of the local practitioners whose appointments were confirmed annually. In addition there was a resident apothecary at the General who initially acted as secretary. He would look after the patients in the honorary medical staff's absence and attend the physicians' and surgeons' visits, which might only be once a week. He dispensed medicines as prescribed and was expected to deal with most administrative problems. In effect he was the general dogsbody. Apprentices and pupils could be taken on by the medical staff but not by the apothecary, and they had to pay for the privilege.

The Medical Act of 1858 made a clear demarcation between orthodox practitioners, which included licensed apothecaries, surgeons and physicians, holding qualifications recognised by their colleges, who went on the Medical Register, and the fringe practitioner who did not. However, it did not outlaw fringe practice altogether as many doctors had hoped. Herefordshire doctors were particularly militant and 69 of them, under the chairmanship of Mr Bleek Lye and including all the honorary staff at the General Infirmary, signed a petition to Parliament asking for the Act to be modified with restrictions to be placed on unqualified practitioners. They also asked for better representation on the proposed General Medical Council, the national body that was to register and control the profession, as it was intended that more than two-thirds of its members would be appointed by the Government. The petition failed. In

	1870-99	1900-18	1919-39	1940-48
Matron	£20 - £30	£30 - £60	£60 - £110	£100 - £350
Probationers				
1st year		£5 - £10	£10 - £25	£25 - £50
2nd year		£10 - £15	£15 - £30	£30 - £60
Assistant nurse				
(untrained)	£10 - £20	£15 - £25	£25 - £45	£40 - £50
Nurse		£30 - £45	£45 - £80	£70 - £140
Sister			£50 - £85	£85 - £250
Cook			£34 - £45	£45 - £130
Housemaid	£8 - £25	£18 - £25	£25 - £35	£35 - £50

*Table 1 The annual salaries of matrons, nurses and domestic staff.
These varied between cottage hospitals until 1943 when they became
standardised nationally*

1858 the Herefordshire Medical Association was established with the aim of
trying to regularise the practice of medicine in Herefordshire. They chased a
few fringe practitioners out of the county but had no real authority.

The hospital matrons were initially housekeepers without any nurse training
and were usually judged on their ability to run the hospital economically. They
were expected to reside on the hospital premises and were provided with
furnished rooms, board and washing. They looked after the welfare of the
patients, were expected to account for all provisions, and kept a diet book. They
were responsible for discipline amongst the nurses and servants and usually the
matron or apothecary had to ensure that at least one of them was on the
premises. Typically, the matron was expected to be respectable, middle aged
and free from the cares of a family.

Up until the latter half of the nineteenth century nurses were untrained and
learnt on the job, being looked upon as servants with associated low pay and
conditions. During the second half of the nineteenth century reforms in nursing
were focussed on training, largely influenced by Florence Nightingale. At this
time there were two means of entry to the profession. In the Nightingale School
in London, lady pupils paid for their training and tended to be educated daughters of prosperous families, subsequently becoming the future reformers and
leaders of the profession. However, most nurses were taken on as probationers
and tended to be daughters of small farmers, or were well educated domestic
servants. They were given two years free training in hospital with strict discipline, at the end of which they sat their local hospital examination and gained
certificates and badges indicating they had completed their training and passed

The nursing and medical staff of the General around 1900.
Sitting right to left are Dr Chapman, the senior sister, the matron, Dr Lilley,
and Mr Turner. Behind the matron is Mr DuBuisson

an examination. As a result of this recognised training and a code of conduct, nursing had become a respectable profession by the end of the century. By 1900, even in the cottage hospitals, there was usually an additional untrained assistant nurse or a probationer. Assistant nurses and probationers were popular with management because their salaries were especially low.

But the introduction of general nurse training created its own problems, for standards varied and there was a demand for registration so that the public could recognize professional competence. Two associations competed to represent the nurses and deal with registration, though with limited success. The Hospital Association registered nurses who had been in training, while the British Nurses Association, which was granted a Royal Charter in 1893 pressed unsuccessfully for state registration. Effective action was initially achieved for midwives with the 1902 the Midwives Act, passed in response to high levels of maternal and infant deaths. Midwives had to be registered with a Central Midwives Board, ensuring that no woman could attend childbirth for gain other than those under the direction of a doctor, unless certified as a midwife.

In 1916 the College of Nursing was formed whose objects included promoting better education, training and uniformity of the curriculum. They advised increased teaching for trainees with a view to nurses qualifying for certificates from the college. Herefordshire's General Hospital was asked to send representatives to a consultation board and the matron, together with Mr Durham, a governor, were nominated. The college wished to maintain a register of all nurses who had obtained suitable certificates of proficiency. However this had to wait till after the First World War. In the meantime the medical staff and house surgeon were increasingly involved in giving lectures to the trainee nurses.

The General Nursing Council (G.N.C.) was established in 1920 to provide state registration for suitably trained nurses and five years later the first state examinations were held. The course for probationers lasted three years with a preliminary exam after the first year and a final exam at the end. Probationers remained popular, but an increasing number of fully trained staff nurses and eventually sisters were employed. When X-ray facilities became available the matron often found herself also acting as a radiographer.

Terms of service were variable. For example in 1913 an assistant nurse or probationer at Kington Cottage Hospital was allowed two hours off a day for exercise, when feasible, and three weeks' holiday a year. As from the early 1920s the College of Nursing not only advised on nurse training but started to negotiate terms of service. As a result nurses at the General Hospital were soon allowed one half day off duty per week which resulted in the matron having to engage three more probationers. But working conditions in general remained poor, and in 1935 critical articles appeared in local papers, prompting three senior sisters to write a letter stating that they were satisfied with the conditions under which they worked and that the hours were not excessive. Nevertheless, by 1937 it was agreed that night nurses at the General Hospital would be allowed two nights off a week. Discipline, however, remained strict—even when off duty nurses were not allowed to visit the cinema without permission.

In 1943, following the Rushcliffe Report, pay and conditions of service were agreed through a central committee and were accepted by the hospitals. Salaries rose dramatically and the government refunded half the increase. Terms of service were also agreed nationally. In 1943 nurses' hours were restricted to 90 every two weeks and they had to have three hours off each day when they could leave the hospital.

As well as nurses, hospitals employed servants including cooks, maids and porters, actual numbers depending upon the size of the hospital.

In 1895 a group of nurses in London who practised massage were appalled by publicity associating some masseuses with immoral massage establishments. They set up the Society of Trained Masseuses which examined and certified their members bringing acceptable standards and respectability to a new profession. In 1900 the society was given legal recognition and status becoming the Incorporated Society of Trained Masseuses.

After the war there was continued development in rehabilitation, especially of wounded soldiers. In 1920 the Incorporated Society of Trained Masseuses was granted a Royal Charter and amalgamated with the Institute of Massage and Medical Gymnasts to become the Chartered Society of Massage and Medical Gymnasts, which supervised the profession. Ten years later they introduced examinations in electrotherapy.

It was during the first half of the nineteenth century that legislation placed an obligation on local authorities to provide adequate inpatient care for lunatics. The County Magistrates, on whom the obligations then rested, decided that the privately run Lunatic Asylum that had been provided alongside the General Hospital was unsuitable, in both size and facilities. They therefore joined with Hereford City and the surrounding counties to jointly build a 250 bed asylum at Abergavenny which opened in 1852, and which was soon enlarged to accommodate 500 patients.

In spite of this the asylum became overcrowded, resulting in the decision to build the Hereford County and City Lunatic Asylum at Burghill, north of Hereford, which opened in 1872. In 1935 an annexe to the Mental Hospital opened at Holme Lacy House which was used to accommodate up to 107 female patients, most of whom were private and voluntary.

During 1875 and subsequent years a series of Public Health Acts made local authorities responsible for controlling infectious diseases—the most feared of which were cholera and smallpox, with powers to also provide infectious disease or isolation hospitals.

Hereford City Corporation opened their isolation hospital at Tupsley, Hereford, in 1893. It was enlarged a few years later and an annexe was built some distance away to house smallpox cases. Tupsley Hospital was mainly used to isolate cases of scarlet fever and diphtheria.

In 1904 Hereford Rural District Council built Stretton Sugwas Hospital for infectious cases in the district. In the 1930s it was expanded to provide a service for the whole county, except for the city.

Just before of after the turn of the century isolation hospitals or facilities were also established at Burley near Bromyard, at Kingswood just south of Kington, at Ebnal on the outskirts of Leominster on the Kingsland road, at Birtley just north of Lingen and at Drybrook in the Forest of Dean in Gloucestershire. The last named facility was eventually superseded by an isolation hospital at Camp Meadow on the outskirts of Ross. All of these small hospitals were closed in the 1930s, except for the one at Bromyard which became the County Smallpox Hospital.

Early in the twentieth century further legislation made the county council responsible for providing accommodation for the isolation and treatment for patients with contagious tuberculosis. In 1923 the Nieuport Sanatorium with accommodation for 64 inpatients, including 29 children was opened at Almeley, just south of Kington.

Under the National Insurance Act of 1911 manual workers and all others with incomes under £160 a year had to contribute 4d a week to an approved society. In addition their employers paid 4d and the State 2d. In return the insured person, but not his dependents, became entitled to a cash benefit when sick, to the services of a general practitioner and payment for drugs. There was no provision for hospital treatment and the cash benefit for patients in hospital would go the relatives and not to the hospital. As a result, hospital staff feared that a lot of their work might be taken over by general practitioners treating seriously ill patients at home.

In 1911 two associations represented doctors. The British Hospital Association (B.H.A.) was formed in 1884 to represent the voluntary hospitals, but up until the National Insurance Act it had been poorly supported. The British Medical Association (B.M.A.) had been formed in 1856, arising out of the Provincial Medical and Surgical Association, which originally started as the Worcestershire Medical and Surgical Society. The original main aim was to spread and increase medical knowledge in every department of science and practice. Although starting in Worcester it rapidly became provincial and finally national under the guidance of its most famous member, Sir Charles Hastings, honorary surgeon at Worcester Royal Infirmary. The B.M.A. tried to represent all doctors, but in practise they often supported general practitioners in disagreements with their hospital colleagues.

On this occasion both associations opposed the National Insurance Act because it did not provide for hospital treatment. On their advice the staff at the General Hospital announced they would no longer treat as charitable cases anyone insured under the Act except as an emergency. They soon withdrew their opposition as in practice the Act had little effect on hospital admissions.

In 1930 the Poor Law Unions became Public Assistance Institutes (P.A.Is) directly under the control of the county council who appointed a Board of Guardians. Financing of paupers still came from the rates.

The county council also continued to provide chronic sick and midwifery services. The demand for better hospital facilities for these services grew during the 1930s and the Herefordshire County Council Hospital (later known as the County Hospital) opened in 1940, adjacent to Hereford P.A.I. The council planned the hospital to simply provide services for which they were responsible—the chronic sick, midwifery and infectious diseases—and it had been agreed they would avoid providing acute services competing with the general. But the Second World War intervened, the hospital was made part of the Emergency Medical Services and the government built ten huts to accommodate wounded soldiers and increased its facilities to treat acute illness and injuries, with a modern operating theatre and X-ray Department. Disagreements arose with the General Hospital over payments and provision of services, and so a Joint Advisory Committee was appointed in April 1940, with Captain Lionel Green, chairman of the Hospital Management Committee of the County Hospital, as its chairman. More understanding was achieved but a Ministry of Health report in 1942 recommended even better co-operation over nursing services and division of cases, and a common consultant staff.

Management, however, remained under different structures. Local authorities appointed committees to oversee their larger hospitals, though day to day administration lay in the hands of a medical superintendent who was also responsible for the medical care of the patients. The smaller hospitals were often run by the local medical officer of health as part of his duties.

This structure, the numbers of hospitals and the services offered changed with the advent of the National Health Service in July 1948. During the war there was widespread acceptance in the country that some form of co-ordinated Health Service was necessary. The standard of care fluctuated widely over the country with many of the municipal hospitals being ill-equipped and staffed. The voluntary hospitals were increasingly in financial difficulties, and there was also a new awareness of medical and social problems.

Many suggestions were promulgated. The doctors' view, expressed by the B.M.A., favoured central control with regional delegation, having medical representation at every level. They were split on the merits of a salaried service as opposed to charging fees for each patient, but fiercely opposed having a medical superintendent, as in the municipal hospitals, with clinical control over the medical staff. They believed this arrangement would limit their clinical freedom.

In 1944 the Coalition Government issued a white paper which proposed that groups of counties and county boroughs should combine to provide joint boards to run hospital services under central government control, with grants to voluntary hospitals. The doctors felt that this would make the hospitals subservient to local authorities and destroy the voluntary system. The Emergency Committee of the General Hospital supported the B.H.A. objections to the white paper, while the Hereford Trades Council took the opposite view and threatened to advise their members to contract out of the contributory scheme if the doctors kept on opposing it.

In the event, the white paper was overtaken by the election of a Labour Government. Aneurin Bevan, Minister of Health, produced a second consultative white paper in March 1946 which was followed by the N.H.S. Act in October, with implementation on 5th July 1948. The Act laid down the principle that service to all patients would be free. The hospitals were to be nationalised and administered by 12 Regional Boards under central government control, the Boards consisting of 22 to 32 people chosen by the Minister for their suitability for the task, after wide consultation with all interested parties. Initially one-third were to be doctors.

The Boards would then appoint hospital management committees either for each large hospital or for a district formed from a group of related hospitals after consulting with local authorities and the medical and dental staff of the hospitals concerned. Consultants and specialists would be salaried but allowed to work part-time in the service if they wished. The hospital doctors thus obtained most of their aims, so ensuring their commitment to the N.H.S. General practitioners lost their hospital appointments but retained their independence, while local authorities lost control of their hospitals.

On the 5th July 1948 the remaining six voluntary hospitals and the eight municipal hospitals came under the authority of the Herefordshire Hospital Management Committee (H.H.M.C.), which was itself responsible to the Birmingham Regional Hospital Board. In addition the P.A.I.s in Bromyard and Ross were nationalised and also came under the H. H.M.C. Over the next 12 years it became practical to rationalise and plan services for the whole of Herefordshire.

The services at the County and General hospitals were amalgamated with a single nursing school and one matron in charge of the three acute hospitals. Specialist medical services were developed with the appointment of visiting specialists. All the isolation hospitals were closed except for Stretton Sugwas. In the market towns the surgical work in the cottage hospitals was restricted while local services were based at them. By 1959 the hospital service was reorganised and providing comprehensive medical care for the people of Herefordshire, adjacent counties and parts of mid-Wales.

CHAPTER 2

The Hereford General Infirmary
from Inception to the Twentieth Century

Once sufficient funds had been collected, the hospital's governors decided to establish a temporary infirmary in a building on the north side of Eign Street, outside Eign Gate. In his address following the laying of the foundation stone for Victoria Ward in 1887, Mr Thomas Cam, whose grandfather was one of the original surgeons in 1776, stated that the institution began at no.42 Eign Street, the second house east of the railway bridge, as it was then. All the numbers were subsequently changed, and no.42 has become no.162. The house is a three storey tenement building with a two storey extension at the back. Each storey has three rooms, and the building contains a cellar with a low ceiling. It is still serving the public in the 1990s, but as a Chinese take-away.

At a governors' meeting in November 1775 it was agreed that the temporary infirmary would open around Lady Day, 25th March, the following year. Requests were made to help with its furnishing, notably for bedsteads, cheap and wooden, without posts, 6 feet 4 inches long and 3 feet wide, and also coverlets, blankets and sheeting.

The management of the infirmary was to be controlled, under its Rules, by the governors who could attend and vote at all meetings. Proxy votes were allowed for those who could not attend. The governors would decide on policies within the Rules, confirm contracts, appoint the honorary medical staff and all the officers of the institution. The lord lieutenant of the county and the bishop of Hereford would be requested to act as patrons; a subscriber of £5 and upwards for two consecutive years and a benefactor of £50 or over would be designated a vice-president; two or more trustees would be elected in whose name the property and investments of the institution would be held; whilst each

The old or temporary infirmary,
the light coloured tenement building,
now no.162 Eign Street

year a person of distinction would be elected a steward to chair the annual general meeting.

On the 26th March 1776 the temporary Hereford General Infirmary opened, initially for patients with injuries following accidents and who therefore required no tickets of recommendation. The first weekly board meeting for the admission of ill patients via the system of tickets was held on Thursday 8th May 1776.

In the Autumn of 1775, Edward Harley, Earl of Oxford had offered the charity a generous plot of land on the north-east bank of the River Wye as a site for the new infirmary, land which included Bartonsham Meadow to the south-east. This gift was gratefully accepted. Edward Harley had been born at Eywood, Titley, in north Herefordshire, and before he inherited the title in 1755 had been M.P. for Hereford. He was still Chief Steward of the city. The next few years were dominated by the planning of the new infirmary, the building work being repeatedly postponed because the governors were reluctant to proceed until donations had provided a capital of £6,000. Meanwhile the temporary infirmary was having difficulties in accommodating the number of patients being recommended, and 18 months after opening the weekly board informed the governors that it was full, with seven patients waiting for admission. A year later the governors finally accepted that the infirmary was totally inadequate for the numerous patients recommended. Unfortunately a further delay was caused by the bank of the River Wye, on the site of the proposed infirmary, becoming eroded by floods. The bank was rebuilt, with the help of stones donated by the bishop, but it cost £308.

On the 1st of March 1781, the foundation stone was finally laid by the Rev. Dr Thomas Talbot, in the presence of the Mayor and Corporation of the City of Hereford in all their regalia, many friends of the charity, and a vast crowd. The architect and builder was Mr William Parker of Hereford, who owned a quarry at Lugwardine, and who later helped to build the county gaol and the spire of Kington Church.

The plans show a three storey building with two ground floor wings. The ground floor of the main building contained a committee room, surgery, physicians' room, kitchen, dining room, and accommodation for the apothecary. The wings provided a wash house, a brewery, bathing facilities and quarters for the matron. The brewery was required as beer was both prescribed for the patients and consumed by the staff. On the first floor there were six wards for 27 patients and on the second floor five wards for 28 patients. There were also cellars and attics. The final cost was well above expectations, at £4,803.

The new infirmary was opened in August 1783 without any ceremony. Indeed the governors had doubts about whether the income would be adequate and there were further appeals for subscribers. Meanwhile the temporary infirmary was rented out as a workhouse to All Saints Church, and 25 years later it was advertised for sale being described as 'All that messuage or building, called the old infirmary, together with the yard and premises thereto belonging, situate within Eign Gate aforesaid, and now occupied by the parish of All Saints as a workhouse.' It was sold a year later to private buyers.

Hereford Infirmary from the gardens of the Bishop's Palace

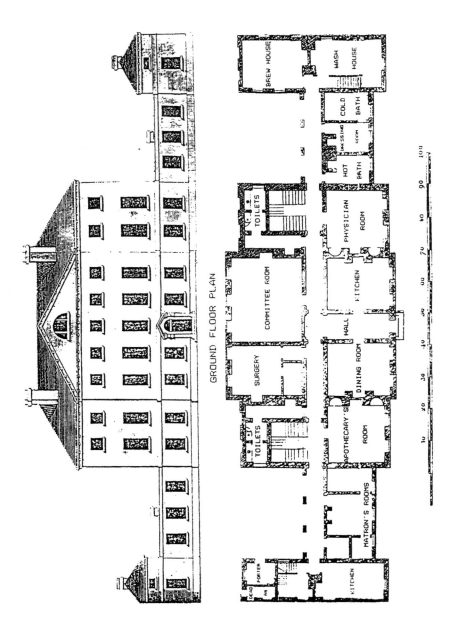

Diagram of the General Infirmary in 1785, including the ground floor plan

Every summer there was a well advertised annual general meeting to revue the state of the charity and approve the accounts. Honorary auditors were appointed, and trustees and bankers replaced when there was a vacancy. The meeting was usually held on the morning of the Hereford races or assizes, no doubt in the hope of a good attendance, the venue being either the Town Hall or the Swan and Falcon Inn. It was followed by a cathedral service with a sermon and collection for the infirmary, the proceedings being rounded off by an 'ordinary', a meal usually costing 2s 6d, at a city inn. On the evening of the first annual general meeting there was a musical performance at the music room adjacent to the cathedral, as well as a ball in the College Hall, south-east of the cathedral.

The quarterly governors meetings would examine the matron's books, usually accept her accounts and grant her petty cash for the next quarter. Tenders for the next quarter's supplies consisting of butcher's meat, bread, malt, butter, cheese, milk, groceries, coals, candles, soap, etc., were always awarded to the lowest bidder. Governors were appointed to the weekly board and visitors selected, from amongst the subscribers, to inspect the infirmary regularly and ensure the patients were being properly treated and not neglected. Special Meetings were held when required to deal with appointing senior staff or to discuss urgent problems.

At the weekly board meetings more information was sought about patients seeking admission. They were expected to provide information about age, general fitness and duration of illness. If coming from some distance, the subscriber recommending that patient was asked to send information to the secretary in advance, if possible drawn up by a physician, surgeon, apothecary or other capable person.

The honorary medical staff were usually made governors and most were involved with management. Each physician and surgeon was allowed to recommend urgent inpatients and outpatients for treatment. By the end of the century the medical staff were also granted admission rights for non-urgent patients. Each week there was a nominated physician and surgeon who were available for emergency admissions and care of the patients.

In 1794, the governors issued instructions that no surgeon should prescribe drugs for any patient without consulting with one of the physicians, except for emetics (drugs to produce vomiting), purges (laxatives) or opiates. No operation, except as a result of an accident, was to be performed by a surgeon without the prior consultation of physicians and surgeons. The apothecary was made responsible for informing all the medical staff about these cases and organising the meeting. These instructions indicate the rather low status accorded to the surgeons and their then limited training.

The governors were equally ruthless in trying to ensure that unsuitable cases were not admitted. The case of any patient who had stayed over two months was reviewed and if improvement was unlikely even with further treatment, they were discharged home or to the workhouse. They decreed that no scrofulous, a soft tissue swelling often tuberculous, or venereal cases were to be taken into the infirmary without the consultation and agreement of the majority of the physicians and surgeons.

The staff owned several dogs which become a nuisance, so the governors decreed that only one dog was to be kept in the infirmary as an alarm to provide protection at night. They also resolved that when the price of provisions was high, no more than 25 patients should be admitted to the infirmary; any additional inpatients would require the consent of three of the medical staff.

Fundraising continued and by 1800 there were 81 benefactors of £20 and over and approximately 200 current subscribers. These included additional country gentry, including Michael Biddulph of Ledbury, Rt. Hon. Lady Frances Coningsby of Hampton Court, Sir John Cotterell of Garnons, Sir James Hereford of Sufton, and Uvedale Price of Foxley. Several benefactors came from outside Herefordshire, including the bishop of Durham, the Marquis of Bath, and the Governors of Guy's Hospital.

Dr George Harris, who initially subscribed 3 guineas annually, subsequently donated £20 and when he died in 1796 left a legacy of £5,000. He was a doctor of law, an advocate and legal adviser to three dioceses being chancellor of Durham, Hereford and Llandaff. His father had been bishop of Llandaff and previously dean of Hereford in 1729. Two wards, Upper and Lower Harris were subsequently named after him.

The first detailed accounts available are for the year to March 1785. Expenditure totalled £680 and consisted of: Housekeeping and running costs £468, drugs and medicines £103, salaries £78 and administration £31. The ordinary income, excluding benefactors' donations, was £664. Of this, subscriptions provided the vast majority at £603. Other income included church collections of £7, dividends from invested capital £10, the Board of Parish Paupers and contributions for servants totalled £31, rent from the old infirmary £6 and miscellaneous items £7. These latter included selling sermons, books, coal ash, grains and suet, and charging for the use of cold baths.

Every year there were subscriptions in arrears. Repeated reminders were made with threats to publish the names of the defaulters, threats which never seem to have been carried out. The weekly board would inspect the treasurer's books from time to time and write off subscriptions that had become 'desperate, or extremely dubious, through death, removal, misfortune, or change of mind.'

Up to 1790 the income and expenditure remained relatively unchanged, but by the mid-1790s the income had dropped to £460 p.a. The governors sent out a circular letter appealing for more subscribers, whilst an article in the *Hereford Journal* explained the important advantages of the infirmary, proven by the last 21 years, and appealed for more financial support. The accounts for the year to March 1800 showed a slight increase in income to £491, with over 90 per cent of the income still coming from charitable sources. But expenditure kept increasing and these accounts also showed expenditure on items that would never be countenanced in the later N.H.S.—wine and beer. One of the more unusual duties of the apothecary was to distribute wines and spirits to patients as prescribed by the medical staff. In the year to March 1800 the annual cost of wine for the patients was £7 while the cost of malt and hops for the hospital's brewery came to £76; the total consumption of beer was around 100 gallons. Attempts to economize included the infirmary owning and milking its own cow. Nevertheless, the infirmary ended the century with a current account deficit of over £306.

The governors elected members of the honorary medical staff after the posts had been advertised. Initially two physicians, Dr Francis Campbell and Dr John Cam were appointed; both had previously been mayors of Hereford. Dr Cam was born in Llanwarne and studied medicine at Cambridge.

Three surgeons, Mr Thomas Cam, Mr Richard Hardwicke and Mr William Cam were appointed. As the Rules stated that only two surgeons were required it seems likely that the appointment of Mr William Cam was truly honorary in nature, as he played little part in the life of the infirmary.

When they retired or died, successors were appointed as

Mr Thomas Cam, honorary surgeon 1839-67

27

	Date appointed	Years of service to advent of N.H.S.
John Cam, M.A., M.D.	1776	16
Francis Campbell, M.D.	1776	12 + 8
Thomas Blount, M.D.	1792	28
G.H.H. Symonds, M.D.	1788	8
Samuel Hughes, M.D.	1799	25
John Bleeck Lye, M.D.	1820	44
Maineswete Walrond, M.D.	1825	13
William L. Gilliland, M.D.	1838	28
Henry Graves Bull, M.D.	1864	21
Alfred Rickards Smith, M.D.	1866	31
Paul M. Chapman, M.D., F.R.C.P.	1885	34
James H. Lilley, M.A., M.D., (Cantab), M.R.C.S.	1897	21
George H. Hamilton Symonds, M.D., M.B., C.M.(Edin.)	1909	15
John Steed, M.B., C.M., M.D.	1919	12
Patterson, L.R.C.P.	1919	10
J.R. Bulman, M.B. Ch.B. (Edin.)	1924	22
F.O.T. Strange, M.B., B.S.(Lond.), M.R.C.S.(Eng.), L.R.C.P.(Lond.)	1929	19
John E. Wells. M.D.(Dublin), B.Ch.	1931	17
Charles W. Walker, MC., M.A., M.D., Ch.B.	1946	2

Table 2 Honorary Physicians of the General Infirmary

set out in tables 2 and 3. Dr Campbell was followed by Dr Samuel Hughes who graduated in Edinburgh. One of his friends was Robert Burns, the Scottish poet, who presented him with one of the first copies of 'Scots Wha Hae' and which was later donated to Hereford City Council. At present it resides in the city library.

Mr Thomas Cam had three sons who all became surgeons. His eldest son, Thomas jnr., succeeded him and in turn was followed by the next brother, Samuel. The youngest, John, became a surgeon in Bath and his son, another Thomas, later joined the staff when Sam died in a riding accident.

Mr Hardwicke was followed by Mr Thomas Cotes, the son of the Rev. Digby Cotes, rector of the parish of Abbey Dore. He was a lively character who, in 1787, when he was a surgeon in general practice in Hereford and a governor at the infirmary, brought a charge against Mr Hardwicke for a breach of the Rules, which was found to be unwarranted. When Mr Hardwicke died Mr Cotes offered his services as an honorary surgeon, and surprisingly was appointed.

Thomas Cotes appeared to make a name for himself in registering grievances and complaints. In 1794 he complained to the governors that he had been

	Date appointed	Years of service to advent of N.H.S.
Surgeons		
Thomas Cam, L.S.A.	1776	18
Richard Hardwicke, L.S.A.	1776	18
William Cam, L.S.A.	1776	18
Thomas Cam, jnr. L.S.A.	1794	6
Thomas Cotes, L.S.A., M.D.	1794	23
Samuel Cam, L.S.A.	1800	38
John Griffiths, sn. L.S.A., M.R.C.S.	1817	20
John Griffiths, jnr. L.S.A., M.R.C.S.	1837	2
Charles Lingen, L.S.A., M.R.C.S., F.R.C.S., M.D.	1838	26
Francis Braithwaite, M.R.C.S.	1839	14
Thomas Cam, D.L., J.P., F.R.C.S.	1839	28
John Freeman Morris	1853	6
Henry Vevers, M.R.C.S.	1859	33
Thomas Turner, J.P., F.R.C.S., M.R.C.S.	1864	44
Richard Thomason, M.R.C.S., A.S.A.	1867	30
Edgar G.F. Morris, L.S.A., L.R.C.P.(Edin), M.R.C.S.(Eng.)	1892	27
Edward DuBuisson, L.R.C.P.(Lond.), M.R.C.S.(Eng).	1897	25
J. Arthur Wood	1908	11
William Ainslie, M.C., M.D.(Aber.), F.R.C.S.(Edin.)	1919	18
William B. Butler, M.R.C.S., L.R.C.P.(Lond.)	1919	7
Blanche E. Walter Stallard, M.D., B.S.(Lond.)	1922	10
Richard Wood Power, B.A., M.B., B.Ch., F.R.C.S.I., D.P.H., L.M.(Dublin)	1926	22
Bernard Scholefield, M.A., M.D.(Oxon), F.R.C.S.(Eng.), M.Ch.(Oxon.)	1932	16
William Moir Brown, M.B., Ch.B.(Edin), F.R.C.S.(Edin.)	1937	11
Dental Surgeons		
Mr George McAdam, L.D.S.R.C.S.	1882	16
Mr Peyton G. Levason, L.D.S.R.C.S.	1898	25
Frank S. Machin, M.R.C.S., L.R.C.P, L.D.S.R.C.S.(Eng)	1923	25

Table 3 Honorary Surgeons of the General Infirmary

improperly treated in the infirmary by the matron. It appears the matter was discussed privately and no action was taken. The following year he again complained, this time that medicines belonging to the infirmary were being clandestinely taken away by the matron, Mrs Diane Moore. The weekly board found that many of the accusations against her were well founded, but she asked for a pardon and made amends, so was allowed to stay. However a nurse was immediately dismissed.

Those members of the honorary medical staff who retired after many years of distinguished service were usually elected to the post of Honorary Physician or Surgeon Extraordinary. This allowed them access to a few beds in the infirmary and made them available for consultation and advice in difficult cases.

Although originally the governors appointed the apothecary, they later allowed the medical staff to take over this duty as long as they were unanimous in their choice. Mr Perkins, the first apothecary and secretary died in January 1780 and was followed by a succession of apothecaries. When a Mr Blackfield resigned, with little warning, he was found to have debts of £50. Although these were eventually repaid, his successors had to give the treasurer an assurity of £100—this at a time when the apothecary with secretarial duties was paid £40 p.a. plus board and lodgings! In 1799 the office of secretary was separated from that of apothecary, and the salary was split between the posts.

The first matron, Mrs Jones, had resigned in January 1781. Two candidates advertised their applications in the local paper to gain support from the governors and Mrs Diane Moore had been elected. After 13 years she requested a rise in salary and as a result it was increased from £10 to £15 p.a. She became the subject of Mr Cotes' complaints and in 1797 several further charges were brought against her and she was eventually dismissed. Immediately after this the apothecary was instructed to have locks fitted to the drawers that contained the wine—it would appear that Mrs Moore had several weaknesses.

There is little information about the nurses and servants. There was certainly a head nurse with an assistant nurse on both the male and female wards. The servants included a cook, a maid and a scrubber or laundry maid. The average wage for a nurse or servant was 3s 6d a week or just over £9 p.a.

The Rules allowed for a chaplain on an informal basis, with no salary until near the end of the century. It was then that an annual subscription was provided by the bishop and clergy to fund a permanent post until the infirmary could provide the funds, which happened within a few years. His duties were to read the Church of England morning service to the patients every Wednesday and Friday.

Initially patients who died in the infirmary were buried in the cathedral close until it was closed. Subsequently they were buried in the parish from

	Date appointed	Years of service
Mrs Jones	1776	5
Mrs Diana Moore	1781	16
Mrs Margaret Brown	1797	1
Mrs Ann Gwatkin	1798	6
Mrs Mary Hartford	1804	22
Mrs Susan Davies	1826	8
Mrs Elizabeth Pritchard	1834	20
Mrs Hallum	1854	18
Mrs E.J. Markham	1869	4
Mrs H. Baker	1872	17
Miss A.A. Sharpe	1887	11
Miss K. Elphick	1899	4
Mrs Marion Measures	1903	9
Miss P.A. Blake	1912	4
Miss M. Steers	1916	2
Miss E. Tidman	1918	1
Miss Annie C. Bell	1919	2
Miss Constance Keys-Wells	1921	2
Miss Anabel Cameron	1923	14
Miss V. Langdon	1937	10
Miss E.M. Cordery, S.R.N., R.F.M, S.C.M.	1947	

Table 4 Matrons at the General Infirmary/Hospital

which they came. If not parishioners of any city parish, they would be admitted to the burial grounds of St Owens.

The annual report to March 1785 showed that 175 inpatients and 447 outpatients had been treated. The average bed occupancy was 30 and it stayed around this level until the mid-1790s when it gradually decreased, the report for the year to March 1800 showing an average bed occupancy of only 23. The number of inpatients discharged, who had died or who were made outpatients totalled 159. Of these 24 were accident cases. The outcome was as follows:-

Cured	97
Relieved	24
Misbehaviour	3
At patients request	1
Incurable	0
Dead	5 (mortality 3%)
Made Out-patients	29

The number of new out-patients attending was 166, for whom the outcome was:

Cured	138
Relieved	11
Non attender	3
Made In-patients	14

The figures were 'laundered' to a certain extent for the category 'cured' was defined as restoration to temporary health, whilst 'relieved' would cover cases that might be incurable but who had received some benefit. The mortality rate was kept low by ruthlessly applying the Rules to exclude admitting the dying and incurable—the Annual Report was made as optimistic as possible because the infirmary depended on continuing support from the public.

Growth 1800 - 1849

The financial crisis looming over the infirmary at the end of the eighteenth century rapidly disappeared for in 1800 Dr Harris's legacy of £5,000 was received together with three years' interest of £600. In the next few years the income and expenditure were approximately balanced.

During the first half of the nineteenth century the infirmary trebled its activity and the two wings were enlarged, with the average number of inpatients steadily increasing to 71 in the year to March 1850. As there is little evidence from other provincial hospitals that medical conditions or treatment changed significantly till anaesthesia was introduced in 1847, the increased activity up to this date is likely to be due to greater confidence in the infirmary's care.

In the year to 25th March 1850 the number of inpatients discharged, who had died or were made outpatients was 586. This included 165 accident cases and was made up as follows:

Cured	268
Relieved	49
Discharged for misbehaviour	3
Own request	6
Incurable	2
Absconded	4
Dead	13 (2.2%)
Made outpatients	241

The total number of outpatients attending was 655, of whom:

Cured	254
Relieved	41
Non attenders	336
Known to be dead	4
Made inpatients	20

The number of non-attenders appears large as it included those whom failed to keep follow up appointments, though presumably the majority of these were either 'cured' or 'relieved'.

The privileges of subscribers to recommend patients were often added to or modified. Early in this period a subscriber of one guinea was allowed to recommend one 'poor ruptured person' as an outpatient who could then be provided with a truss at half the original cost. Only if a groin rupture threatened life, by damaging an entrapped segment of bowel, would surgery be considered—in any event it usually resulted in death.

In 1834 the Poor Law was changed, resulting in larger district union workhouses controlled by Boards of Guardians. The infirmary Rules were therefore modified to encourage paupers to be admitted if authorised and financed by the relevant Board of Guardians. The charge made was 3s 6d a week. The Board of Guardians also had to agree to remove the patient when requested and, in case of death, pay for the cost of the funeral.

Two years later the dean stated that the annual cathedral service held on the day of the infirmary's Annual General Meeting had been postponed as only 14 ladies and eight gentlemen had turned up. Other motives may have been behind this move, for although holding the

For over 35 years Captain Prendergrass R.N., was an active governor, being at times chairman of the both the governors and the weekly board. On his retirement in 1848 his friends presented the infirmary with his portrait in appreciation of his services. The medal he is wearing is the 'Naval General Service Medal' with a single bar, awarded to those who had fought in the Napoleonic wars

meeting on the morning of the third day of the races might suit the governors, it did not always please the clergy. Over the years the date of the meeting was changed several times, but usually returned to the date of the races.

In response to a bitter squabble over the appointment of an honorary physician in 1838, a resolution clarifying the use of proxy votes was passed restricting such votes to peers, members of parliament, ladies, persons prevented from attending by illness or infirmity as certified by their medical attendant, all governors over 70 years of age and those resident beyond 10 miles from the city.

In 1839 it became the tradition that the high sheriff of the county was requested to accept the office of president during his year in office, with the main responsibility of chairing the Annual General Meeting. Most of the high sheriffs accepted this post over the next hundred years. A new post of life governor was created and was awarded to people who had given particular help and service.

John Morris

Meanwhile, changes were being made to the building. In 1824 the first porter's lodge had been built adjacent to the main entrance, which at that time was at the back of the infirmary half-way along Nelson Street. It cost £59 and is now used as a workshop.

With increasing numbers of patients being admitted the infirmary's 55 beds were inadequate. Store rooms were fitted with extra beds and the attics were considered for additional staff accommodation. In 1834 it was decided to expand the infirmary by building another storey onto the two wings. Fortuitously Mr John Morris of Kington, a wool stapler and former High Sheriff of Radnorshire, had bequeathed £10,000 to the infirmary. Subsequently two wards, Upper and Lower Morris, were named after him. The extensions were opened in August, increasing the available accommodation to around 70 beds.

In 1844, because of further demands for more beds, the laundry was appropriated as a sick ward and a new drying room was added at a cost of £130. There were times when the infirmary managed to cope with over 80 inpatients.

Subscribers could not live forever, and there were three minor financial crises over these years as income from this source dropped. The governors response was to appeal widely by letters and advertisements in the *Hereford Journal* and *Hereford Times* stressing the distressed state of the infirmary and its good works. After one of these appeals £200 was raised. The bishop also came to the rescue by agreeing that a Sunday should be selected when the clergy should preach suitable sermons in every church in the county to be followed by a collection for the infirmary. Thus started the tradition of the annual Hospital Sunday. As a result of these appeals the books were balanced and capital investments did not have to be realized.

The accounts for the year to March 1850 reflect the gradually changing nature of the infirmary's funding and expansion of its activity. Income had now climbed to £1,857, of which 54 per cent now came from dividends on investments of £33,582. Subscriptions accounted for £624, not that much more than had been the case in 1785, with the balance of £180 being made up of small donations, legacies and miscellaneous. Housekeeping costs including fuel and administration still formed the major expenditure at £1,056, then came salaries for the non honorary staff at £312. Wine, cider and malt for brewing (alcohol was still being prescribed) amounted to £158, drugs and medicines £132, leeches (for bleeding) £22 and trusses £14. The accounts for the year show a positive balance of £158.

When Dr Walrond, a physician, retired after 13 years service, there was a bitter contest over his successor. The likely problem was that the most favoured candidate, Dr Gilliland, was the resident superintendent of the Lunatic Asylum in the infirmary grounds, which carried a certain stigma. At a special meeting of the governors the proceedings began with a disagreement as to who was entitled to chair the gathering. Once that was resolved, one governor who had not paid her subscription was then disqualified. Two governors, J.E. Gough, Mayor of Hereford and John Griffiths, honorary surgeon, claimed double votes, once as a subscriber and secondly as right of office. Surprisingly this was allowed. Eventually Dr William Gilliland was elected honorary physician by 53 votes to 45. Of the 98 votes cast 36 were by proxy.

When Thomas Cam was elected honorary surgeon by 48 to 32 votes on the death of his uncle, Mr Sam Cam, he was the fourth member of that family in succession to be appointed honorary surgeon. Subsequently the family was mentioned in a Parliamentary Select Committee on medical education, where it was suggested that social connection could be more important than ability in gaining these prestigious posts. In 1839 a third honorary surgeon was appointed, Mr Francis Braithwaite.

By 1820 apprentices and pupils were appearing. All wanted medical training and were prepared to pay for it. Originally the apprentice was looked upon as a learner of a craft and was bound to or had a contract with his master to work for a specific time in return for training. The pupil was looked upon as a scholar who was taken on for training. Both terms appeared to become inter-changeable over the next few years. The infirmary took on both indoor apprentices, who were resident and participated fully in all the activities of the hospital, and outdoor apprentices who were non-resident and attended the outpatient clinics and dispensary. They worked under the instruction of the house surgeon. Indoor apprentices had a contract for three to five years and were provided with board and lodging. By 1833 they were paying the infirmary £150 and the house surgeon £20 for the first three years, and if the training continued for a further two years they paid £100 to the infirmary and £10 to the house surgeon. There were similar arrangements for the outdoor apprentices who would pay the house surgeon £10 for a three-year course.

Mrs Hartford was elected matron in 1804 and stayed for 22 years. Shortly after being appointed, she was accused by Mr Cotes of embezzlement, but this was not established. However, much abusive and improper language passed between them. The governors admonished her, asked her to adhere strictly to the rules and behave respectfully to the medical staff and make any complaints directly to the governors. The dispute was probably related to the medical staff's instructions about their patients for shortly after this event they were asked to put such instructions in writing.

These reprimands to the matron do not appear to have done her any harm as shortly afterwards her tea allowance was raised to 4 guineas a year and she was awarded gratuities at regular intervals. Gratuities were used as rewards for good performance and avoided the permanent raising of salaries.

The next matron was Mrs Susan Davies, who resigned after six years as she had become blind. As she was unable to maintain herself, the governors granted her a year's salary as a parting gift.

During this period nurses continued to have no formal training but learnt while on the wards. A charwoman was engaged to do the washing thus relieving the men's nurse of this task. Nurses working on the male wards were paid more, probably because the men were more trouble, though in 1849 wages still continued to reflect the low overall status of nurses.

Meanwhile, the chaplain was reprimanded when it was discovered that there had been no religious services in the infirmary for five consecutive Sundays. The chaplain explained that he did not consider that Sunday services were part of his work. Although this was accepted by the governors he nevertheless resigned. The Rev. Gretton was then appointed at a salary of £30 p.a. to specifically perform services on Thursdays and Sundays. In addition he was not to appoint another clergyman as a substitute without permission of the weekly board. A few years later the chaplain was made a governor.

In March 1845 there was an outbreak of erysipelas, a soft tissue infection which spread from patient to patient. In the absence of knowledge about the infection the response at this period was to increase ventilation and whitewash or colour all wards, offices and passages.

Ether anaesthesia was first used in England in December 1846. In the following February, in the presence of a great number of medical gentlemen, the new technique was demonstrated at the infirmary when a 13 year old boy was anaesthetised using inhalation of ether vapour. Mr Charles Lingen amputated the boy's leg due to a long standing disease of the knee joint, probably tuberculous. Afterwards the youth recalled he had been dreaming he was on the River Wye enjoying himself. The operation lasted under a minute, indicating the earlier necessity for speed before anaesthesia was available.

Shortly afterwards, a prisoner at the County Gaol had a tooth extracted by Mr Joseph Levason, dental surgeon, having been anaesthetised by the inhalation of ether vapour administered by Dr Graves Bull, medical officer of the the gaol, using an apparatus of his own construction.

Despite these successes, there were warning voices about the dangers of ether, especially as it was highly inflammable with the subsequent risk of explosion. Also, ensuring that ether anaesthesia produced the correct level of consciousness required experience and skill or death could arise as a result of the anaesthetic. Sometimes an anaesthetic failed, usually because of difficulties in getting a tight connection between the inhalation apparatus and the patient. The first death under anaesthesia in Hereford occurred in March 1847, after which there was a reluctance to advertise the procedure and it was stressed that anaesthesia was used at the patient's request.

Chloroform anaesthesia, which was safer and rapidly became more popular than ether, was first used in Hereford in March 1848 when Mr Lingen amputated both hands of an unfortunate man who had had them macerated in a chaff cutting machine.

However the advantages of anaesthesia were so apparent for both patient and surgeon that its introduction steadily increased the range and number of operations.

Renewal and Expansion, 1850 - 1899

In 1865 it was decided that better access to the front of the infirmary was necessary. The single entrance, off Nelson Street, gave access to the back of the building, and led to congestion of patients, staff and traders. A piece of land that included the site of the old Castle Mill, between the infirmary and Castle Green, was obtained from the city council and enclosed by a boundary wall and railings. A new lodge was built and the entrance gate was moved to the new position, giving direct access to the front door.

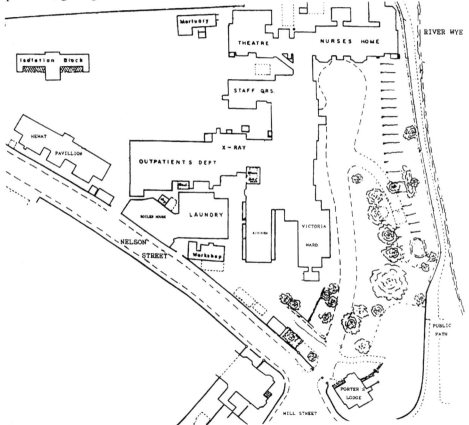

1935 plan of the grounds showing the entrance to the front of the building established in the 1860s

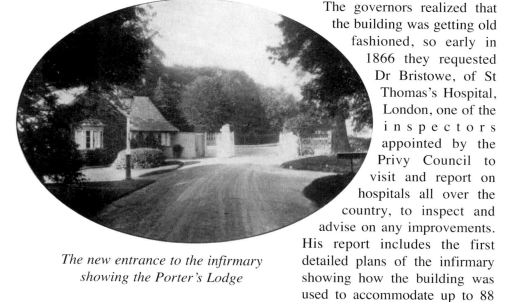

The new entrance to the infirmary showing the Porter's Lodge

The governors realized that the building was getting old fashioned, so early in 1866 they requested Dr Bristowe, of St Thomas's Hospital, London, one of the inspectors appointed by the Privy Council to visit and report on hospitals all over the country, to inspect and advise on any improvements. His report includes the first detailed plans of the infirmary showing how the building was used to accommodate up to 88 patients and staff, and provide outpatient facilities, a laundry and brewhouse. Dr Bristowe was critical. The wards were too small and difficult to supervise, the corridors were long, narrow and dark while the ventilation was poor. The water closets were badly placed, being adjacent to the inner walls and so tending to infect the interior. The outpatients' and admission rooms were badly placed and scattered while he felt the laundry and brewery should not be part of the infirmary building.

His recommendations were therefore numerous. He planned to provide seven wards on the first floor, including one with 16 beds, and six wards on the second floor, with one having 14 beds. He also suggested that one end of the infirmary should accommodate mainly males and the other females to avoid excessive mixing of the sexes. In total he planned accommodation for 84 patients—53 males and 31 females.

A special meeting of governors in February 1867 approved the report and the necessary alterations were carried out over the next few years at a cost of £1,235. Larger wards extending from the front to the back of the building were made on the first and second floors, by joining three rooms together and including the passages between them. The large ward on the first floor became Oxford Ward, named after the Earl of Oxford who donated the original land, while the ward on the top floor became Talbot Ward after the Rev. Thomas Talbot, the infirmary's founder. The manual lift was extended to reach the attic,

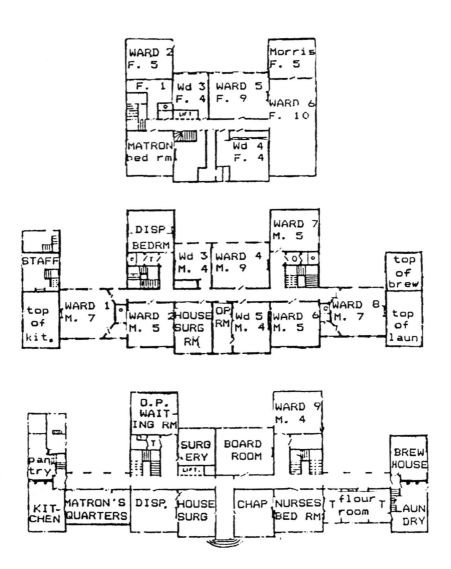

The layout of the infirmary in 1866 prior to Dr Bristowe's recommendations,
with the ground floor at the bottom, first floor in the centre
and second floor at the top.
The attics contained the nurses' bedrooms.
M = Male, F = Female, T = Toilets, W.C. or bathroom.
The total number of beds was 88, of which 50 were designated for men
and 38 for women

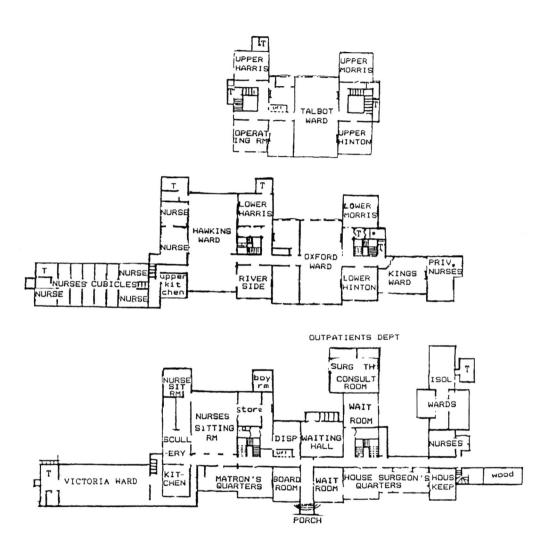

The layout of the infirmary in 1899, with the ground floor at the bottom (the outpatient department was in fact added in 1904), first floor in the centre and second floor at the top. The wards have been named.
T = Toilets, W.C. or bathroom

*The rear of the infirmary in 1899, showing the glass cupolas
over the staircases and theatre*

which was floored to make two new rooms for servants. The nurses' room on
the second floor became an operating theatre with a glass cupola.

Each of the two main staircases at either end of the building was extended
to the second floor, and roofed over with a glass cupola, which provided both
light and ventilation. Water closets were removed from the wards and replaced
with multiple bathrooms and toilets. Gas lighting was installed with 54 separate burners.

The resident officers' apartments were altered and refurbished. Sitting
rooms and bedrooms were provided for the house surgeon and matron on the
ground floor. There was also a nurse's bedroom. The out-patient and dispensing
departments were rearranged to become more functional with a waiting room,
a surgery, a prescribing room, a serving room and an apothecaries' shop.

The old lodge and adjacent buildings were converted into a wash house and
laundry. The old 'dead house' or mortuary was at this time situated in the front
garden and it was agreed to move it to the back of the infirmary. In 1875 the
city council agreed to finance a new public mortuary adjacent to the back of the
hospital, but it was not built until the end of the century.

In 1876 it was decided not to brew any more ale in the infirmary but to buy
it from a brewer. A year later it was resolved that the old brewhouse at the south
end of the buildings should be converted into a ward and disinfecting room for
casual cases of infection which might occur in the infirmary. It was also often
used to accommodate nurses.

In 1882 Mr Francis Hawkins, chairman of the Board of Management that had succeeded the weekly board, donated £1,000 out of a total cost of £1,840, to improve the accommodation on the female side and a two storey building was erected, attached to the back of the north wing. The upper floor was a large and handsome ward containing 28 beds for female patients and was named after him. The ground floor was used as a kitchen and outpatient department, until it became a nurses' sitting room in the next century. The following year Mr Hawkins donated further money to erect a porch at the front door of

Francis Hawkins

the infirmary to prevent draughts, which had become a problem.

Early in 1887 the medical staff persuaded the Board of Management that a separate children's ward was necessary and helped to mount a public appeal for

Hawkins Ward, as it appeared in the annual report in 1929

funds to commemorate Queen Victoria's Jubilee. Dr Thomas Turner spoke at a public meeting at the Guildhall and pointed out that when children were recovering from illness they needed youthful company, toys and amusements rather than being surrounded by older people in an adult ward. Following an appeal in the local press, £1,255 was raised with a further £1,150 donated by Mr Arthur Hutchinson, a member of the Board, and his family. Eventually £3,096 was collected.

The foundation stone was laid in November 1887 by Mrs Cam, whose husband, Thomas Cam, Surgeon Extraordinary, was now chairman of the Board. The new two storey block was built onto the north end of the building and was opened in November 1888. The ground floor became the children's ward accommodating 16 children, and was named Victoria Ward, whilst the first floor provided accommodation for the nursing staff. Mrs Cam persuaded 18 donors to provide a cot each, which would be named after them.

Eventually a separate isolation block, containing two wards each accommodating three patients, with its own access road, was built in the grounds to the rear. It was opened in 1897, but within months the ceilings fell down due to a defective cask of cement being used. Fortunately nobody was injured. Isolation wards were often empty and the temptation to use them for other purposes was strong so that it is not surprising that a year later they were being used to accommodate nurses.

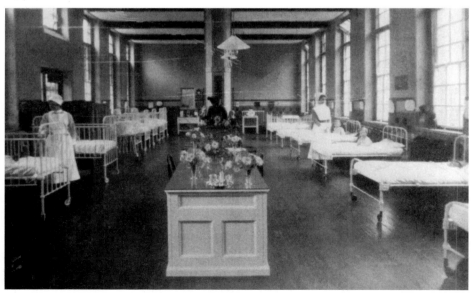

Victoria Ward, as it appeared in the annual report for 1925

By the end of the century many of the infirmary's wards had been named, mostly after benefactors, but the origin of Upper and Lower Hinton Ward is uncertain. From the 12th century Hinton Court and estate, situated opposite the infirmary, south of the river, was owned by the cathedral, hence its Old English name, *higna-tun*, 'the monks town'. It was rented by several governors of the infirmary. The first was a Mrs Elizabeth Smith of Hinton who had donated £150 to the infirmary in the 1790s and later Mr Richard Powell, one time treasurer to the infirmary, lived there, making it likely that the wards name came from the estate.

The ward adjacent to Hawkins Ward was called Riverside Ward as it overlooked the river. It later became a pathology laboratory. A ward on the first floor, next to Lower Hinton Ward was called King's Ward. Whilst there were several governors called King there is no evidence that the ward was called after any particular one of them.

In 1882 the water supply to the infirmary became unreliable, probably because more water was being used, and often no supply was available on the upper floor. Up till then the infirmary had a huge storage tank on the second floor holding 2,564 gallons, filled from its own supply. The infirmary was duly connected to the mains in Nelson Street, but problems continued. The supply was poorly filtered and the house surgeon reported that he had found several tadpoles and horse leeches in his bath water. A filter was rapidly acquired. The pressure still fluctuated and sometimes would not fill the huge storage tank. A year later the city council laid larger pipes, but the pressure remained variable and arrangements were made for the pressure to be maintained on Wednesday and Friday to fill up the tanks, because Thursday was the weekly bathing day at the infirmary.

In 1894 there was an extensive review of the hot water and heating systems. Prior to this date there were three inadequate sources for supplying hot water consisting of a solid fuel boiler on each floor. Only one hot bath was possible at a time and many basins had no hot water supply. A new solid fuel kitchen range and boiler was installed, together with two new boilers on the first floor. The boiler on the second floor was retained. Heating of the wards had previously been by open fires but now a central heating system was installed with radiators in the wards and corridors. A solid fuel furnace was placed in a new excavated cellar, below the original building, called 'the stoke hole', to heat three boilers. Dr Chapman, honorary physician, was able to report to the Board of Management that since the introduction of the new heating apparatus the temperature of the wards was more uniform and the comfort of the patients in getting to and from the toilets was much improved.

In December 1893 the House and Grounds Committee was formed with responsibility for the state of the buildings and grounds. This led to an improvement in general maintenance, including a new roof in 1896. That same year an earth tremor caused cracks in ceilings and walls. Meanwhile, the infirmary grounds saw changes as Dr Henry Bull, a physician, took a lively interest in them, designing the front garden and donating trees for the back.

As early as 1863 the City Council had been keen to construct a riverside path in front of the infirmary to link up Castle Green with Bartonsham Meadow to the south. This was turned down by the governors, who were reluctant to give up any land and considered such a public path as a potential nuisance to the patients. The request was renewed in 1893 and was reluctantly agreed to with strict conditions—the path would be locked at night and a fence would be built to discourage rubbish being thrown into the infirmary grounds. The public gained a useful asset, even though the following year the River Wye swept away the pathway. It was rebuilt by the council using stone, iron rods and concrete when the river was low. The governors were also concerned about people bathing in the river in front of the infirmary, probably for moral reasons, and sought the support of the police to prevent this happening. However the annoyance was not always one-sided. The infirmary had a punt moored at the river bank, adjacent to the Victoria Suspension Bridge, which annoyed a neighbour. As a result a mooring for the punt was rented for £1 p.a. from the adjacent St James's Vicarage.

The Riverside Walk in 1896 (Alfred Watkins)

The Board of Management continued to be given increasing responsibility, and now consisted of an elected chairman, the president of the infirmary, the vice-presidents, the honorary medical staff and six governors. However, often as few as four people turned up. In 1896 they were given the authority to appoint all paid officers, including the chaplain and secretary.

The Board was often exchanging letters with the Boards of Guardians running local workhouses in Ledbury, Leominster, Dore, Hay-on-Wye and others as far away as Rhayader, Abergavenny, and Crickhowell, all of which had subscribed to the infirmary and were given tickets for their paupers. Either they were slow in paying their subscriptions or were criticised for not keeping to the printed Rules, sending patients who were unsuitable, or on the wrong day or without proper documentation.

The appointment of medical staff by the governors had resulted in canvassing in spite of it being forbidden. In 1896 it was therefore resolved that future vacancies were to be filled by an elective committee of 23 governors— 10 elected by the Annual Meeting and 10 by the Board. The president, the mayor and the chairman of the Board were to be the three *ex-officio* members. It was also decided that an honorary physician or surgeon who had reached the age of 70 years or had held the appointment for 25 years should retire.

On another front the governors brought the attention of the medical staff to the greatly increased amount of wine and beer consumed. In 1865, 12 gallons of Cognac Brandy had been ordered at 25s a gallon and a further 16 gallons three years later at 20s a gallon. Mr Arthur Levason, a governor and dental surgeon, expressed anxiety at the amount of stimulants being consumed by the officers, nurses and servants. There is no record whether these comments had any effect. Ale and porter remained under the control of the matron.

Over the half century capital projects had been financed by public appeals and a few large private donations. The investments in the capital fund had been protected and in December 1889 stood at £49,311. The county council made several requests during this period for loans from the infirmary to help finance various projects, particularly the new Lunatic Asylum at Burghill. As a result, over £8,000 was lent to the council, guaranteed by the rates, to be repaid over 30 years, allowing the infirmary to benefit from the interest.

Several trust funds were established for specific purposes. Thus in 1887, following the death of Dr Henry Bull, the Bull Convalescent Fund was set up by his friends with an initial capital of over £300. Its purpose was to defray the cost of sending infirmary patients to a convalescent home, seaside or country residence for a change of air and scene. Good food and rest were considered beneficial to restore health and strength. The governors regularly allocated the

	Date elected	Years in office
Board of Management		
Mr Francis Hawkins	1880	6
Mr Thomas Cam	1887	3
Mr W.G. Barton	1890	4
Mr Joseph Carless jnr.	1894	6
Mr James Hutchinson	1990	2
Count L. Bodenham-Lubienski	1902	1
Lt. Gen. Sir Edward Hopkins, K.C.B.	1903	8
Sir Geoffrey Cornewall	1911	15
The Honourable R.C. Devereux, D.L.	1926	3
The Very Rev. the Dean of Hereford R. Waterfield	1929	7
House Committee		
Count L. Bodenham-Lubienski	1902	6
Col. Hewat	1909	3
Sir H. Archer Croft	1912	4
Col. Hewat	1916	7
Major Owen Croft	1923	6
Col. H.E.P. Pateshall	1929	16
Mr R.M. Bentley	1945	3
Executive Council		
Col. H.E.P. Pateshall, D.S.O., D.L., J.P.	1934	3
Mr G.A.C. Thynne	1937	11

Table 5
Chairmen of various administrative committees of the General over the years

income each year sending patients to various homes such as the Royal Alexandra Convalescent Hospital at Porthcawl, the Royal West of England Sanatorium at Weston-Super-Mare, the Salt Baths at Droitwich and the Royal Mineral Water Hotel at Bath.

In 1891 the Executive Committee of the Venn Memorial Fund asked the governors to take over the running of the fund, which at that time stood at £610. The capital was to be invested and the income used to assist patients who had incurable conditions. The fund was set up in memory of John Venn, 1802-90, one of Hereford's greatest philanthropists, who was vicar of St Peter's and St James's churches from 1832-70 and for seven years from 1864 was chaplain to the infirmary. In 1835 he established an outpatient dispensary in Hereford which 50 years later was seeing nearly 4,000 patients a year. He was responsible for setting up many charities including the Society for Aiding the Industrious. This society received funds from donations and its functions included providing baths and a swimming pool, letting allotments of land for gardens, opening a soup kitchen in severe weather, lending up to £15 at low interest rates and providing benefits for invalids. It also regularly donated £100 to the infirmary.

Despite all this activity, financial troubles were once more rearing their head towards the end of the century, and by 1899 the annual accounts showed a deficit of £1,300, almost a third of the expenditure. The proportion of income from investments at 60 per cent, and subscriptions at 30 per cent had changed little over the previous 50 years, but both totals had fallen with interest rates declining and some of the more liberal subscribers dying and not being replaced. In addition, charitable giving from churches and individuals was now being shared with the newly emerging cottage hospitals. On the expenditure front, all the costs had increased. The cost of fuel in 1899 had trebled since 1849 while the costs of surgical and medical supplies had increased fivefold. Drugs were now supplied by Messrs Chave and Jackson, a pharmaceutical business still trading in Broad Street. The governors were facing the most serious financial crises in the history of the infirmary. The solution was to be found early in the next century.

Two Professions, 1850 - 1899

The latter half of the 19th century was the golden age for the medical staff because not only were they well qualified and competent at their profession and contributed greatly to the infirmary's administration, but many played a prominent part in the life of the city and countryside. At the same time the nurses, partly due to the influence of Florence Nightingale, stopped being looked upon as servants and started the long struggle to become a great and respected profession.

Dr Bleek Lye resigned in January 1864, after nearly 44 years service and died shortly after from cancer of the stomach. He was described as a tall commanding figure with a store of personal anecdotes which he would relate in a racy style at fitting moments, often cheering up the sick ward. During his funeral most shops closed and the bells of the cathedral, St Nicholas and All Saints churches tolled all morning. He was replaced by Henry Graves Bull, who was elected unanimously. Dr Bull was born at Pitsford, near Northampton. He studied medicine at Edinburgh University where he won two gold medals for essays on cerebral disease and the chances of infants surviving. He also gained the prize for surgery, a case of amputation instruments—not the most appropriate gift for a potential physician. He even learnt Italian in order to understand a reference in one of his papers. He died quite suddenly of cancer of the stomach on 15th January 1885 after 21 years of service to the infirmary, aged 67. He was a magistrate, a tireless physician, an innovator, a very active manager and a founder member of the Hereford Medical Association. Along with the Rev. John Venn he established the Hereford Society for Aiding the Industrious and was a founder member of the Free Library. In addition he was the life and soul, a founder member, and at times president and editor of the famous Woolhope Naturalists' Field Club, whose purpose was to study Herefordshire in all its aspects and publish the results. Their most publicised activity during his time was their Annual Fungus Forays. A plaque in his memory is on the wall outside his house in St John Street.

Dr Henry Graves Bull,
honorary physician 1864-85

Dr Paul Chapman was elected to replace Dr Bull after two other candidates were considered to have inadequate qualifications. During a lively discussion, Mr Henry Vevers, honorary surgeon threatened to resign if a Dr Matthews, one of the other candidates, was appointed, a discussion in which the honorary solicitor Mr W.J. Humfrys was invited to define a physician, but wisely declined to do so.

Initially there was one resident house surgeon, appointed by the governors on the recommendation of the Board of Management. By the end of the century the Board were given the authority to make these appointments without referring to the governors. However, qualifications in both medicine and surgery were required by candidates, who were also to be single, between the ages of 25 and 40. The appointment was even limited to two years. The house surgeon was only allowed leave if he provided a suitable locum or replacement at his own expense; one house surgeon was reprimanded for taking leave when there were seriously ill cases in the infirmary. The house surgeon's duties involved carrying out the instructions of the medical staff in looking after their patients and attending ward rounds. There were also many additional tasks including investigating and reporting damage to the fabric of the buildings. He ordered surgical instruments and medical reference books for the staff and engaged additional night nurses when required.

The Board would, however, often express their appreciation of the house surgeon's work. A certain Mr Giles, for example, was thanked for looking after scarlet fever cases, which either must either have developed in hospital or had been admitted in error, with such kindness and attention that he was given £10 to enable him to have a well earned holiday. In 1898, in view of increasing work and complaints by a succession of house surgeons that they required additional help, the governors accepted plans for appointing an assistant house surgeon.

During this period pupils continued to be taken on for training, usually staying for one to two years. Contracts were drawn up by the infirmary's solicitor and fees paid in advance by the pupil's parents or guardian. Pupils could also take their meals at the infirmary upon payment in advance of 10 guineas p.a. for lunch and 21 guineas for dinner. The sons of gentlemen connected with the infirmary were offered a reduction, and the medical staff continued to bring their own articled pupils with them into the infirmary without payment. Short term pupils, often medical students, were also accepted for a fee payable to the infirmary. The only additional equipment purchased for the pupils appeared to be disarticulated skeletons.

During this half century there were five matrons appointed. Although they still played a major roll as housekeeper and were in charge of the nurses and servants, they were increasingly expected to have nursing experience and be prepared to teach. Miss Markham of Swansea was appointed in 1869 at a salary of £50 p.a. with rooms and board. The following year she was allowed a month's leave during which the Board accepted that her sister, who was also a nurse, could deputise for her. She resigned 18 months later after a disagreement about visiting hours and attempts to restrict the newspapers and periodicals available for the patients.

Mrs Baker, aged 33, who came from Bath was then elected and served for 15 years. She had a little girl who was allowed to stay in the infirmary with her. The matron and officers were usually charged £2 a year for beer, but as Mrs Baker kept to wine and spirits she was only charged £1.

In 1887, after advertising in the *Lancet* and local papers, Miss Annie Sharpe was appointed matron and served for 12 years. During this time the Board gave her the authority to summarily dismiss any porter, nurse or servant guilty of misconduct, misbehaviour, insolence or neglect. When she left, there were 71 applicants for the vacant post and Miss Katherine Elphick, Lady Superintendent of the North London Hospital for diseases of the chest was elected at a salary of £90 p.a. and served for just over four years. One official visitor on a routine inspection of the infirmary was duly impressed by finding her engaged in making sheets for the patients.

In 1875 the governors decided to train their own nurses and promote them according to their ability, in the hope that they would remain in the infirmary. A programme for training probationary nurses was approved and three trainees were appointed on two year contracts. No specialised tutors were taken on and the teaching was carried out by the medical staff, house surgeon, matron and senior nurses. The medical staff were enthusiastic about their new role because they hoped it would lead to better trained nurses to look after their patients. Of the 13 girls who followed this route and on whom we have information, eight completed their training of whom all but one obtained permanent posts in the infirmary. Three were dismissed, one for insolence, another for neglect of duty and the third for drinking alcohol early one Christmas morning. Of the other two one was given a month's notice for continued ill health, and one left early.

With the increase in conditions suitable for operative treatment, new nursing skills were constantly required. In addition the male and female divisions were subdivided into medical and surgical wards, and when Victoria Ward opened an additional head nurse was appointed. By the end of the century the permanent staff consisted of two sisters and 15 nurses.

The matron continued to enforce discipline in the nurses. One nurse was discharged because she gave opium pills and brandy to a patient without orders. One nurse left without notice and her father paid compensation. A fine of 6d was levied on any nurse who broke a thermometer. There were also complaints from subscribers and patients against the nursing staff for misconduct, insobriety and charging for washing clothes which were all investigated and usually found lacking substance.

In spite of the strict discipline, compassion survived and one nurse was given a gratuity of £5 for extra help she had given during a smallpox outbreak. Three nurses died in post and in two cases their families or friends were given temporary financial help. At one stage the nurses expressed dissatisfaction over their diet and asked to be allowed 1 lb of bacon each per week as an alternative to cheese; this was accepted. The Board also thought they should have green vegetables in addition to potatoes. From 1874 the nursing staff were provided with uniforms, obtained from Greenlands Store in High Town.

There were lighter moments too. In once case a probationer nurse, Helen Latham, volunteered to play an ugly old charwoman with a black eye and a red nose in one of Dr Chapman's plays when no other nurse would volunteer. He rewarded her with a 'pale green muslin dress, trimmed with wet looking imitation grass and tiny frogs' to her apparent delight.

Near the end of the century there was an increasing demand for a private nursing service to provide nurses in private homes and temporary help in other institutions and in 1892 the governors agreed to establish such a service. Trained nurses were based at the infirmary, under the control of the matron, who was to receive an additional salary of £20 p.a. The nurses were paid a minimum salary of £24 p.a. and were to wear the uniform of the institution. When not engaged in private nursing they were available to attend hospital patients. Initially four nurses were to be engaged and would be accommodated in the attic.

The private nurse was allowed eight hours out of 24 for rest and outdoor activities and permitted to attend a place of worship on Sundays. She was to keep secret any personal details about her patients and their household. The nurse would not be expected to do servants' work nor would she eat in the sick room or with the servants. Nursing was starting to come of age.

The accounts for this private service were kept in a separate fund from those of the infirmary. It soon proved popular and profitable and the fund paid the infirmary £150 p.a. to cover expenses as well as contributing larger donations from time to time.

By the end of the century the servants at the infirmary included a cook, a kitchen maid, a laundry maid, a house maid, a scrubber and a porter. An old servant named 'Kitty' who had been at the infirmary for 40 years had become too old and infirm to work so the Board granted her a pension of 5s a week, but this was not to set a precedent.

The porter-cum-lodge keeper was provided with a free suit of clothes and was allowed three weeks leave after three years in the post. One of his duties was to milk the infirmary's cow night and morning. In 1869 a house boy—a term covering youths well into their twenties—was appointed at 3s 6d a week, and provided with a greatcoat. He was a general dogsbody for the porter, cook and matron. The matron had to dismiss one house boy for misconduct with the kitchen maid. He disappeared along with his greatcoat, but attempts to take him before the magistrates were abandoned as the Hereford Infirmary was not an incorporated body so could not maintain an action at law.

The governors did not hesitate to reprimand the chaplain if he did not honour the Rules. One chaplain started evening services in place of the stipulated morning ones, and when it was drawn to his attention he resigned. He was expected to be in priest's formal attire when he visited, but by the 1870s nonconformist ministers were recognised and encouraged to visit their own church members. Following the Rev. John Venn the Rev. W. Duncombe was elected chaplain by 51 votes to 22 and he raised money to provide a harmonium for the infirmary.

Treatment, 1850 - 1899
By the end of the century the infirmary could accommodate 107 patients, 47 males, 40 females and 20 children. In addition there were two isolation wards each with three beds. In the year 1899 the number of inpatients discharged or who had died was 570, of which 233 were accident or emergency cases, and 35, or 6 per cent, had died. The total number of inpatients discharged appears to be similar to that of 1849, but the figures are difficult to compare because almost half of the discharges in 1849 were made outpatients and so the outcome of treatment is not obvious. The number of new outpatients treated was 2,856. a threefold increase over the 50 years, made up of 1,200 new patients referred with letters of recommendation, 1,295 patients arriving as casualties, 263 dental patients and 98 patients referred for surgical appliances.

It was during this period that the first glimpse of specialisation began to appear. Although anaesthesia had first been used in Hereford in January 1847 it was usually administered by the house surgeon, and there were no specialist anaesthetists till the next century. Even so, various pieces of specialised equipment began to appear and in 1871 an apparatus for administering laughing gas was donated to the infirmary.

In 1882 the governors had accepted Dr Bull's suggestion that a dental surgeon should be appointed who held a 'Licentiate of Dental Surgery' and be resident in Hereford. He would attend once a week to extract teeth which would be done without tickets of recommendation from governors being required. Advice and treatment of other conditions such as oral deformities, irregularities of teeth or fractures would require tickets.

In 1888 a special lamp for examining the eyes and throat was provided. Five years later a cardiographic apparatus to take tracings of the heart was procured for Dr Chapman who became the pioneer of cardiology in Hereford. Three years later he was found using this equipment in his private practice, which stimulated some comment. It was subsequently agreed that he would be allowed to use the equipment in this way, but only with permission from the Board. In 1894 he gave three notable lectures at the Royal College of Physicians on 'The Physics of the Circulation'. A patient, Mr Higford Burr, donated £1,000 to provide a ward for urological problems resulting in two

X-rays in 1896. There is a high vacuum tube above the lady's hand and a high voltage induction coil being controlled by the operator. Its battery supply is below the table

small male and female wards being given over to diseases of the bladder and associated conditions.

Information about Röntgen's discovery of X-rays reached London in January 1896. The following November the governors sanctioned Dr Chapman to purchase a Röntgen apparatus costing £30 for the use of the infirmary. There were no dedicated X-ray sets at that time and the suppliers put together their apparatus from a collection of components available in laboratories, consisting of a high vacuum tube which produced radiation when a current was put through it, and a high voltage induction coil to control the current energised by either primary batteries or accumulators charged from a dynamo. The low power of this equipment meant exposures ranged from one to 10 minutes to X-ray a hand while denser parts of the body could take up to 60 minutes. Examinations were limited to locating foreign bodies and bone fractures at the body's extremities. There was no protection from radiation. The equipment could also be used with a fluorescent screen which was more popular than taking a permanent photographic record.

By 1899 there are detailed records in the annual reports of all the conditions which had been treated that year. They included, in descending order of number of treatments, 24 cases of anaemia, 23 of rheumatism, 20 of pneumonia and tuberculosis of the lungs, 17 of heart attack, 12 of stomach ulcers, eight of degenerative osteoarthritis, eight of bronchitis, seven of pleurisy and six of influenza. The commonest conditions dealt with at the Accident and Casualty Department included 58 cases of simple closed fractures, seven of

Screening

compound fractures with bone exposed, 33 wounds, 26 varicose ulcers and 10 burns.

Until the 1870s infection frequently complicated surgical operations leading to a high mortality rate. In the 1860s Louis Pasteur showed that micro-organisms were responsible for infections and Lord Lister in Glasgow applied this knowledge by introducing antiseptic surgery, using carbolic acid sprays in the theatre to kill these organisms. Antiseptic surgery was then replaced by aseptic surgery, where the emphasis was on excluding organisms from the theatre environment mainly by cleanliness. Aseptic surgery was introduced to the infirmary in the 1890s. A probationer nurse described Mr Turner, the honorary surgeon, who used to practise antiseptic surgery, as being handsome, tall and very wise but sometimes naughty. This 'naughtiness' took the form of marching up to the operating table in his top coat, with collar and cuffs of sable, during an operation presumably being carried out by the house surgeon, and peering into the open wound, to the fury of the theatre sister who was trying to teach her nurses about aseptic surgery.

In 1899 there were 174 operations performed for 75 conditions with a mortality rate of 6.7 per cent. General anaesthesia was administered in 164 cases, using chloroform or ether, while local anaesthesia was used in nine cases and no anaesthetic at all in one case The commoner operations included 22 cases of draining abscesses, 14 removals of tonsils and adenoids and a similar number of amputation of fingers and toes, nine cases of removing dead, infected bone, five of superficial innocent tumours, five amputations of breasts for cancer, five circumcisions and four repairs of groin ruptures. Major surgery was uncommon, as just two cases of major amputations through a thigh or arm, one of exploring a depressed fracture of a skull and just one appendicectomy indicate.

There was a relief fund to provide patients with support stockings for leg ulcers, equipment for club feet, money to get home or attend another hospital and simple necessities such as slippers.

In 1853 a weekly diet for the patients was approved by the governors. Breakfast each day consisted of a pint of broth or cocoa, the mid-day meal rotated between 4 ounces of cooked meat with vegetables, meat soup with potatoes, and baked pudding, whilst the evening meal altered between between a pint of broth, 2 ounces of cheese and and half a pint of beer, or milk pottage (bread soaked in milk). The men were allowed slightly larger helpings, and were offered 16 ounces of bread per day against the women's 12 ounces. At dinner men were allowed one pint of beer and women half a pint, and tea and some coffee was also available. It does appear that this diet was often modified and fish dinners might be provided, or a pint of milk or beeftex in the evening.

Unsurprisingly, there were complaints about the food especially about it being cold. The medical staff were asked to review the menu, but pronounced the diet liberal. However, to keep the food hot, tin covers were purchased and meals served in the wards, though the matron complained that serving meals in the wards made patients more hungry and increased costs. In 1877 the patients complained that the butter was too salty. The Chairman of the Board visited and tasted it, pronouncing that the butter was indeed salty, but good and the patients could either wash the butter in cold water or do without. There were complaints about delays in admission and in being seen and on one occasion about a child being sent home in an unclean condition. These complaints were all investigated and usually pronounced groundless. Occasionally a fault was admitted as in the poor treatment of a head injury, a case where two nurses treated a patient roughly, and when a child with a cleft palate was fed with a spoon. However, only an apology appeared to be required. Grateful letters were also received from patients or subscribers.

Several patients were discharged for misbehaviour such as using abusive language to the nurses or going out without leave. Bringing in a bottle of whisky resulted in instant discharge. Less serious offences such as smoking were punished by withholding the beer allowance from the culprit, if known, or if unknown, from the ward.

The governors were very sensitive about publicity over mortality rates, the use of beds and the expense of long stay cases. For example, when two children who had fallen off a tree in Castle Green were brought in dead and registered in the house surgeon's book, the governors subsequently ordered the report to be struck out. The medical staff were also directed that if incurable cases were admitted they were to be discharged before they became too ill to move. Patients in the hospital for over two months had their cases reviewed and unless there was a chance of effective treatment they were discharged, either to their union workhouse or home to relatives. There was controversy in 1894 about who was responsible for the proper treatment of a corpse in hospital, following a complaint, which was denied, that a child's body had been put naked into a coffin. It was decided that the matron would be responsible in future.

CHAPTER 3

Herefordshire General Hospital from 1900 to the advent of the N.H.S.

Charity is not enough, 1900 – 1918

At the Annual General Meeting in 1900, the Mayor, Mr W.A. Humfrys, who presided, was concerned about the annual deficit. The governors had already set up a committee the previous year to secure the long term financial position without either selling investments or reducing beds, but it had not yet reported. The committee reported a few weeks later and after lengthy debates a series of radical changes were agreed—administrative support was to be strengthened so as to increase financial supervision; private paying patients were to be encouraged; and local authorities were to be charged for services which the hospital provided for them. This radical change to financing the hospital was made possible by having commercially minded governors such as Mr H.P. Bulmer and Mr Frederick Bulmer with experience of their cider business. In addition the name of the institution was altered to The Herefordshire General Hospital to improve its status and image—the name 'infirmary' had become associated with chronic sick wards, whilst the word 'General' was retained because it implied that patients would be accepted from any part of the country and not just from Herefordshire, subject to tickets of recommendation.

The committee suspected that part of the reason that expenditure had risen was due to a lack of financial control. The secretary's work had been confined to book keeping and managing the finances, while the matron's duties were too great to allow her to supervise expenditure in any detail. Therefore, a new post of superintendent was established to try and contain costs. He would be full time and resident, keep the books and oversee the expenditure. It was expected that he would also have time to seek more financial support. The previous secretary,

Mr Beddoes, graciously resigned and was thanked for 13 years of service and Mr Arthur Pierce was appointed to the new post at a salary of £150 p.a. However, within two years the Board of Management decided that any savings resulting from improved control of expenditure did not justify the continuation of the post and it was terminated.

In the course of time, the composition of the Board of Management was modified to consist of 12 Governors elected at the Annual General Meeting, a third retiring yearly but eligible for re-election. Cleverly, the third who retired would be those who had attended the least number of meetings. Only one honorary physician and one honorary surgeon would attend. The slimmed down Board, which was meant to be more effective, took over the work of the quarterly governors meetings, and met monthly. But good intentions don't always work out and within five years there were 48 members of the Board, which had been persuaded to include representatives from diverse groups to gain their support. The Board therefore appointed a House Committee to deal with most day to day matters.

The House Committee first met in November 1902 and thereafter every Monday, which became the only day of the week when non-emergency eligible patients were admitted, because everyone involved would be present. It regularly appointed sub-committees to advise on matters such as the upkeep of the buildings and grounds, nursing and fire precautions. In 1905 the committee increased the number of visitors to three gentlemen and three ladies. The words 'Objects of Charity' printed on the tickets were considered objectionable, and were replaced by 'Deserving Objects of Assistance' which doesn't sound much better to modern ears.

Meanwhile plans to increase income were slowly maturing. The first paying patient was admitted in January 1901, a charge being levied both for maintenance and for treatment by the medical staff. In return paying patients were given better food and had flexible visiting times. In 1907 semi-private patients, who had an income below a certain limit, were introduced. They were charged less than private patients, but were not looked upon as charitable cases. However, private patients were slow to take advantage of the facilities and though yearly receipts from this source rose to £174 in 1916, they then decreased again. Both the city and county council were charged for the treatment of certain types of tuberculosis, mainly of bone, that were not spread by direct contact and for the provision of a venereal disease service. As the treatment of cases referred and paid for by the local authorities were not charitable patients, the staff were usually paid a fee, but often only after much wrangling.

In the Education Act of 1907 the education authorities were given powers to carry out health checks on new pupils, and arrange and pay for suitable treatment where necessary. School children were referred to the hospital following routine medical inspections, notably for treatment of infected tonsils and adenoids and for ear diseases. The medical staff, following advice from the B.M.A. suggested that these referrals should stop as it was taking work away from the child's own general practitioner. Indeed the local papers printed stories about 'the Doctors Revolt', but this soon collapsed. The contributory schemes also started to produce more income, and during the war the Government also contributed funds towards the treatment of wounded and of discharged soldiers.

Nevertheless, in spite of all these new sources of income charity was still important. In 1900, in order to encourage more subscribers and benefactors, their privileges were increased and modified. Privileges were also extended to the clergy who held collections on behalf of the charity. But within two years it was realized that the hospital had been issuing tickets of admission beyond the limits of its finances, so the Rules were once again changed to give fewer tickets to supporters and to restrict the time for which these were available. There was initial anxiety that people needing admission might not be able to get tickets but this did not happen, as many subscribers instead increased their subscriptions.

Some individuals chose to dedicate a bed for £500 or a cot for £250, which would be named in memory of a nominated person, whilst the interest on the capital qualified the donor for tickets of admission. In 1909, Col. Hewat, a chairman of the House Committee, along with his family endowed a bed in memory of his son Arthur Henry Hewat with priority to be given to young men under 21 with conditions of the lungs. In 1916 eight little girls died when taking part in a concert in the Garrick Theatre to aid the troops, when their inflammable costumes caught fire. A cot was endowed in Victoria Ward in their memory. Single donations were raised from entertainments such as fêtes, balls, concerts and horseracing. Certain annual events were the source of steady support. Hospital Sunday collections continued. A May Fair was held in Hereford every year and a 'May Fair Hour' became an annual event where the proceeds taken over a designated hour were donated to the hospital. The Industrious Aid Society offered £100 for five years.

Queen Alexandra started a Rose Day street collection in aid of hospitals to mark the 50th anniversary of her coming to England. The first collections in Hereford began in 1914 and raised £38. They continued and developed into a well organised campaign each year which was sometimes spread over several days. Collections were ultimately organised into 10 districts, involving 21 hotels and cafés and 14 street collectors.

Some individuals or groups chose to give towards a particular project. For example, the officers of the disbanded Herefordshire Militia donated £126 for operating theatre improvements. In 1909 a Samaritan Fund was established to

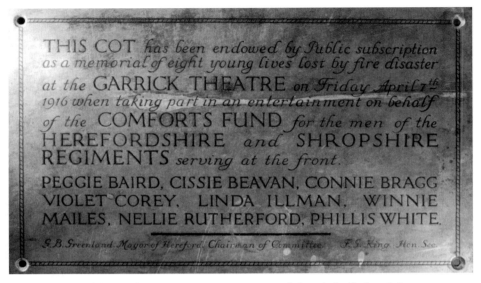

THIS COT *has been endowed by Public subscription as a memorial of eight young lives lost by fire disaster* at the GARRICK THEATRE *on Friday April 7th 1916 when taking part in an entertainment on behalf* of the COMFORTS FUND *for the men of the* HEREFORDSHIRE *and* SHROPSHIRE REGIMENTS *serving at the front.* PEGGIE BAIRD, CISSIE BEAVAN, CONNIE BRAGG VIOLET COREY, LINDA ILLMAN, WINNIE MAILES, NELLIE RUTHERFORD, PHILLIS WHITE. *G.B. Greenland Mayor of Hereford Chairman of Committee   F.S. King Hon. Sec.*

Tablet endowing a cot in memory of the eight little girls
who died in a fire at the Garrick Theatre

supply artificial limbs, false teeth and other surgical appliances for patients who could not afford to pay. In 1915, stimulated by the loss of limbs in wounded soldiers the 'Guild of the brave young things' was formed to help with providing artificial limbs.

By 1918 annual income had risen to £8,228, an increase of nearly three times that for 1899. Charity still proved the largest source at 59 per cent; although the percentage was down, the actual amount had increased by over £2,000. Paying patients and selling services to local authorities raised 9 per cent, contributory schemes 7 per cent, Government grants 23 per cent and miscellaneous items 2 per cent. The source of funds had radically changed over 18 years and this change was to continue.

Expenditure had also steadily risen but only to £7,606. A comparison of patient cost was made with other hospitals in England and the costs in Hereford Hospital came out the cheapest at £1 3s 4d per bed per week.

There was no major building work during this period, though improvements had been made in consulting room facilities for physicians and for outpatient surgery, a larger nurses' dining room had been provided along with improved sleeping accommodation for domestic servants. In 1905 an Electric Light Committee was set up to advise on electric light installation at the request of the medical staff as electricity was now necessary in certain treatments, whilst the lighting in the operating theatre was unsatisfactory. When an operation had to be carried out by artificial light, the gas lighting needed to be supplemented by oil lamps held by nurses, a practice that was inconvenient and dangerous. Electricity was duly installed.

The governors were anxious that the hospital should be kept up to date and January 1910 invited Sir Henry Burdett to visit and advise on the hospital's state. Sir Henry, who had been superinten-

The verandah on Victoria Ward

dent at Queen's Hospital, Birmingham, was a recognised authority on hospitals. He reported that the hospital was not up to date in spite of £10,000 being spent on it over the previous 20 years, and advised the building of a new wing. But no action was taken because of the expense.

In June 1913 a verandah was built onto Victoria Ward financed by Mrs Hewat, the wife of Col. Hewat. The telephone system was also steadily improved and by 1914 there were telephones installed between the wards, although there was only one outside line.

By 1900 the first junior house surgeon had been appointed at a salary of £35 p.a., but there were difficulties in allocating duties between the senior house surgeon and after 12 years the post was abolished. The senior house surgeon's duties included giving lectures to the nurses, for which he could get an extra £5 to £10, and keeping an inventory of all the surgical instruments belonging to the hospital.

The system of the house officers wearing white jackets when on duty started in 1908. Being a house officer had its risks and Mr Meyrick James was assaulted by a drunk patient, irritated because his truss was not available. In 1915, during the First World War, as so many male doctors were being called up to serve in the forces a lady house surgeon, Mrs Blanche Walter Stallard, was appointed.

In 1904 Miss Nicol was appointed as the dispenser, and was also put in charge of the stocks of wines and spirits. She, too, was allowed to take on a pupil.

	Date appointed	Yrs service to 1948
Physician in charge of the Cardiology Department		
Charles W. Walker, M.C., M.A., M.D., Ch.B.	1937	11
Anaesthetists		
Meyrick James, M.B.(Brux), M.R.C.S., L.R.C.P.	1912	
W. Ainslie, M.D., F.R.C.S.	1914	5
C.H.G. Philp	1914	
Blanche Walters Stallard, M.D., B.S.(Lond.)	1919	3
J.A. Pritchard, M.R.C.S., L.R.C.P.	1922	9
S.L. Corry, M.B., B.S.(Adelaide)	1927	
W.G. Maule, M.B., B.Ch., B.A.O.(Dublin)	1929	15
W. Moir Brown, M.B., Ch.B.(Edin.), F.R.C.S.(Edin.)	1932	1
Anne Pillans, L.R.C.S.(Eng.), L.R.C.P.(Lond.), L.R.F.P.S.(Glas.)	1933	2
H.S. Perrot, M.B., B.Ch., B.A.O., B.A.(Dublin)	1935	13
Charles Langley Owen, M.A., M.B., B.Ch., F.R.C.S.(Eng.), L.R.C.P.(Lond.)	1936	5
Madeline Malcomson, M.B., Ch.B.	1937	8
G.R. Malkin, M.R.C.S.(Eng.), L.R.C.P.(Lond.)	1939	9
G.H. James, M.R.C.S.(Eng.), L.R.C.P.(Lond.)	1939	9
Eleanor Russell, M.D.	1941	1
Marie E. Potter, M.B., Ch.B.(Birm.), D.A.	1942	6
Helen Wood, M.B., Ch.B., D.A.	1945	1
A.H. Zair, M.A., M.R.C.S.(Eng.), L.R.C.P.(Lond.), M.B., B.Ch.(Cantab.), D.A.	1945	3

Table 6 (above and opposite)
Specialists appointed at the General Hospital

It was during these early years of the twentieth century that some of the specialties accepted as a matter of fact today became established. For example, in 1903 a bacteriological laboratory was opened and Dr Herbert Jones was appointed honorary bacteriologist, even providing his own research equipment. In fact the laboratory seems to have been essentially used for research and there is no evidence that it provided any significant service for the hospital.

Although the first X-ray equipment was provided in 1896 the Electric and X-ray Department was only established in 1907 by converting one of the outpatient waiting rooms when it was agreed to spend £150 on modern X-ray and high frequency apparatus. This time Mr Albert Simpson, a Governor, donated shields to protect the operators from radiation. The electrical equipment consisted of constant (D.C.) and alternating (A.C.) current to stimulate muscles

	Date appointed	Yrs service to 1948
Assistant Orthopaedic Surgeons		
Richard Wood Power, B.A., M.B., D.P.H.(Trin. Coll. Dublin)	1925	1
Brian Thomas, B.A., M.B., B.Ch., M.R.C.S., L.R.C.P., F.R.C.S	1947	1
Ophthalmic Surgeons		
Norman H. Pike, M.B., Ch.B.(Lond.)	1918	4
H. Woodward Barnes, M.R.C.S.(Eng.), L.R.C.P.(Lond.)	1922	26
Ear, Nose and Throat Surgeons		
John B Cavenagh, M.C., M.R.C.S., L.R.C.P., D.L.O.	1926	22
Ian W. MacGregor, M.B., Ch.B.	1926	22
Psychiatrists		
G.W. Flemming, M.R.C.S., L.R.C.P., D.P.M.(Eng.)	1934	3
T.E. Burrows, B.A.(Cantab), M.R.C.S.(Eng.), L.R.C.P.(Lond.), D.P.M.(Eng.)	1937	11
Bacteriologist		
Herbert Jones L.R.C.S.I., D.P.H.	1904	
Pathologists (Not honorary but paid)		
W. Stewart, M.D.	1934	8
R.E. Jones, B.Sc., M.R.C.S., L.R.C.P., D.P.H.	1942	6
W.H.J. Baker, M.B., B.S., M.R.C.S., L.R.C.P.	1947	1
Radiologists		
W. Ainslie, M.C., M.D., F.R.C.S.	1929	6
Malcolm Milton Melrose, M.R.C.S., L.R.C.P.	1935	13

and nerves for diagnostic and therapeutic purposes. The theatre sister acted as radiographer. With the constant necessity to repair and upgrade X-ray equipment, a fund was established to cover the costs and a scale of fees for private patients was soon produced.

In 1912 Meyrick James was appointed as the first honorary anaesthetist to the hospital under the general direction of the operating surgeon. This relationship did not survive for long as the anaesthetists struggled for equal clinical status. Two years later it was agreed that a joint appointment of two anaesthetists should be made. The dental surgeon's suggestion that the hospital should buy their anaesthetic gas from him at half the price was also accepted. As he also wished to keep some of his anaesthetised patients in hospital, a maintenance charge of 2 guineas was agreed. While no fee was charged for extracting teeth, the provision of false teeth required a ticket of recommendation.

Four matrons were appointed during this period. Although now requiring nursing experience and involved in teaching probationers, housekeeping remained a major responsibility. Mr Michael Biddulph of Ledbury, a governor serving on the nursing committee, was reported as saying about the matron that 'a woman who could keep 40 other women in order was a person of great merit.'

Early in the 1900s the house porter was in the lift when the rope holding the cage broke, causing the lift to fall from the first to the ground floor and pitching him out. He was admitted to the hospital and subsequently awarded two weeks' holiday. This incident resulted in an insurance policy being taken out for an annual premium of 1 guinea against claims by employees.

By 1901 the permanent nursing staff by day consisted of four sisters or charge nurses and eight other nurses, while at night there was one sister and four nurses. There were additional probationers in training and there was a policy to encourage and promote nurses trained at the hospital. Indeed, by 1907 it appears that all the nurses, with the exception of maternity nurses, had been recruited from those who had completed three years training in the hospital. Nurses who had not had a surgical training were retrained. There was also a need for some nurses to develop special skills and they were sent away on courses for specialist training. Sister Goodridge, in charge of Oxford Ward and the operating theatre, attended Guy's Hospital in London to learn about the sterilisation of dressings.

In 1903 Miss Heins, a masseuse, was asked to lecture the nurses on massage. During the First World War a masseuse called Miss Lara was particularly popular with the wounded soldiers and was given a presentation in November 1918. With increasing war casualties requiring rehabilitation, outpatient facilities for massage, mobilisation exercises, heat and electrical treatment were made available.

The war resulted in many changes. In September 1914 The War Office were offered the use of 60 beds for sick and wounded soldiers on terms to be agreed. Some of these beds would only be available after six to 14 days warning. Owing to the demands of civilian patients the allocation was later reduced to 35, and a marquee for wounded soldiers was provided in the meadow behind the hospital, but it was never used. In October 1914 the first convoy of wounded soldiers arrived by train and the stationmaster and Red Cross Society were responsible for conveying the soldiers across the city to the hospital. Over the next four years 28 convoys containing 610 wounded soldiers arrived and were treated. During the same time 166 local troops were looked after.

Any recruits needing an operation to enable them to join the army were treated without a ticket, whilst Hereford Territorials wounded and returning home were treated free. Soldiers in camps in Hereford were admitted at 1 guinea a week.

In 1914 some of the wounded soldiers were of Belgian nationality and the Rev. Canon Dolman was asked to make arrangements for their spiritual care as they were Roman Catholics. So many people wished to visit the Belgians that visiting had to be restricted.

In October 1915 wounded soldiers transferred from Cardiff were considered more suitable for a convalescent hospital than a general hospital and were passed on to the Red Cross which ran two convalescent hospitals in the city at Hampton Grange, Hampton Park Road, Tupsley and Beechwood in Venn's Lane. The honorary staff had appointments at both hospitals.

In 1918 the Military Authorities agreed to transfer up to 10 of their beds to the Ministry of War Pensions for discharged and disabled soldiers. The rules for wounded soldiers, who were in the general hospital, were relaxed and they were allowed to smoke and visit the city in the afternoon. They tried their luck when they suggested it was customary to issue the wounded with beer or spirits, a suggestion turned down by Lt. Col. C. Rundle, the local commanding officer, unless prescribed by the doctors.

A munitions factory with an average output of 70,000 shells a week was erected on the Rotherwas estate in 1916, employing over 5,000 workers. This also increased the work of the hospital, fortunately only due to sickness rather than any explosions at the factory. They showed their appreciation by donating the proceeds of their pantomime, Cinderella, to the hospital.

In the year to December 1918, 922 inpatients were seen, an increase of 50 per cent since 1900. Included were 214 sick and wounded soldiers received by convoy direct from the seat of war and also 20 discharged soldiers treated under arrangements with the Ministry of War Pensions. The average bed occupancy was 86 with a stay of 34 days. The number of operations had doubled to 442, in which chloroform was used 340 times, gas 100 times and ether six times — the use of gas and ether could be combined. 2,255 outpatients had attended.

The hospital was still subject to complaints but, as earlier, most were refuted. In one notable exception, the parents of an infant, who had died in hospital and whose body was confused with another newly born infant and taken away in error were offered an apology and given expenses of 7s 6d.

Buildings Galore and Financial Chaos, 1919 - 1939

With the war over a period of massive modernisation and development began. In 1919 an electric lift was provided, due to a generous donation from the Red Cross, replacing the previous hand powered one. Two revolving huts were placed in the grounds behind the hospital so that convalescent patients could catch the sun or avoid the wind.

The nurses' accommodation had been a disgrace to the hospital with nurses having to be boarded out and a decision had been taken to build a nurses' home. But in 1918 this was temporarily deferred and instead Wolseley Villa in Mill Street was purchased to house up to 12 nurses. This provided only brief respite and a new plan was proposed to build a nurses' home at right angles to the hospital's southern wing at a cost of £13,222, using a donation from the Red Cross of £4,500 augmented by appeals. The foundation stone was laid on 2nd October 1920 by Mrs Hewat, wife of Col. Hewat, current chairman of the House Committee. Built of brick with a slate roof it could accommodate over 30 nurses on three floors. It was a great occasion on 1st April 1922 when it was opened by the honourable Miss Violet Biddulph in the presence of the high sheriff, the mayor and city councillors, the bishop, the governors and 500 guests. Four previous matrons also attended. The following report appeared in the *Hereford Times* in February 1926. 'The Nurses Home gives glorious river views and looks

Wolseley Villa in Mill Street used for nurses' accommodation

out upon the distant Black Mountains on one side and Dinedor Hill on the other. It houses an assistant matron, 8 sisters and 28 probationers in separate bedrooms with hot and cold water laid on. On the ground floor are a sisters' sitting room, a nurses sitting room, a study with well filled bookshelves and a spacious recreation room.'

Since the last operating theatre renovation in 1909, surgery had made vast strides, and by 1922 the number of operations performed was 678, nearly two and a half times greater than in 1908. Indeed, surgical cases now made up 70 per cent of the total inpatients. After inspecting theatres in 13 hospitals it was resolved that a separate operative wing be built on the site of the isolation block. When the

Bas relief medallion of Col. James R.C. Hewat

wing opened in 1925 it provided two operating theatres with associated anaesthetic rooms. Most of the finance, which came to £5,014, was provided by the

The front of the hospital seen from the avenue showing the porch and, on the right, the nurses' home with its flat roof

The nurses' recreation room as seen in the annual report for 1929

trustees of the late Mr Benjamin St. John Attwood Matthews, a governor who was high sheriff in 1891 and had lived in Pontrilas Court.

A report in the *Hereford Times* commented on the new theatres. 'Outside the theatres there was a board telling what operation was being performed and by which surgeon. Nearby there was a telephone communicating with all the wards. From a double lobby one entered a room set apart for the surgeons and

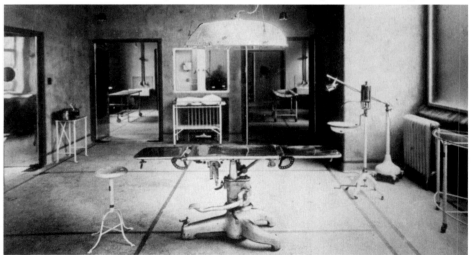

The operating theatre opened in 1925

Aerial view of the General Hospital.
At the back on the left is the Hewat Pavilion opposite the isolation block.
Forward from the pavilion is the new outpatient department on the ground
floor, Davey Ward on the first floor and the maternity unit on the second
floor. On the right hand side in front is the completed nurses' home

nurses to clean and scrub their hands before putting on gowns. From the left side of the lobby an anaesthetic room is entered, which leads through a further door into a theatre packed with modern equipment.' Two years later the electrical supply failed twice, once during an operation. In response an emergency lighting supply with its own generator was rapidly installed by a local firm, Harding Bros. With orthopaedic cases increasing, an 'open air ward' or orthopaedic pavilion was built at the back of the hospital adjacent to Nelson Street. It opened in 1927 to accommodate 20 patients and was named the Hewat Pavilion in appreciation of all the continued interest and generous financial support Mrs Hewat had given the hospital following the death of her husband. The ward and balcony had no front wall and was open to the elements, for fresh air was considered to be good for all, but particularly beneficial in some cases of tuberculosis.

Some patients spent many months in the ward and survived to tell interesting reminiscences. Several people who were patients in 1931 recall a bird cage which they used to tap with a stick to encourage the occupant to burst into

The Hewat Pavilion

song. A gentleman, now in his 70s, remembers being in the ward for six months with cancer of the leg when he was aged 12. He was often taken to a bathing station at at Bartonsham Farm and was referred to as a walking miracle. At night a canvas curtain was pulled across the balcony for protection and to retain some warmth.

By the mid-20s it was recognised that a massive new building programme was necessary to cope with increasing demand and complexity of medical knowledge. In 1927 the governors considered an ambitious scheme to accommodate 160 patients, which included a surgical block with 70 beds, a new out-patients department below a 25 bedded ward, enlargement of Hawkins Ward, a small Maternity Unit, new accommodation for pathology, administration and kitchens, additional nursing and domestic accommodation and a private nursing home for 16 patients. The estimated cost of this proposal was put at £72,057, to be set against an annual income of £13,800 and invested capital of £56,348. At a special meeting on 10th September 1927, the governors approved the plans by 54 votes to 47. An appeal was launched for funds but after 15 months it failed to match expectations so the plans were modified to accommodate

Major George Davey

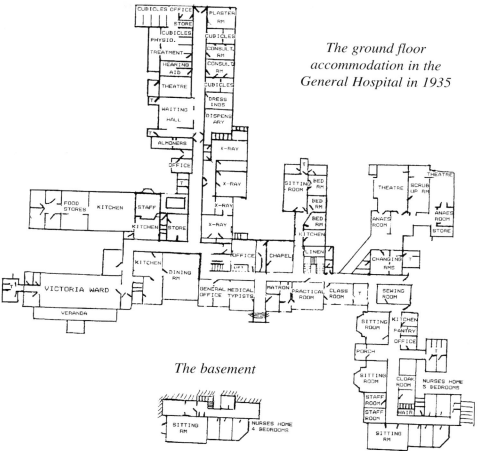

The ground floor accommodation in the General Hospital in 1935

The basement

140 patients and the idea of a private nursing home was abandoned. The first part of the scheme was estimated to cost £50,777. However, even these plans continued to cause great controversy due to the size of the project and the cost involved. In 1929 this resulted in the resignation of the Chairman of the House Committee, Major Owen Croft, and a governor, Capt. Lionel Green. Four governors turned down the post of chairman before Col. Henry Evan Pateshall, who lived at Allensmore, came to the rescue.

One of the main supporters of the project was another governor and committee member, Major George Davey of Kinnersley Castle who had played a prominent part in the building appeal and contributed £5,000 himself. In October 1929 he laid the foundation stone of the main extension which was to be built onto the back of Hawkins Ward block. The ground floor contained the Outpatient Department and kitchen premises. The first floor contained a female

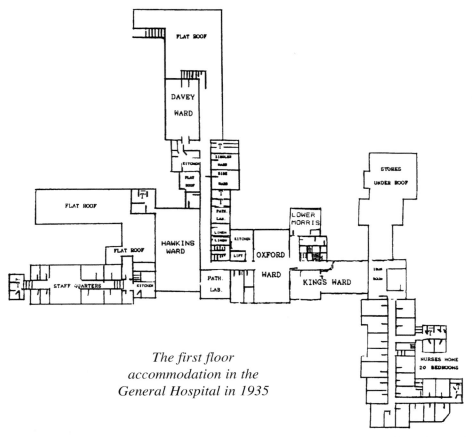

*The first floor
accommodation in the
General Hospital in 1935*

ward subsequently called Davey Ward after him, and the second floor housed a new maternity department with a labour room and a six bedded ward for complicated midwifery, together with accommodation for private patients. Hawkins, King's and Talbot wards were also reconstructed and modernised.

The new block was formally opened in March 1931 by Sir John Cotterell, the Lord Lieutenant. He mentioned that during earlier debates he had opposed the project on account of the costs, but was generous enough to praise the results. By 1930, although £32,602 had been raised towards the cost of the new buildings, it was accepted that funds would not be available to complete the whole project. It was therefore decided to abandon plans to build a surgical wing, though additional nursing accommodation, oil fired heating and steam sterilisation was installed at a cost of about £15,000.

By now there were 56 nurses and this was expected to increase to 62. The nurses' home was therefore extended by building onto the south and west side

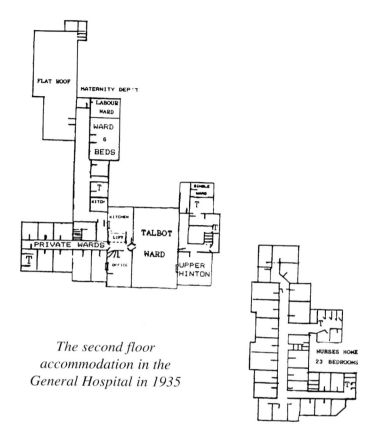

*The second floor
accommodation in the
General Hospital in 1935*

of the existing home to provide 24 additional bedrooms. The new addition was opened in 1933 providing each nurse with a separate bedroom.

Oil fired heating was installed to reduce costs, the new boilers replacing the previous boilers in the 'stoke hole', and the central heating system was extended with extra heating provided for the main kitchen, Davey Ward and the maternity department. Two boilers placed in a new boiler house near the laundry provided steam sterilisation for the theatre, casualty room and labour room.

When the previous isolation ward had been replaced by the new operating theatre, an isolation room had been made available in Hawkins Ward. This facility was lost during the ward reconstruction. As a result, in 1934 a new isolation block was completed as a separate building at the back of the hospital on the old vegetable garden. It had six beds for infectious diseases arising in the hospital and for midwifery cases with puerperal fever, a spreading infection in the soft tissues around the womb following childbirth which at that time carried a significant risk of mortality.

However, a new steriliser proved too big for the proposed room in the isolation block, perhaps an indication of chaotic bureaucracy. Another embarrassment occurred when the hospital was overrun with rats and a professional rat catcher had to be employed. He was not completely successful, for four months later there were still rats in the pantry. The total number of beds in the hospital had now reached 150, including eight for private and five for semi-private patients.

The need for a chapel was highlighted when Mr Butler, a surgeon, was delayed seeing a patient because the chaplain had to take a service in the ward. When he did get access his patient was dead! A solution was found and the old outpatient waiting room was converted into the Florence Nightingale Chapel and dedicated by the bishop of Hereford on the 5th October 1932. It was to be used by all denominations. The matron, Miss Cameron, raised money for the stained glass windows by initiating a county-wide campaign of a Mile of Pennies.

In 1922 a telephone girl was employed during the day at 7s a week, the resident staff attending to calls outside her hours. Soon the telephone system linked up wards and departments.

A wireless service for patients was discussed for 10 years before a system was installed by Hereford Radio Relays in 1935. There were problems due to interference from electrical apparatus in the hospital and numerous aerials were erected to enhance reception. The programmes and times of listening were regulated by the matron, but there is no information about her choices.

The Florence Nightingale Chapel

Shortly after the end of the First World War wounded soldiers were excluded from using the front grounds after the matron reproved them for shouting to girls across the river. Some years later the city council wished to purchase land for playing fields opposite the hospital. The House Committee opposed this as they did not want noisy crowds, as might attend a football match, but agreed it could be used for children for what they optimistically hoped would be comparatively noiseless games. Their views seem to have been honoured.

Throughout this period continued efforts were made to increase charitable giving but in 1939 the total was £500 less than it had been in 1918. In 1920 a Capt. Chubb was appointed as a paid canvasser for subscriptions on a commission basis, but he only lasted a year. As it was considered that farmers were providing limited support for the hospital, but contributing significantly to the numbers of patients attending through agricultural injuries, they were encouraged to set up a Herefordshire Farmers Hospital League. This was duly formed and contributed £442 in its first year.

The Herefordshire and District branch of the League of Mercy regularly contributed several hundred pounds. In 1939, under the guidance of their president, Col. Sleeman, they raised more money in 1939 than any other branch in the country and donated £260.

These inter-war years were the time for many donations, raised by every conceivable activity—social, sporting, and artistic. These included a sacred concert, handbell ringing, a comic football match and a motor and cycle carnival. One of the most bizarre was when a record salmon weighing 59.5 lbs, caught at Whitney-on-Wye by Miss Doreen Davey, daughter of Major George Davey, was donated and realised £17 10s 0d. There was a lovely donation in 1936, when Mr Sid Wright, a well-known city greengrocer, offered to present a gift of fruit each fortnight to a lonely patient selected by the matron.

The Bambino Guild were pledged to support children and regularly gave generously towards Victoria Ward, often in kind. An annual Pound Day was started in 1922 when people were encouraged to give at least a pound of produce. One year 7,569 lbs were donated with a value of £250 15s 0d. By 1928 an annual egg collection was instituted—it required 20,000 eggs, suitably preserved, to satisfy the hospital for one year.

In 1932 a yearly potato growing competition was started. The hospital provided 1 lb of potatoes for each competitor and the person who grew the heaviest crop was presented with the Challenge Cup. Needless to say the hospital was awarded all the potatoes from every competitor, which helped meet the estimated yearly consumption of 18 tons.

Poor people who could not afford to be private patients, and were not in any contributory scheme, still needed a subscriber's ticket and a doctor's recommendation to obtain admission. Although they were looked upon as suitable cases of charity, if they had any income they were expected to contribute towards maintenance and expenses.

Charges for private and semi-private patients provided £2,645 during 1939, with further income generated by providing services to local authorities and central government. If cases referred from the local authorities were covered by the hospital's contributory scheme charges were remitted. When the school dental officer referred children for tooth extraction under anaesthesia a payment of 10s a case was agreed. As these cases were not charitable both the dental surgeon and the anaesthetist charged a fee.

The finances throughout the inter-war years were a source of great anxiety. In each year expenditure exceeded income by between £300 and £5,000, resulting in a cumulative deficit of nearly £20,000 by 1939, though in that year a small surplus was made. The income for 1939 was £21,858, of which, despite all the efforts made, only 20 per cent came from charity, whilst 43 per cent came from payment for services, which included receipts from private practice, and 37 per cent from the new contributory scheme. Expenditure in 1939 amounted to £20,861, salaries accounting for 34 per cent, two-thirds of which was spent on nurses. The cost of nursing services had risen seven and a half times since 1918, due to the increase in both numbers of nurses and in salaries paid. The number of patients admitted had increased by almost three times and the treatments available had become more complex and expensive. The average cost per patient for the seven years to 1934 was £2 14s 0d per week, but by 1939 it was £3 6s 6d.

The various building projects and accumulated deficits were largely cleared by realizing the hospital's capital investments. Over £45,000 was realized in this way, after permission was obtained from the Charity Commissioners and the Court of Chancery to change the use of the capital, as part had been endowed by benefactors for a specific use. This left investments of just £13,816 that could be used to cover future deficits.

Repeated demands for interested groups to be represented on the Board of Management resulted in a continued increase in its size, eventually reaching the unmanageable total of 135 in 1933. Recognising the problem, Mr Orde, the secretary of the Central Bureau of Hospital Administration, was invited to advise. As a result an Executive Council was formed to control the activities of the hospital under the direction of the Board which would only meet twice a year or for specific purposes. By October 1937 the Board of Management had increased further to 150 members, and its function was almost identical with that of the governors meeting. It therefore dissolved itself, setting an example which few subsequent committees have followed, Mr Orde quoting a great philosopher: 'Nature as she omits nothing necessary for the purpose, so she ruthlessly eliminates all that is superfluous.'

The Executive Council initially consisted of the chairman and vice-chairman of the Board and 30 elected members, 10 of whom were to retire every year, but be eligible for re-election. The Council met monthly and elected numerous sub-committees including the House Committee. A Medical Committee, that included all the honorary staff, met weekly and advised the House Committee. A further Joint Committee of lay members and representatives of the medical staff elected by their Medical Committee advised on matters involving both lay and medical interests. In May 1935 the county council requested representatives from the hospital to help to establish a municipal hospital and four governors and Mr Ainslie, a surgeon, were appointed.

In April 1928 complaints were made about the secretary, Mr S. Evans. He resigned and extensive investigations of the books revealed a deficit of £76 which was finally recovered from him in November. The succeeding secretary was dismissed in August 1929 for falsifying the accounts; a warrant for his arrest was subsequently issued, but he had fled to Canada. However, as the secretaries were covered by a Fidelity Guarantee Insurance Policy the total sum missing of £433 was recovered. After these lapses, the central administrative office and staff were reorganised with the appointment of a supervisory manager at 120 guineas p.a., a secretary at £250 p.a. and an assistant secretary at £2 5s 0d a week. An office boy was also appointed at 10s a week.

There were lighter moments, as for example in May 1937 when the secretary was thanked for the work he had done in connection with the Herefordshire Beauty Queen Competition. Shorthand typists were also making an appearance and one was dismissed for irregular behaviour. Complaints were also received from neighbours about the visible transport of coffins from the hospital. As a result the management requested that the undertakers removed coffins either at night or in the early morning in enclosed vehicles.

Doctors and Specialities, 1919 - 1939

At the start of the inter-war years there was one house surgeon. By the end there was a resident surgical officer (R.S.O.), a casualty officer or junior house surgeon and a house physician. Several of the junior doctors went on to be appointed to the honorary staff.

Dr Walter Stallard resigned in July 1919 after acting as house surgeon for over three years. There was then a succession of house surgeons, one of whom had to explain why he carried out a major operation, the removal of gall stones, without supervision. However an inquiry decided that he had adhered to the

From left to right: Mr Richard Wood Power, surgeon; Dr John Wells, physician; and Mr Bernard Scholefield, surgeon

Rules and exonerated him. The governors clarified the Rules at the next Annual Meeting and confirmed that major operations must be performed by a member of the honorary staff or under their supervision, except in urgent cases, when the facts and reasons should be reported at the next meeting of the House Committee.

In May 1924 Mr Richard Wood Power was appointed house surgeon. He was working out his notice at Cheltenham when he was injured by an explosion in the operating theatre due to a spark igniting inflammatory anaesthetic gases. Fortunately he recovered in time to take up his new appointment.

In 1925 Dr Frederick Strange was appointed to the new post of house physician. His duties included looking after medical inpatients, attending medical outpatient clinics, performing post-mortems, giving emergency anaesthetics and looking after the pathology laboratory. Attempts to pay the house physician less than the house surgeon soon failed, which was not surprising in view of the workload expected of him. In 1930 it was agreed that the resident medical staff should be supplied with beer, not exceeding two bottles a day. Undoubtably a reward for long hours of work.

In 1934, in order to staff the accident department adequately a casualty officer or junior house surgeon's post was created. The original house surgeon's post was made more senior and became the resident medical officer with authority over the two house officers. This appointment usually lasted a year while the house officers served six months.

In general, the honorary staff appointed during the inter-war years were less well qualified than some of their predecessors in the latter part of the nineteenth century. Only three out of six honorary physicians held an M.D., while the surgeons were a little better with four out of the six holding fellowships of Royal Colleges.

Early in 1919 Dr Paul Chapman resigned aged 67 after 33 years as an honorary physician. He had rewritten an article on heart disease in Bristowe's medical textbook and, as an outstanding academic, had given three lectures to the Royal College of Physicians on the physics of the circulation.

After the war Dr William Ainslie joined the Wargrave House practice and as a surgeon at the General Hospital he tackled many branches of surgery including abdominal, orthopaedic, ear, nose and throat (E.N.T.), midwifery and gynaecological surgery as well as acting as a radiologist. He also had many other interests and was elected vice-chairman of Hereford United F.C. in 1929. As a long standing member of the Herefordshire Burns Club he was famous for his sparkling wit. Unfortunately he was also absent minded and apparently on one occasion while visiting a patient in the country, his wife, who had accompanied him, got out of the car for a walk, while he completed his consultation.

William Ainslie, honorary surgeon 1919-1937,
addressing a rather small haggis

On the way home he lifted his hat on passing his wife, but neglected to stop and left her behind. After 25 years he resigned his surgical appointment, but continued to serve on the House Committee. The county council then appointed him as Consultant Obstetrician and subsequently Hereford City Council appointed him chief steward, the eighth holder of the office since 1836. While running the X-ray Department he had developed a mobile X-ray apparatus powered from his car engine to take to road accident victims. At various times he had also acted as orthopaedic superintendent to the outpatient department and surgical consultant to the Victoria Eye Hospital.

Dr Moir Brown who succeeded Dr Ainslie as a surgeon at the General Hospital, having previously been an anaesthetist and then assistant surgeon

Early in 1923 Mr DuBuisson retired after 25 years of surgical practice. He had been also medical officer for the Much Dewchurch district under the Hereford Board of Guardians. Unmarried, he lived in Castle Street with his sister and his dog Jock. He was followed by Dr Blanche Walter Stallard who had been appointed the first female house surgeon in 1915. After the war she became an honorary anaesthetist and then applied for the surgical post. It was not long after the publicity over the suffragette movement and a proposal at the Board of Management that it was undesirable to appoint a lady surgeon at this precise time was defeated by 16 votes to 11.

In 1932 members of the honorary staff had been absent when they had commitments in the hospital. It was agreed that if they were absent for any appreciable time the Chairman of the House Committee must be notified in writing. In addition, all three physicians were reprimanded for being on leave at the same time.

With the science of medicine rapidly providing new methods of diagnosis and treatment this was the age of specialisation. The work of dental surgeons and anaesthetists increased steadily; the X-ray Department expanded to include treatment by radiotherapy; ophthalmology was rationalised; new departments were formed in laboratory medicine, orthopaedics, E.N.T. medicine and in psychiatry.

Most of the honorary staff appointed to a specialty were on limited and renewable contracts and did not have the same status and security as the honorary physicians and surgeons. The anaesthetists were appointed annually while the appointments of the ophthalmic surgeon and dental surgeon were for

Mr Edward DuBuisson, honorary surgeon between 1897 and 1922, with his dog Jock

seven years. Interest in postgraduate education for doctors was encouraged by the honorary staff and in 1922 the General Hospital hosted a series of lectures organised by the University of Bristol.

In 1922 it was decided to set up a new bacteriological laboratory, so that specimens need not be sent away for examination, thus saving time and money. Mr Butler, honorary surgeon was placed in charge. By 1926 blood transfusions were being given regularly and appeals for donors were made. Initially each donor was paid a guinea, a generous incentive to initially attract apprehensive volunteers. This practice soon ceased and has never been reintroduced.

In 1934 a part-time post for a pathologist was approved and Dr W. Stewart, pathologist at Worcester, was appointed at a salary of £125 p.a. This was the first senior member of staff to be paid by the hospital. A fully equipped pathology laboratory was installed on the first floor in the old Riverside Ward.

By 1939 the foundation of a modern laboratory service had been established and soon developed into several departments. In that year the Department of Haematology, which dealt with the structure of blood, provided 359 complete blood counts and compatible blood for nine blood transfusions. The Department of Biochemistry, the study of body chemistry, provided blood sugar estimations in 242 cases and stomach acid levels in 19 cases.

The Department of Histology, which involves studying the microscopic structure of body tissues, carried out 346 examinations mainly of tumours. There were also 17 post-mortem examinations performed.

In 1935 the first specialist radiologist, Dr Malcolm M. Melrose, was appointed as the honorary radiologist in charge of the X-ray Department, now officially called the Electro-Therapeutic Department. In 1920 Sister Gummer, who had radiological experience, was appointed as surgical and X-ray sister at £70 p.a. Nurses continued to be trained to act as radiographers as long as they agreed to stay on for at least two years. The department opened for routine work three mornings a week, expanded to provide emergency cover and by 1937 had a staff consisting of a senior resident radiographer and an assistant. The assistant in 1939 was a Mrs Flatau-Berwin who had come into the country on a servant's passport from Europe, to escape German persecution, but the Board of Trade refused to let her work as a radiographer for six months.

The X-ray Department was constantly needing new and more modern equipment. Several transformers were installed and portable X-ray equipment was purchased allowing X-ray examinations to be carried out in the wards and departments. By 1937 strict rules were introduced to prevent X-rays leaving the hospital, as doctors carried them away to their private consulting rooms or other hospitals, a problem still with us today. In 1939 there were 2,254 examinations performed.

As well as providing diagnostic X-rays the department expanded to include therapy with radiation. An ultra violet ray lamp was purchased to treat superficial skin lesions. The use of radium and X-rays for treatment, particularly for malignant conditions was also making its appearance. By 1923 the occasional patient was being referred to London for radiotherapy at the cost of 6 guineas, plus the expense of transport. Two years later radium was hired so it could be used in the hospital and in 1932 the hospital became affiliated to the Birmingham National Radon Centre. They supplied radon seeds, which were implanted to produce local radiation. In 1936 a Deep Therapy Unit, under the control of Dr Melrose, was established for radiation treatment by deep X-rays, mainly for cancer. During 1939, 918 such treatments were given.

In the inter-war years the numbers of honorary anaesthetists increased from one to six, until most anaesthetics were being given by specialists.

After the war eye cases were still dealt with both at the General Hospital and at the Victoria Eye and Ear Hospital. In 1922 talks were held between the two hospitals to agree on working arrangements, but the only result was to decide on the appointment of a joint honorary ophthalmic surgeon, to replace Mr Norman Pike at the General Hospital, who had resigned, and Mr Lindsay, honorary ophthalmic surgeon at the Victoria Hospital. Mr H. Woodward Barnes was appointed to this post on a yearly basis. The following year there were complaints about excessive delays in outpatients being seen, but suggestions that all ophthalmic work might be transferred to the Victoria Hospital were opposed. Further attempts at co-operation, initiated by Mr Barnes himself in 1925, resulted in nurses at the General Hospital being able to attend courses at the Victoria Eye Hospital. In practice ophthalmic work at the General Hospital steadily diminished and had ceased by 1934.

In 1925 provision for maternity cases was revised. It was confirmed that no provision would be made for uncomplicated cases, whilst adequate facilities would be provided for complicated cases in Upper Harris Ward, the old theatre and anaesthetic room. Accommodation improved with the opening of the new maternity block and the isolation wards, which took over the care of puerperal fever cases. In 1932 the establishment of a Cardiovascular Department, to study heart problems, was being considered. Dr Logan Jack, a general practitioner at Kington, offered to place his portable machine for taking heart tracings at the disposal of the hospital and to attend once a week to take electrocardiograms, but the offer was not accepted. In 1937 Dr Charles W. Walker was appointed honorary assistant physician in charge of the Cardiovascular Department.

After the Great War there were many orthopaedic problems associated with wounded soldiers, and tuberculosis of bones was common. As a

Dr Charles Walker

An old walking aid found in the cellars of Wolseley Villa. London's Science Museum considers that this type of equipment was in use from the 1890s

result, in 1919 a new clinic in orthopaedics was established and the hospital was recognised as an orthopaedic centre. In December 1925 Mr Wood Power was appointed as honorary assistant orthopaedic surgeon. It was also agreed that four orthopaedic beds would be provided for children in Victoria Ward and 16 adult beds in the Hewat Pavilion. Miss Bauser was appointed masseuse in charge of the orthopaedic clinic with Miss Bird as a part-time masseuse. By 1937 the staff of the massage department were supervised by a medical officer in charge of their department and were no longer considered part of the nursing staff. All patients coming to the massage department had to be seen initially by an honorary member of the medical staff before commencing treatment.

Almoners, equivalent to the modern social worker, started to appear, but had to refer all outpatients to an honorary physician or surgeon at least once a month. In 1925 the ladies on the Board of Management formed a committee and with the help of the Red Cross provided an aftercare service for discharged patients.

In 1926 a separate E.N.T. Department was considered necessary and two part time honorary surgeons were appointed. In 1932 the County and City Mental Hospital at Burghill requested that an outpatient service for nervous and mental disorders be established at the General Hospital. The medical staff agreed and suggested that the service should be called the Psychological Clinic.

In 1934 Dr G.W. Flemming, was appointed as honorary psychiatrist to the general hospital to be followed three years later by Dr T.E. Burrows, both of them being superintendents of the Mental Hospital at Burghill. Thus it was that by 1939 the General Hospital had developed the range of services expected in a district hospital.

The Carers and the Cared for, 1919 - 1939

The inter-war years saw the training of nurses being regulated nationally and increasing time and effort was spent at the General on teaching and training. The honorary medical staff, house surgeon and matron gave regular lectures to the nurses, covering medicine, surgery, ophthalmology, gynaecology,

Mr Ian Wyness MacGregor, appointed as assistant surgeon to the E.N.T. Department in 1926. He became a naval surgeon during the Second World War

anatomy, physiology, drugs and practical nursing. Even the cook was asked to help and instruct the probationer nurses in cooking. Medals and prizes were given out for general proficiency, physiology, hygiene and practical nursing.

The number of probationers nurses in training at the General Hospital increased from 18 at any one time to 45 by 1939. Immediately after the First World War there was difficulty in attracting probationers so their salaries were increased to £12, £16 and £20 p.a. respectively for their three years in training. Part of the exam was held in Hereford and part in Birmingham.

In 1926 nine nurses passed the examination and became State Registered Nurses (S.R.N.s). However, the results in the late 1930s deteriorated and in December 1937, 13 out of 18 nurses failed. Sister Langdon duly resigned as sister tutor. A Nursing Committee was formed, including both doctors and nurses and Miss Rudland Hills was appointed sister tutor at £180 p.a., from which time the exam results steadily improved.

After the Great War the private nursing service was re-established with two nurses employed at £70 p.a. However, it never reached its previous popularity

The medical and nursing staff in 1922.
Sitting, left to right: Mr Ainslie; the senior sister; Dr Patterson;
Mr DuBuisson; Miss Key-Wells, the matron; Dr Symonds; Dr Walter Stallard;
and Miss Bird, the masseuse. The men standing from left to right are:
Mr Bradley, one of the secretaries; Mr Butler; Dr Whitecroft,
the house surgeon; and Mr Baxter, the other secretary

and was soon abandoned. By 1939, as well as probationers there was a permanent staff of 10 sisters, whose salaries varied between £80 and £115 p.a., and
five staff nurses.

In 1926 a night sister was insubordinate to the matron, refusing to carry out
instructions about preparing a male patient for an abdominal operation. It
seems likely that she was asked to shave the pubic hair. She was suspended and
asked to resign. The Medical Committee made no comment, causing 13 nurses
to ask to appear before the House Committee in support of the sister. The
House Committee interviewed them and upheld the matron, which caused
several nurses to resign.

Immediately after the war an outbreak of influenza incapacitated five nurses
and admissions had to be restricted to urgent cases only. In the 1930s several
nurses developed tuberculosis of the lungs some of whom were transferred to

the Nieuport Sanatorium at Almeley. On a more cheerful note the nurses requested a tennis court and this was provided in the grounds, beyond the isolation wards, and they organised competitions and prizes.

In 1926 it was estimated that 25 rooms were needed for the domestic staff, who were accommodated either above Victoria Ward or in the attics. By 1935 the ward maids were only paid £24 p.a. and in 1938 there was difficulty in getting a cook so the matron travelled to Edinburgh to interview three candidates and appointed Miss Sellars at a salary of £110 p.a. This was also the time that bed bugs infested the maids' sleeping quarters necessitating evacuation and fumigation.

As well as a house porter, two night porters were appointed in 1928 because of the increasing operative work at night. There was also a head porter and a laundry engineer. Porters were provided with a uniform of a jacket, waistcoat and trousers.

In 1939 the number of inpatients admitted was 2,688, nearly three times as many as in 1918. 152 beds were available, and the average number of patients in hospital at any one time was 115 with an average stay of 16 days. 1,550 operations were performed, three and a half times the number in 1918. They included the following: -

	Nos.
Removal of tonsils and adenoids	291
Appendicectomy	250
Repair of groin rupture, (hernia)	116
Removal of part of the thyroid gland in neck	37
Removal of the womb (hysterectomy)	33
Removal of a breast, (mastectomy)	18
Removal of Gall Bladder (cholecystectomy)	17
Amputation of leg	10
Removal of part of stomach (gastrectomy)	8

4,650 new outpatients were also seen. The commonest procedures on outpatients were 779 cases of extracting teeth, and 394 dealing with fractures.

By 1923 insulin was available for the treatment of diabetes, a condition characterised by excess sugar in the blood, and an apparatus was purchased on the request of Dr Symonds, honorary physician, for estimating blood sugar levels prior to treatment. As insulin was expensive there was an instant reluctance to purchase it, especially as Dr Patterson, another honorary physician considered that the case for insulin was not yet proven. A few months later the treatment was accepted but each patient had to first be considered by a liaison committee.

Upper Hinton Ward was now allocated to private patients. Fees in 1933 were 7 guineas for maintenance a week plus a theatre fee of one guinea. There was a reduction for beds that had restricted views. Private patients had to be nursed by members of the hospital staff and be under the care of a member of the honorary medical staff, although a visiting surgeon was allowed to operate.

Private maternity patients or complicated maternity patients, paid for by the county council were now accepted. Maternity patients, who had been booked in, were charged half price from the expected date of confinement until they were admitted, so as to cover the cost of having a reserved bed left empty should labour and admission be delayed.

By 1938 an increasing number of private patients were occupying beds and the House Committee became anxious that charity cases might have their admission delayed or even be excluded. They told the honorary medical staff not to overcrowd the hospital with their private patients, except in emergencies.

Complaints were increasing perhaps because people were getting more confident and outspoken at the same time as their expectations of the hospital were rising. In 1921 an article appeared in the *Hereford Times* saying that a doctor was not always available at the hospital. Some truth was found in the allegations, but as there was only one house surgeon resident and he had duties all over the hospital, it is easy to see how delays in seeing patients could arise.

There were the usual complaints from patients about food, lack of blankets, premature discharge from the hospital, delays in being seen, lack of kindness and neglect. All were investigated and most found to be lacking substance. In the late 1930s the Federation of Women's Institutes investigated the food provided in the hospital and expressed satisfaction with its quality and the system of preserving eggs for the winter. It was noted that porridge was provided for winter breakfasts.

But despite best endeavours there were several unfortunate episodes. A man died during the night in 1919. As the county telegraphic office was closed, the matron sent a postcard to the relevant district nurse, asking her to break the sad news to the deceased's wife, who was in labour. The matron thought that the postcard would be as quick as a telegram—she was proved wrong as an inexplicable delay took place. In future postcards were not to be used.

In 1921 a patient was taken to theatre for an operation by Mr Ainslie. He was delayed and asked Dr Walter Stallard, who was the honorary anaesthetist, to operate. However the house surgeon refused to give an anaesthetic on the grounds that the operation was 'irregular' and the patient was returned to the ward. Mr Ainslie admitted he should have asked one of the honorary surgeons instead. The house surgeon offered to resign and this was inexplicably accepted. One suspects he must have upset other colleagues on other occasions. It was agreed that in future patients would not be taken to theatre until the operating surgeon was actually present.

In 1923 a patient died in theatre after a tooth extraction. The House Committee called for the clinical notes to be produced, but the medical staff objected to clinical notes being inspected by lay people on the grounds of confidentiality and this approach was backed up by the B.M.A. Two years later the Committee again wanted the right to inspect clinical notes. A compromise was agreed that case notes would be available to a member of the honorary staff who would answer questions.

In 1937 a patient died shortly after being transferred to the Hereford Public Assistance Institute, the renamed old workhouse, where he was not expected and no accommodation was available. The resident surgical officer was instructed that no patient was to be transferred to any institution unless he was assured that proper arrangements had been made.

Patients also complained of unnecessary suffering due to operations being performed under local anaesthetics, particularly during the removal of goitres from the neck. The House Committee bravely suggested that a general anaesthetic might be used. The reply must have been forceful as the Committee hastily reassured the medical staff that they had no intention of presuming to interfere with the treatment of patients.

There were complaints from medical practitioners that the telephone was not being answered and information about discharged patients was often late. These are continuing problems today. In an extraordinary decision reversing a previous ban on smoking, the House Committee allowed the matron to sell cigarettes and tobacco to help purchase heated food cabinets. On a more positive note a patients' library was established and Mr Mines, a governor, acted as honorary librarian while the Red Cross provided a regular supply of books.

There were numerous outbreaks of scarlet fever, diphtheria, measles and chicken pox necessitating temporary closure of wards and transfer of infected patients to the infectious disease hospitals. More serious was an increase of tuberculosis in patients in the 1930s.

To mark the Jubilee celebrations in 1935 the patients were provided with a special dinner with beer, stout or cider. Cigarettes were provided for the men and chocolates for the women and the hospital was represented in the procession through the city.

From 1938 preparations for war were started. The Ministry of Health had designated the General Hospital as a suitable base hospital, but initially would not finance any air raid precautions, in spite of the proximity of the munitions factory across the river. Eventually they paid for sandbagging and wire mesh for window frames, anti-shatter paint for windows, cellophane strips for theatre windows and wire for protecting lantern lights. Anti blast walls were placed in front of Victoria and Talbot wards. Three stirrup pumps were purchased. Early in 1939 auxiliary nurses in large numbers were being trained in the hospital while provision for treating wounded servicemen was organised and suitable financial arrangements agreed with the government.

War and then a Health Service, 1940-1948
In the early days of the war there were anxieties about the availability of supplies of fuel, water and food. There were no facilities for storing boiler fuel, but the local coal contractor was holding 40 tons for the hospital's exclusive use. The hospital used 1,000 gallons of water an hour and should the mains be hit in an air raid within a radius of a quarter of a mile, hose pipes could be used but if outside that distance, tankers would be needed. The city surveyor was confident that in a crisis the hospital would get an adequate supply of water as the city was investing in a flexible water pipe and a mobile pumping plant. The Stores Committee estimated the amount of tinned food in stock and found there was enough for 10 weeks, whilst retailers gave an assurance that the hospital would be given priority. Precautions against fire in an air raid were taken—two members of the Auxiliary Fire Service attended the hospital, access to the river water was also arranged in case the mains were damaged, additional stirrup pumps were provided and the resident staff were trained to deal with incendiary bombs.

Effective blackout proved difficult, especially in the Hewat Pavilion and isolation block. But blackout rules were laid down and the responsibilities of every member of staff clearly explained. Any person failing to carry out his duties was threatened with penalties of 5s for the first offence, suspension for the second and an appearance before the appropriate committee for the third. Only one unfortunate nurse was fined 5s.

Volunteer stretcher bearers were on duty each night. For a time the use of the upper floor for patients was abandoned due to the perceived difficulty in evacuating them. During an evacuation exercise, half the patients in the Hewat Pavilion could not be moved out of their beds, so only mobile patients were subsequently admitted there. In view of anxieties about air raids, nurses sleeping on the top floors of Wolseley Villa and No.1 Nelson Street, both used as nurses' homes, were to be accommodated on the ground floors.

By January 1941 Civil Nursing Reserve sisters were available and helped to man the General Hospital as well as the auxiliary hospitals. As the auxiliary hospitals were not fully used for war casualties and had empty beds, civilian

	Date appointed	Years of service till 1948
Temporary Assistant Physician		
Jean Edwards, M.D., M.R.C.P.	1940	5
Squ. Leader R.F. Dawson, M.D., M.R.C.P.	1942	3
Temporary Assistant Surgeon		
Squ. Leader A.C. Lysaght, F.R.C.S.(Eng.)	1943	
Assistant Surgeon		
W. Moir Brown, M.B., Ch.B.(Edin.), F.R.C.S.(Edin.)	1933	4
C. Langley Owen, M.A., M.B., B.Ch.,		
F.R.C.S.(Eng.), L.R.C.P.(Lond.)	1937	8
Squ. Leader J. Hughes	1942	1
Squ. Leader A.C. Lysaght	1943	2

Table 7 Staff appointments made leading up to and during the Second World War

patients were admitted for convalescence at 1s 6d a day. There was also a rush of volunteers who manned a canteen in the outpatient department in co-operation with the Red Cross.

At 6 a.m. on the 27th July 1942 a single German bomber dropped two 550 lbs bombs which hit the transit shed of the Royal Ordnance Factory at Rotherwas killing 19 people and injuring many more. One bomb exploded in the shed whilst the second was deflected, shot out of the door, bounced along the ground and across the perimeter fence before exploding in the house of the police superintendent of the factory, killing him, his wife, one son, a daughter-in-law and her mother. Only his younger son survived as he had moved into an adjacent granary to make room for the visitors.

For the sake of security, no information about this incident was available till after the war. Records at the General Hospital show that 19 people were admitted that day as 'air raid victims', including the 16 year old surviving son of the police superintendent, who had no major injuries, but was suffering from shock. That young man, Ken Hursey has since told his story in the *Hereford Times* of 24th July 1997. Two of the injured subsequently died.

Two accidents also took place at the munitions factory. In September 1941 a serious explosion occurred in a mill, inside a protected area where explosives were being mixed. Three men died and six sustained injuries requiring treatment at the hospital. In the evening of 30th May 1944 three consecutive major explosions occurred. A fire started in a large filled bomb and spread to other bombs, mines and explosive devices. The equivalent of thirty-one 2,000 lbs bombs exploded, sending up a sheet of flame 2,000 feet high and devastating the filling house and surrounding area. Two people died outright and 30 sustained injuries. Reference was made to the coolness of the 800 workers in going to their shelters, and to the skill and sympathetic treatment of the injured at the General Hospital, which was visited shortly afterwards by Sir Andrew Duncan, Minister of Supply.

There were two accidents in the hospital unconnected with the war. In January 1943 a large gas cooker, which was in two sections, had the gas turned on in one section by error and a pudding put in the second section which was then lit. Five windows and a ceiling were lost in the resultant explosion. In the following June a fire occurred in the isolation block resulting in £40 worth of damage. In dealing with the fire the engineer, Mr Chave, broke his upper dentures, which a grateful hospital replaced.

During May 1944 all leave was stopped because of the likelihood of casualties following D Day. It was also arranged that two mobile surgical teams from the hospital would be available for duty at Ronkswood Hospital in Worcester if necessary.

During the war no building and little maintenance was carried out. There was some excitement in 1946 when the hospital became overrun with cats and they had to be carried off by the R.S.P.C.A. An increasing number of cars were causing congestion, particularly during visiting times and Mr Hyde, Chairman of the Working Mens' Representative Committee bravely offered to control the cars in the hospital's grounds on a Sunday, the start of a long saga of conflict that continues today. In 1947 ward duty rooms were provided and extensive redecoration was carried out both inside and outside the building.

During the war income and expenditure at the hospital was brought into balance mainly by government grants for treatment of war casualties and from better control of expenditure. However, this did not continue and the last complete year of annual accounts produced for 1947 showed a deficit of £19,899. Income was £33,067, an increase of 24 per cent on 1939. Charitable income kept up well at £5,693 but now accounted for only 17 per cent of the total—half a century earlier this source had provided 95 per cent of the total. It included annual subscriptions, interest from decreasing investments, church collections, donations, and numerous charitable activities. Some donations came from new sources, including the proceeds of a football match between Belgian and British soldiers stationed around Hereford, the Hereford Butchers' Retail Buying Association and the Hereford City Darts League. Payments for services provided £16,911, just over half of the total, and included £9,330 from private patients and services provided for the local authorities. All patients who had incomes over £420 p.a. were now considered private and paid a maintenance charge. By 1948 this was 9 guineas a week for a front ward with a view and £8 18s 6d for a back ward, such wards being designated as private wards. Semi-private patients who had incomes below the private level but who were not eligible to join the contributory scheme were charged a little less. The Hospital Contributory Scheme produced £10,463, making up 32 per cent of the total, a slight decrease during the previous five years. The contributions were raised in 1942 from 3d to 4d a week and in February 1943 the income limit for contributors was increased from £312 to £420.

Expenses between 1940 and 1947 more than doubled to £52,966. Salaries accounted for 43 per cent, the increase being partly due to nationally negotiated levels of pay for nursing and domestic staff and partly to an increase in the numbers of staff to comply with new regulations. Maintenance costs for patients rose to £8 0s 2d per week, a rise of nearly two and a half times over eight years.

During the war, the Air Council allowed medical specialists in the armed services, who were stationed at Credenhill Camp, to help out when members of the honorary staff were called up to serve in the forces. In 1941 the resident surgical officer was dismissed because of dissatisfaction with the manner in which he was performing his duties. A complaint from the house officers about the food being cold, of poor quantity and variety resulted in an additional kitchen maid and a qualified cook being appointed. Hot plates were installed in the nurses' dining room. It was also about this time that the House Committee resolved that, with the exception of the night sister or her deputy, members of the nursing staff were forbidden to visit the resident medical officers' quarters; there must have been an interesting incident to necessitate this rule.

One of the main tasks facing the administration during this decade was how to co-ordinate the hospital services with those of the new municipal hospital, the County Hospital, which opened in 1940. This had unexpectedly developed acute services thus putting them in competition with the General and causing disagreements over the provision of services. These were partly overcome and in 1947 a joint appointment of an assistant orthopaedic surgeon, Mr Brian Thomas, was made. There was a steady in crease in secretaries, typists and telephonists.

During this decade the X-ray Department increased its activity and in 1947 performed 6,267 examinations. In April 1946, the radiologists decided that all patients requiring barium meal or enema examinations, where radio-opaque barium is either swallowed or inserted into the back passage and the relevant area scanned, could only be referred to the department from a hospital clinic.

The general practitioners often liked to refer their patients direct to the X-ray Department as this was quicker and they remained in charge of their patients' care. However, the radiologist felt that at times unnecessary or inappropriate referrals were being made and they wanted the cases screened by a specialist in an outpatient clinic. The first early battle for open access for general practitioners was lost, but it was to be a continuing battle in years to come.

Radiotherapy treatment improved when the Birmingham United Hospitals agreed to provide a monthly advisory service by sending specialists to Hereford to discuss the suitability of patients for radiotherapy. In 1944 there was a critical letter in the *Hereford Times* stating that the radiotherapy service for Hereford patients was of poor quality and involved repeated visits to Birmingham. This prompted a reply by the medical staff, who stated 'That for the past two years, under the terms of the Cancer Act 1939, radium specialists from Birmingham visit the general hospital once a month and arrange to carry out the very latest methods of treatment, in consultation with the honorary medical staff, either at the general hospital or in Birmingham.' In 1947 the number of deep X-ray treatments was 1,012.

In 1943 a Rehabilitation Treatment Centre was established under the supervision of Mr Moir Brown and run by a trained masseuse, Miss Moore. In the same year the Chartered Society of Massage and Medical Gymnasts changed its name for the fourth time to The Chartered Society of Physiotherapists. Following this the title of masseuse faded out and the modern title of physiotherapist replaced it.

In 1946 a fully qualified male rehabilitation officer, Mr Ballanger, who had trained as a gymnast, was appointed at £330 p.a., and functioned from a Red Cross hut in the hospital grounds. In 1947, to satisfy sceptics, the medical staff reviewed the working of the rehabilitation unit and were

Mr Brian Thomas, assistant orthopaedic surgeon in 1947. He worked with Mr Richard Wood Power to establish a fracture clinic

Dr William Baker, junior pathologist, in 1947. His appointment covered both the General and County hospitals, and he had a laboratory in each. He was also acting director of the Public Health Laboratory Service in Hereford and the coroner's pathologist

satisfied that full and effective use was made of the personnel and equipment. Indeed, 7,282 treatments were given in 1947.

In May 1944 it was resolved that school children with E.N.T. problems, for whom the local authority were responsible, would in future be referred to the County Hospital. In 1942 a Hearing Aid Centre had been established, initially in the Dental Room, under the direction of Mr Alfred Peters who was on the approved list of the National Institute of the Deaf. Patients had to be referred by the surgeon in charge of the E.N.T. Department. Tests and advice were free but hearing aids had to be purchased from Messrs Alfred Peters and Son. In 1947, 76 patients had attended for consultation. Mr Peters died that year but was soon replaced by Mr Conrad Browne.

In April 1940, Miss M. Barker, the sister tutor, was asked to sleep out, due to lack of accommodation, and resigned. She was not replaced, the work being covered by the assistant matron and subsequently local results of the examinations set by the G.N.C. were very poor. In December only 12 out of 22 candidates passed the preliminary examination and one out of seven the final examination. Whilst there was criticism of the G.N.C. that the preliminary examination was too theoretical, great efforts were made to improve nurse training. Dr Strange joined the nursing sub-committee and more lectures were provided by the medical staff. By 1943 pupil nurses were attending a three months unpaid preliminary course prior to starting their formal three year training. Should they fail the resultant state examination twice their appointment would be terminated. However, if they joined the staff after completing their training they would be posted to night duty or the maternity ward, posts which must have been unpopular.

There was, at times, a shortage of nurses, partly due to an increase in need, and partly due to a loss of nurses with some being called up to serve with Queen Alexandra's Imperial Military Nursing Service Reserve, coupled with a failure of some student nurses to pass their examinations, whilst others resigned. There was also a lack of accommodation for nurses. Rooms and properties around the General were rented including 2 Nelson St., St James's Vicarage, and two floors at Sarum House in St Ethelbert Street. In 1946 a warden was appointed to look after Sarum House.

Apart from concerns over recruitment, training and accommodation, nursing had its lighter side. At Christmas a matron's fund was available to spend on decorations, patients and staff. Dances were organised for the sisters and nurses, being held sometimes in the nurses' home, the Booth Hall or the Green Dragon Hotel. One Christmas Mr Moir Brown donated £5 to the nurses in the private patient ward to be spent on silk stockings. On another occasion Nurse Williams in Victoria Ward fainted and in a gallant act Private Coltman, a patient recovering from a fractured thigh, leapt to her assistance — and refractured his thigh.

It wasn't only difficult to retain nurses. There was also a steady turnover of cooks and maids, increasingly subject to restriction in hours of work and nationally agreed wages. Unfortunately one of the maids contracted tuberculosis and died in Nieuport Sanatorium, near Almeley.

The porters were on duty for up to 65 hours a week and not surprisingly there was difficulty in finding candidates. In 1941 additional appointments allowed an acceptable rota for four porters. By 1945 they too were subject to central pay agreements. The standard working week was 51 hours and the rates of pay 1s 8d an hour for the first 48 hours and thereafter 2s 1d an hour. The resident engineer in

Miss E.M. Cordery, matron, in 1947

1948 had his pay increased from £416 to £520 p.a., as recommended by the Institute of Hospital Engineers.

It was agreed with the clergy that information on the religious denomination of all in-patients should be noted on the case sheet. When patients were in danger of death, the relatives were responsible for communicating with their own clergy, otherwise the local clergy would be called. If a newborn baby was not expected to live a sister or nurse could baptise the baby in the absence of a minister.

In the year to December 1947 there were 3,025 patients admitted. The average bed occupancy was 121 of the 154 beds available, with an average stay of 15 days. 1,685 operations were performed. The number of new outpatients seen was 7,029. All these statistics indicate a steady increase in activity.

The hospital appeared to suffer from a minor epidemic of patients falling out of bed. One patient fractured his arm and another his toe. The Rev. Killgour, a previous chaplain, jumped out of bed and sustained a cut to his left eyebrow which required suturing.

One patient who had just been operated on for tonsils and adenoids was placed behind a screen. A nearby patient hearing choking sounds drew the staff's attention to the problem and the patient was found to be bleeding from his throat, from where a tonsil had been removed. Fortunately he survived. The subsequent inquiry stated that the nurse who was meant to look after the patient had left the room for a few moments.

There was also an inquiry into complaints by a private patient, Mrs Lynch, that she had had inadequate midwifery attention and had been prematurely discharged. Prominent people supported her complaint including Sir Ernest Shepperson M.P. and Lt. Col. Winser Clive, commanding officer of the Grenadier Guards. A Ministerial Inquiry confirmed the complaint, perhaps suggesting that influential complainants were more likely to be successful. Another private midwifery patient was scalded by spilt tea and so was not charged for her maintenance or medical fees. The hospital itself did not seem to suffer any financial penalty for any of these incidents.

Epidemics became less common, although scarlet fever closed the childrens' ward in February 1941 and in 1947 an outbreak of infantile paralysis stopped non-urgent operations in children.

In 1948 one of the first customer surveys was carried out to discover to find out if the patients would like the chapel services relayed to the wards. A majority were in favour.

Over the years a ghost story about a 'Grey Lady' had been gaining credence. Apparently, soon after Queen Victoria's Jubilee, a child had died in Victoria

Ward, after which an apparition of a lady dressed in grey with a nun's cowl used to visit the cots in the ward every night. If she gave any of the patients a glass of water they were said to die the following day. Breezes along the corridors were ascribed to her presence. She was thought to live in the attics and was said to ring bells in some of the empty rooms near Talbot Ward, causing the nurses to search for the cause.

In January 1948 there were discussions with the Ministry of Health about financial assistance but they would not help unless the hospital had an overdraft of £7,000. This soon occurred, the hospital became bankrupt and the Ministry came to its aid.

As the 5th July 1948 approached, the day appointed for the commencement of the N.H.S., it was realised that there was a residual sum of money in a medical staff fund. The staff therefore resolved to a have a dinner at Brockhampton Court to mark Dr John Bulman's retirement as an honorary physician. The bill for the 14 doctors came to £3 for food and £105 for liquid refreshments. Given that disparity, it was unsurprising that one of the diners had rather overindulged and required assistance in getting home. Lots were drawn to decide who would undertake this duty as his wife had a reputation of being particularly fierce. He was duly delivered to his home, propped up in the porch, and the bell rung—but the good samaritans rapidly fled.

With the creation of the N.H.S., 172 years of the General Hospital as a voluntary institution came to an end. It had grown over these years into a sophisticated modern hospital providing an extensive range of services available to the people of Herefordshire and surrounding counties. The governors and staff had responded to constant change, coping with modernization and expansion of its buildings, medical advances, social changes and above all numerous financial crises.

CHAPTER 4

Bromyard Cottage Hospital

In 1869 Bromyard was a small market town with a population of 2,978. It had a small trade in tanning and malting. By road it was 14 miles from both Worcester and Hereford and the railways had yet to reach the town.

The town had limited provision for looking after the elderly and sick. The Jackson Almshouses in Cruxwell Street provided accommodation for seven widows while the union workhouse at Linton, on the Worcester road, served 33 parishes with accommodation for 160 people, including wards for the sick. A charitable dispensary in the market place, supported by subscriptions, donations and fundraising saw several hundred patients each year.

Early in April 1869, 10 of the most prominent supporters of the idea of a cottage hospital issued a statement in the local press proposing that one be established in the town and calling for a public meeting to support the project. Six of the 10 came from two prominent and influential families—the Barnebys and the Arkwrights. Mr William H. Barneby of Bredenbury Court, was one of the main landowners and philanthropists in the district and he was supported by three other members of his family, his brother Mr J.H. Barneby-Letley of Brockhampton and two uncles, Mr William Barneby of Clutter Park and Mr Edmund Higginson of Saltmarsh Castle. The Rev. George Arkwright, who became vicar of Pencombe in 1861, was supported by his elder brother, Mr John Hungerford Arkwright of Hampton Court. The Rev. Nash Stephenson, who had recently become vicar of Bromyard, was another enthusiastic supporter.

A public meeting was duly held on Monday 12th April at Dumbleton Hall which almost 40 people attended. The supporters had clearly been working hard as they were able to produce plans for establishing a cottage hospital and present provisional Rules. After much discussion, the project was approved, the purpose of the hospital being agreed as the treatment of suitable cases of illness or accident amongst the poor in the parish of Bromyard and other parishes within a radius of seven miles. The Board of Guardians of the workhouse agreed that if they referred paupers they would pay maintenance at 2s 6d a week.

The Rules adopted meant that each subscriber had one vote at the annual meeting for every guinea subscribed and each donor one vote for every £5 donated. These contributions also provided them with a ticket allowing them to recommend one patient annually. Larger contributions generated more tickets. To encourage those who subscribed smaller sums it was agreed that if two or three subscribers between them subscribed one guinea, the group would be allowed one ticket of recommendation.

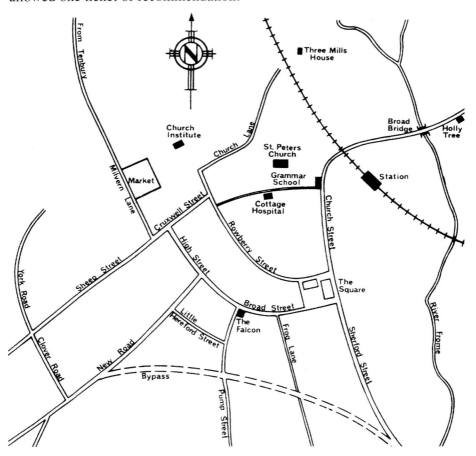

A sketch map of Bromyard showing the cottage hospital site near St Peter's Church

The committee of management was to be elected annually and include four laymen and four clergymen and one of its duties was to encourage as many ladies as possible to supervise the domestic arrangements. The honorary medical officer for the week would attend any meetings.

The meeting appointed Edmund Higginson as president. He had changed his name from Edmund Barneby, when he inherited estates that included eight parishes, amongst them Tedstone Wafre, Edvin Loach and Collington, from his great uncle William Higginson. In 1840 he had built a Victorian castle on the site of Saltmarsh House. He had long had a reputation for looking after the poor and distributed beef and clothing at Christmas time to the surrounding parishes.

By May subscriptions of £164 and donations of £186 had been promised, encouraging the committee to lease The Toll House adjacent to the graveyard of St Peter's Church. By July 1869 furniture had been purchased, a London trained nurse was appointed as resident matron, and the hospital with accommodation for five patients opened without any ceremony.

In 1883 the membership of the committee was modified to include six laymen, five clergymen and all the honorary medical staff, whose votes however would count only as one. Three years later it was resolved that each of the four honorary medical officers should be on the committee for three months in rotation. After the death of Mr Higginson in 1871, the bishop of Hereford became the president. Two joint honorary secretaries were always appointed, whilst it became the custom for the manager of the local branch of the National Provincial Bank to be the honorary treasurer.

The Rev. Nash Stephenson died in 1876 and although his ministry only lasted nine years he had made such an impression that the old pulpit was remade as a memorial to him as well as the stained glass in the east window of the south transept which was inscribed to his memory. His successor as vicar, the Rev. William Martin, was elected on to the committee. Other changes also took place, including Mr George Cresswell, originator of the Penny Fund, from Ocle Court at Ocle Pychard being appointed a vice-president.

At the annual meeting in 1884 a Mrs Prescott proposed an amendment to the Rules to prevent paupers being admitted, claiming that the hospital was for 'respectable people only' and that the workhouse had their own infirmary for the sick. It was pointed out to her that 'if a man was brought low by illness or accident he should not be refused the benefits of the hospital.' As the Guardians of Bromyard workhouse already contributed to the costs of the cottage hospital, Mrs Prescott duly withdrew her amendment.

By 1885 the hospital was considered to be inadequate with cramped, ill ventilated accommodation. Access upstairs was limited by a narrow staircase,

Rev. William Martin, vicar of Bromyard 1877-1913, outside the door to the church

the roof leaked and the drainage was poor. In addition the medical staff wanted a new theatre. To complicate matters the hospital was offered the building for £320, its only saving grace being, it appears, that its five beds provided sufficient accommodation. An argument ensued as to whether to buy and modify the present building or to build elsewhere on land offered to them by a Mr Phipps. Dr Horton, a subscriber, was in favour of building anew and commented strongly on the smell arising from the adjacent St Peter's churchyard. This contained an enormous cesspool, and was used for 'gruntage' by the townsmen, resulting in a very unsatisfactory atmosphere in the wards. The Rev. Martin, on the other hand, who was responsible for the churchyard, was of the opinion that it was the prettiest in the kingdom except for the one at Ross. He said that the smell complained of came from the old part of the churchyard which was not used more than once in 12 months and he thought the smell would gradually die away. His arguments appear to have been persuasive for the subscribers voted to buy the existing building.

Alterations, drawn up by Mr Kempson, an architect, were duly carried out, resulting in a new wing being built onto the back of the building, consisting of an operating theatre downstairs and two rooms and a toilet upstairs. The staircase was widened, the roof repaired and the drains connected to the main town sewer. More space and better ventilation was

Bromyard Cottage Hospital in 1899

provided in the wards. The funding for the acquisition and building work came from legacies and the realisation of investments, and the hospital was partially closed whilst the work was carried out, being reopened at the annual meeting in September 1887.

Ten years later there was further building work which, on the ground floor, provided a matron's parlour and store rooms, and improved the wards whilst leaving the number of beds unchanged at five. At the same time, the front was made more attractive by building a window projecting from the new ward. The hospital was reopened once more in August 1898. The cost of these further changes was £300 which came from savings and left the hospital with no significant reserves.

The income fluctuated around £200 p.a. in the years up to the turn of the century, of which annual subscriptions provided about half. Repeated efforts were made to enrol more subscribers but with limited success as trade was depressed in the mid-1880s. Money boxes only produced between 14s 6d and £4 each year. A Hospital Sunday in the autumn produced amounts varying between £21 and £42 from up to 11 parishes. Only in the late 80s were additional fundraising events instigated. The High Lane Foresters and Bishops Frome Oddfellows organised concerts in 1889 and raised £29 for the hospital. However, many people continued to make gifts of linen, food and books.

A contributory scheme started by the workmen in a local firm, known as Mr Millechap's establishment, produced up to £9 p.a. in 1882. In return the workmen received treatment at the hospital when required. Weekly maintenance payments contributed £10 to £15 annually.

Despite all these efforts, in most years there were small deficits ranging between £6 and £34, although in 1884 the committee congratulated themselves on a credit of £9. The debits were corrected by using small donations while larger ones or legacies were placed in a reserve savings account.

The average number of patients admitted per year up to 1888 was 36, though it varied widely from 23 to 51. As an example, during 1882, 31 patients were admitted of whom 18 were said to be cured, nine relieved, one was incurable, two died and one was still in hospital. The average stay was 24 days, ranging from two to 43 days. The hospital was lax in taking in patients who stayed a long time—the Rules did not clearly specify that only acute medical problems which would respond to treatment were to be admitted. During an earlier year, five patients had stayed from 56 to 209 days suggesting that their treatment was not exactly effective.

Two of the worst cases that the hospital treated resulted from agricultural injuries. In the one Dr William Powell had to amputate a mangled arm, in the second a farmer suffered cracked ribs and bad bruising from an accident with a cart. He had been leading a pony and cart to collect hay, when the mare shied and attempted to run away. He clung to the bridle but was thrown to the ground in front of the cart's wheels.

In the early 1900s four ladies were added to the committee to act as visitors, whilst a House Committee was established to advise on day to day problems. In 1909 there was increasing concern that the hospital was losing touch with the districts round Bromyard which was poorly represented with just two farmers on the committee of management. Several critical letters also appeared in the local press. Rev. Sidney Dodderidge, of Thornbury Rectory, wrote stating that three years earlier, during an appeal for money, his churchwarden had opposed the idea because of a personal grievance against the hospital. Subsequently, however, the same man was persuaded to become a member of the hospital committee.

More damaging, Mr W. Smith of Mayfields said that several people had told him that they felt the hospital was kept more for the benefit of the staff instead

1869	Edward Werge Howey, M.R.C.S., L.S.A. (Broad Street)
1869	Richard Marley, M.R.C.S., L.S.A. (Cruxwell Street)
1869	John Owen, M.D., M.R.C.S. (Nunwell House)
1869	G. Ernest Etheridge, M.R.C.S., L.S.A., L.M. (Cruxwell Street)
1869	John Brown Shelton, M.R.C.S., L.S.A. (High Street)
1872	William Powell, M.R.C.S., L.S.A. (Broad Street)
1880	John William Hinings, L.R.C.P. (Nunwell House)
1885	Thomas Henry Gillam, L.R.C.P., M.R.C.S. (High Street)
1885	Henry Horton (Broad Street)
1899	Philip King Lewis, M.R.C.S., L.S.A. (Nunwell House)
1905	James King Lewis, M.R.C.S. (The Elms, Pump Street)
1913	Edward Ashton Anthony Beck, M.A., M.B., B.Ch. (High Street)

Table 8 Medical staff of Bromyard Cottage Hospital. The year is that in which each doctor is first known to have a hospital appointment, whilst the location in brackets indicates where they were in practice

of the patients. He went on to suggest that if the hospital was closed it would be due to the mismanagement of the committee rather than for lack of subscribers.

It seems likely that some of this criticism was related to the matron, Miss Waddington, having a nervous breakdown, and letting the hospital run down. When she was replaced by Miss Halbrook, there was an immediate increase in inpatients. The new matron became very popular and it was noted that her kindness to everyone day and night was all that could be desired. She also coped without an assistant nurse, an economy which made her popular with management.

1912 was another difficult year with anxieties relating to the National Insurance Act similar to those experienced at the General Hospital. The doctors initially, on B.M.A. advice, threatened not to treat insured patients but then relented.

The Rev. William Martin died in 1913, having been one of the leading supporters of the hospital for 36 years. His death seems to have exacerbated the recurring problems at the hospital, where the annual accounts were in credit in only four of the first 17 years of the century. Although in 1903 a new source of finance appeared with the Cresswell Penny Fund it made only a small contribution. By 1909 there was a cumulative debt of £154, which was paid from legacies and reserve funds in the savings accounts, and a big fundraising effort was made over the next two years. Matters declined again shortly afterwards and in 1913 the subscribers were told that unless additional income appeared the hospital would close. They responded and the accounts were in credit up to 1915.

1869	London trained nurse
1871	Miss Davies
1882	Mrs. E. Soars
1887	Mrs Bridger left after one month as she could not cope with housekeeping
1887	Miss Helen Crawshaw
1903	Mrs Alan Murray
1904	Miss Waddington
1909	Miss Holdbrook
1912	Miss Heriot
1913	Miss Gillies

Table 9 Matrons at Bromyard Cottage Hospital

With the onset of the First World War, subscription income fell and decreasing numbers of patients used the hospital. A general meeting was called on 24th May 1917 at which the financial position was explained. The balance in the bank was just £27 while debts amounted to £50 and there were no reserves. In spite of many people present wanting the hospital to continue it was decided to close it on 11th June. The building was left in the hands of the trustees and rented out temporarily for £21 p.a. Two rooms were retained to store hospital equipment.

On Thursday 18th September 1919 a final meeting was held at Dumbleton Hall of trustees, subscribers and friends, chaired by the president, Col. John Lutley, when it was decided not to reopen the hospital. The building was to be sold or rented and the money used for charitable purposes. Today it is known as Challenge House off Challenge Lane. A sad ending to a great enterprise.

William H. Barneby

Why did this hospital fail after 48 years? It certainly served a smaller district, just 6,000 people, than the other subsequent cottage hospitals in Herefordshire, yet it was prospering up until the turn of the century. After this it failed to obtain adequate continuing support from the district or attract sufficient charitable or private patients. The poor and the working class took very little interest in it. Initial support was dominated by two families and possibly the personality of its main supporter, Mr William H. Barneby, a magistrate well known for his belief in stern discipline, may have antagonised many citizens of the district.

CHAPTER 5

Ross Dispensary and Cottage Hospital

In the late nineteenth century Ross-on-Wye, with a population of just over 4,700, was governed by commissioners chosen under the Ross Improvement Act. The town hosted small firms involved in making agricultural implements, in brewing and in tanning, and there was also an agricultural market.

Five almshouses provided care for 26 elderly and infirm people, and there was a union workhouse covering 27 parishes in Alton Street that could hold up to 200 inmates. The Ross Dispensary, originally opened in 1825 in Brookend Street, was a charitable institution established to help the poor, although patients who could afford to were asked to pay a a small contribution towards their prescriptions. It opened for two hours on three days a week and was attended by a dispenser, a nurse and one of the local general practitioners, being financed by annual subscribers who elected a management committee. In the late 1850s it moved to New Street.

During 1872 the dispensary saw 810 outpatients, and in January that year the management committee decided to establish a cottage hospital in Ross. Many of the leading citizens of the town and district were on the committee including Mr Thomas Blake, a self-made wealthy businessman; George Clive, M.P.; Dr Cambridge Cary Cocks; John Maurice Herbert, a county court judge; Mr John E.S. Hewett, the manager of Capital and Counties Bank; Capt. Kingsmill Power, chairman of the magistrates; and Mr Henry Southall, chairman of the Ross Town Commissioners. Dr Cocks, a long standing general practitioner in Ross, a town commissioner and one of the medical officers for the Ross Union Workhouse, had suggested setting up a hospital in the town some years before but had received no support.

Discussions about establishing a hospital must, indeed, have been going on for some time because the previous November a letter had appeared in the *Ross*

1872—the Dispensary and Cottage Hospital, New Street,
was in the house on the left

Gazette from Rev. Douglas Seaton, another member of the dispensary's management committee and who signed his letter 'a country curate', laying out the need for a hospital in Ross.

In January another letter, signed Theophilus, challenged the working men of Ross to rouse themselves and support this 'noble' work—how could they allow Bromyard to have a hospital and not Ross. Theophilus, who turned out to be Thomas Blake, offered £20 towards the project. The editor of the *Ross Gazette*, Mr William Hill, supported the enterprise and duly offered the project free advertising space.

A public meeting was held in the Town Hall on the 18th of January 1872 which voted in favour of establishing a cottage hospital, if possible in the dispensary as it was so conveniently located in the centre of the town. Already donations of £80 and annual subscriptions of £60 had been promised and the town's three doctors, Dr Cocks, Dr George and Dr Maclaverty offered their services free.

At this and subsequent meetings the Rules were decided. The dispensary and cottage hospital project would come together as the Ross Dispensary and Cottage Hospital (referred to from here on as Ross Hospital) and serve some 13,000 people in Ross within a radius of some seven miles. Those subscribing a guinea or over would become governors and be able to attend and vote at the annual meeting and any special meetings. A management committee of 12 governors and the medical officers was elected annually, and for the first year

Mr Henry Southall, in bowler hat, one of the instigators of the cottage hospital saying farewell to General William Booth, founder of the Salvation Army who had been staying with him

this included most of the previous dispensary committee. It was to be chaired by a president, directly elected at the annual meeting, and Capt. Kingsmill Power was elected as the first president. The bishop of Hereford had indicated his support and was appointed visitor. Four of the county's gentry, the Right Honourable Lord Bateman, Sir J.R. Bailey, Sir Herbert Croft and Mr Michael Biddulph were elected patrons.

Two long serving and respected doctors in the town were awarded honorary posts, Dr Alexander Maclaverty being appointed honorary consultant physician and Charles Edward Thomson, a retired doctor living in the town, honorary consultant surgeon. The honorary medical officers consisted of the medical practitioners in Ross while the matron of the dispensary, Mrs Ennis, was appointed matron of the combined establishment.

The honorary secretary was Mr Henry Minett, a solicitor in the town, Clerk to the Ross Union and to the town commissioners, who had been the secretary and treasurer of the dispensary. The assistant secretary was Mr Frederick Cooper, an auctioneer and agent who had also held a similar position in the dispensary, and was said to have done all the work. Indeed, he became the secretary in 1890 when Mr Minett retired.

By mid-April 1872 four rooms, made available in the dispensary for a rent of £10, were fitted up and furnished as a hospital with the help of gifts and

1872	Alexander Maclaverty, M.D.
1872	Thomas Jones, M.D.
1872	Cambridge Cary Cocks, M.D., M.R.C.S., L.S.A.
1874	Sykes Bramhall, L.S.A., M.R.C.S.
1876	John Winnell George, L.S.A., M.R.C.S.
1876	J.W. Wilson, M.D.
1876	J.H. Powell, M.R.C.S.
1877	John William Norman, L.R.C.P.
1878	William Elliott Price, L.S.A.
1879	Berkley K. Richards, M.R.C.P.
1880	Joseph Bower Siddall, L.S.A., M.R.C.S., M.D.
1881	Edward Michael Molineaux Knapp, L.R.C.P.
1883	Alexander Doig, L.R.C.P.
1885	Henry Mason, L.R.C.P., M.R.C.S.
1893	James Ashford Potts, M.B., M.R.C.S.
1905	Arthur Cutfield, B.A. B.Sc, M.R.C.S.
1905	Arthur Llewellyn Baldwin Green, M.R.C.S., L.R.C.P.
1911	Thomas Scott Shepherd, M.B., B.Ch, F.R.C.S., L.R.C.P.
1916	William Paulson, L.S.A., L.R.C.P.
1921	Walter Holcroft Cam, M.B., B.Ch., M.R.C.S., L.R.C.P.
1921	Charles Allen Adair Dighton, M.B., B.Ch., F.R.C.S.
1929	H.L. D'Olier Duckworth, M.B., B.Ch.
1929	John Leeper Dunlop, M.C., M.B., B.Ch.
1932	David Irving Anderson, O.B.E., M.B., B.Ch.
1932	Anne Fleming Pillans, L.R.C.P., L.R.C.S., L.R.F.P.S.
1932	George Lynn Pillans, M.C., L.R.C.S., L.R.C.P., F.R.F.P.S.
1936	Charles Llangley Owen, M.A., M.B., B.Ch., F.R.C.S., L.R.C.P.
1937	G. Marner Lloyd, M.R.C.S., L.R.C.P.
1939	E. Jean McQ. Lloyd, M.B., B.S., M.R.C.S., L.R.C.P., D.P.H.
1940	William Kerr Russell, M.B., B.S.
1940	Eleanor Hilda Russell M.B., B.S.
1946	William Arthur Derek Jones-Roberts, M.R.C.S., L.R.C.P.

Table 9 Honorary Medical Staff at Ross Cottage Hospital. The year indicates when each doctor is first known to have a hospital appointment

donations from supporters. The female ward was a cheerful room with three beds. On the wall above each bed hung a board to contain information about the occupant and her diet. Below this was a little box containing a bible and prayer book, presented by Mrs Pechell, the wife of Capt Pechell R.N., who was on the committee. Mrs Pechell was an official visitor to the hospital and interested herself in every detail. The male ward also had three beds and had been decorated by Mr Thomas Blake. Upstairs there was an operating theatre and a second room which was kept for emergency use. The kitchen was equipped with a new range and Ross Hospital opened in late April without any ceremony.

The committee of management met quarterly, whilst sub-committees met weekly to decide on the suitability of patients for admission and set charges dependent on their means. Routine cases required letters of recommendation from subscribers which had to be handed to the secretary three days before admission. Once endorsed by a member of the committee the patient had to report to the matron for admission at 11a.m. on the following Wednesday. In 1879 the medical staff were reprimanded for admitting patients, other than emergency or urgent cases, between meetings.

In 1876 a committee of lady visitors was suggested but a general meeting rejected this and instead two interested ladies were appointed to the committee for the purpose of inspecting the establishment weekly. Any suggestions regarding the cooking, linen or general management had to be written down in a large visitors' book which was kept locked up. They were particularly asked to inspect the mens' blankets! The system did not appear to work well, because in 1883 seven members of the committee living in the town took it in turns to inspect the hospital on a weekly basis.

Accommodation in the New Street premises soon proved inadequate and in 1876 Dr Cocks argued for a new hospital. In September 1878 a piece of land known as the Crofts Land, part of the Chase Estate near the town, but well back from Gloucester Road, was bought for £300. Later that year Mrs Stubbs, the wife of the late General Stubbs of Penyard House, who had been on the committee, offered an adjacent strip of land, as long as it was not built on, for the recreation of patients.

Designs were sought from 18 architects from around the country, Messrs Haddon Brothers from Hereford, Malvern and London and their design being subsequently chosen having received the accolade, if it could be called that, of 'Well Considered'. The builders selected were Messrs W. and J. Crow, of the City Saw Mills, Hereford. The estimated cost was £1,200, a figure largely met when the Rev. H.C. Morgan, vicar of Goodrich, bequeathed £1,000. Several smaller legacies made up the balance.

The foundation stone was laid by Colonel Edward Clive, deputising for his father who was ill, the inscription on the stone still reading: 'This foundation stone was laid by George Clive, Esq, M.P., on Easter Tuesday, April 15th, 1879'. Inside the foundation stone was placed a bottle containing information

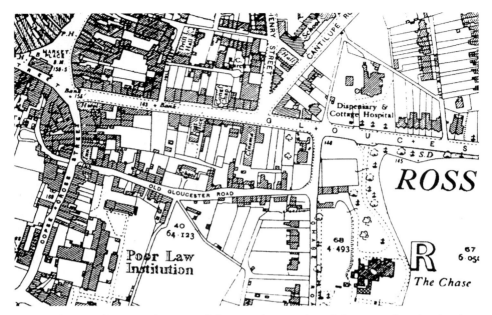

Map of Ross showing the site of the new hospital and the poor law institution

about the hospital and the foundation ceremony, a photograph of the town, copies of the *Ross Gazette* and *Man of Ross* for 10th April 1879 and coins of the realm. The bishop of Hereford, who was attired in full 'canonicals', took part in the ceremony and along with 40 distinguished guests enjoyed a splendid luncheon in the Assembly Room of the Royal Hotel. During the postprandial euphoria, over £20 was pledged in subscriptions.

The hospital was opened in September. The ground floor contained male and female wards, with a southern aspect, each accommodating four patients, with an operating room between them. There was also a two bedded ward for diseases peculiar to women. A sheltered porch led into a wide corridor, which separated the wards from a board room, a waiting room, an adjacent dispensary, a nurses' sitting room, kitchen, scullery, store rooms, toilet facilities and a mortuary. Upstairs was an isolation ward together with nurses' and servants' bedrooms. Part of the grounds became a tennis court which used to be rented out, the rest was planted with shrubs to limit maintenance.

A metered gas supply was provided. A supply of mains water was available but unreliable, so a concrete tank to hold rainwater was placed under the coal shed. It was not till 1897 that the drainage was connected to the sewers in Cantilupe Street, and during the first few years the rainwater tank often became contaminated by sewerage and had to be regularly cleaned out.

Architect's impression of the proposed new 'well considered' hospital

In May 1882 a fire which started in the boiler room caused £200 worth of damage, but was covered by insurance. Five years later an adjacent piece of land was bought for £162 to prevent any future nearby building becoming a nuisance.

During the queen's jubilee year the upstairs ward was fitted out to take one bed and a cot to be used in cases of emergency. It was opened and named the Jubilee Ward by Miss Ellen Barnard of Over Ross, a wealthy spinster who had lived in the town for over 50 years and been a constant supporter of charitable causes including the hospital.

Four years later a consulting room at the back of the hospital called the Kyrle Wing was added at a cost of £120 raised by the Kyrle Coffee House Committee. It was named after John Kyrle, The Man of Ross, the town's most famous citizen, an amiable wealthy philanthropist, immortalised by Alexander Pope. In 1897 an outpatients' waiting room was added, situated in the quadrangle adjoining the Kyrle Wing and dispensary, which had access to the outside and also opened into the dispensary and the consulting room, so allowing patients to enter without having to go through the hospital.

When the hospital opened Dr Cocks had obtained one of Professor Lister's Steam Carbolic Acid Sprays to use as an antiseptic spray in theatre. By 1896 aseptic techniques had come in and the doctors requested a new theatre as the present one was shared with outpatients, increasing the risks of infection.

Initial plans were drawn up costing £300. Then Mrs Alice Foster, of Brockhampton Court, indicated her interest in financing the project and brought in her own architect. The new plans were accepted at a vastly increased cost of £1,500, Mrs Foster and her friends meeting most of the bill. The increase was due to a much higher specification for the theatre, including tiling the walls with salmon and gold tinted minton china squares, whilst the floors were laid with a rich carpet—something at which surgeons today would raise their eyebrows! The instrument cabinets and operating tables were of massive plate glass while the shelves were covered with expensive surgical instruments. It was claimed at the time that the

Mrs Alice Madeline Foster

theatre and its equipment was unequalled outside of London. Mrs Foster was duly made a life governor.

The income of the hospital in 1873, its first operational year, included £4 from charity boxes situated at the hospital, the post office and the King's Head Hotel. Income also came from three firms, including the Alton Court Brewery Co. which ran a contributory scheme where the employees paid 1d a week in return for hospital care when it was required. Some patients were treated free, such as when a child with burns was admitted and the father earned just 14s a week and had five children to support. The work at the dispensary also increased during the first year, when it had been expected that it may suffer.

Over the years, most of the doctors in the town were appointed as honorary medical officers and accepted the Rules concerning their obligations to look after their patients in the hospital and to be available for emergencies. However, in 1880 Dr Bamhall resigned as his duties were interfering with his private practice. The same there was also disagreement between the doctors about how they should be represented on the committee. One view was that the committee should contain no acting medical officer, another that the medical staff should elect their representatives, and a third that they should rotate every few months by seniority. After three years' wrangling the annual meeting decided that they would continue to elect two doctors onto the committee, but without giving them voting rights. Dr Cocks, Dr Richards and Dr Powell immediately resigned. The committee tried unsuccessfully to get them to reconsider and were particularly sad about Dr Cocks who had been such a good supporter of the hospital over so many years.

In 1882 Dr Siddall was outraged when one of his patients was discharged without his agreement. The patient had sustained a severe back injury after falling from a hay cart and was admitted as an emergency. He was unable to pay 3s 6d a week maintenance, had no helpful

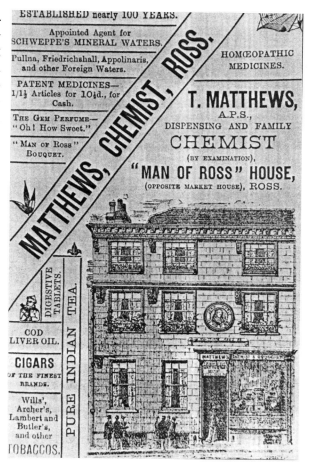

Mr Thomas Matthew's Chemist Shop

friends and was judged a pauper by the committee, who without consulting Dr Siddall discharged him to the Ross Workhouse. The subsequent exchange of letters in the *Ross Gazette* between the doctor and Mr Frederick Cooper, the honorary secretary to the hospital, went on for several months. The committee insisted the Rules had been honoured and were unrepentant, but the publicity must have harmed the hospital.

The first dispenser for the amalgamated institution was Mr Henry Wooler appointed in March 1872 at a salary of £25 p.a. but he died after two years in the post. In 1877 the dispenser appointed was Mr Thomas Matthews who lived above his chemist shop at The Man of Ross, John Kyrle's old house. In 1896

1872	Mrs Ennis
1875	Mrs Morris
1879	Mrs Ann Webb
1880	Miss Maria Hill
1883	Miss Petrie
1884	Miss E.G. Maitland
1885	Miss Perkins
1890	Miss Jane Pye
1896	Miss Lane
1899	Miss Jane Pye
1903	Miss Sibyl Douney
1904	Miss Crawford
1908	Miss Wilson
1912	Miss Shepherd
1939	Miss E.G. Findlay

Table 10 Matrons at Ross Cottage Hospital

he threatened to resign unless changes were made, complaining that with the increase in outpatients and inpatients it took him four days a week to prepare and dispense medicines, which were becoming more complex, resulting in him having to employ a highly paid qualified assistant. Dr Price confirmed that 40 to 50 cases were seen at the dispensary each morning which was now open four days a week. At a special meeting of the governors it was agreed to reduce the duration of an outpatient ticket from two to one month and apply the rules more carefully in selecting suitable cases of charity. Mr Matthews withdrew his threat of resignation.

Mrs Ennis carried out the nursing duties in the wards and theatre as well as being a housekeeper. In 1879 it was agreed that if there were more than three inpatients, the hospital would pay for extra nursing, but it was not until 1896 that an assistant trained nurse was employed. The position of matron was poorly paid, and unsurprisingly there were ten matrons up to the end of the century. Only one, Miss Jane Pye, stayed for any length of time, six years, before resigning to look after her sister. She was subsequently reappointed three years later for a further four years.

Two matrons were forced to resign, Mrs Morris because she had purchased a bottle of port and put it in the accounts as bacon, and Mrs Ann Webb from Presteigne because she was found taking drugs. A youthful matron, Miss Maitland, aged 26, and said to be tall and strong, only lasted ten months. The matron was not allowed a dog but one was allowed to have her husband resident.

The turn round of assistant nurses was also fast as three different ones were employed in as many years. One of these, Miss Drury, complained she was left to do most of the housekeeping, all the cooking and cleaning up of the wards and theatre, while not being allowed to do any of the dressings. She lasted three months but her complaint caused a review of the matron and assistant's duties. As a result a servant was also employed and periodically, a scrubber and errand boy.

The hospital admitted 28 inpatients in 1873, the numbers fluctuating but generally increasing over the years, reaching 92 in 1898. An increasing number of casualties were also seen, up to around 90 a year, whilst others attended for dressings. Some idea of the mix of cases can be seen from the total of 319 patients attending the hospital during the first nine years, of which 99 were surgical cases, 66 medical and 154 accidents. 249 patients were stated to be cured and 47 relieved, whilst 23 died.

Initially no record was kept of how many patients attended the dispensary or had follow up visits. Instead the workload was calculated by noting how many prescriptions were given out, a number that varied between 2,500 and 5,000 a year. Crutches and a wheelchair were lent out free but a deposit was required. Elastic stockings for varicose ulcers were charged for.

There were complaints, as in 1878 when a patient was kept waiting all day without food before being eventually admitted to the Hereford General Infirmary because no bed were available at the cottage hospital. In 1898 a labourer aged 30 died during an anaesthetic given for an operation on his right knee. This resulted in a coroner's inquiry during which Dr Potts and Dr Palin, the medical officers involved, were subject to a 'severe examination'. It was decided that death was caused by a weak constitution and was due to a seizure during the operation as the man had been subject to fits. The jury decided that no-one was to blame.

Ale drinking was popular amongst the patients in the hospital, but it was ordered in small casks in the hope this would help limit its use.

1900 - 1918

In 1903 Lt. Col. Arthur Wellesley Foster, Mrs Alice Foster's husband, became president for the following two years. He was subsequently appointed to the Board of Management of the General Hospital in Hereford. In 1916 and 1917 Mrs Foster herself was president.

In 1904 Frederick Cooper's son, Percival, was appointed an assistant secretary, though they both offered to resign in 1909. Frederick Cooper was the senior partner in Messrs Cooper and Preece, who had acted as agents in obtaining insurance for the Ross Urban District Council, of which Mr Cooper was a member. He was not aware that his firm was involved in these negotiations which disqualified him from membership of the council. The magistrates found him guilty but stated that they did not believe he had intentionally done anything wrong. He was fined 7s and both father and son took the honourable course and offered to resign from their position with the hospital. They were both persuaded to withdraw their resignations. In 1916 Mr Percival Cooper enlisted and was killed in action. Mrs Aga Le Grand, Mr Cooper's daughter was appointed assistant secretary till she left for India in November 1918.

In the early 1900s the hospital buildings were upgraded and modern facilities added. In 1902 a wooden hut was built to accommodate a wheelchair

Fundraising for the hospital in 1910—a mock operation

ambulance and stretcher to bring patients to hospital from the surrounding parishes. A telephone service was provided for £3 p.a. Electric light was installed and paid for by Mrs Moffat of Goodrich and Lt. Col. Arthur Foster. In 1908 two new bedrooms and a sitting room were added at a cost of £140 paid for by a building fund organised by Dr Cutfield. Sir Henry Burdett, a national expert on hospitals, visited the hospital and criticised the sanitary arrangements. As a result a new bathroom was provided and the lavatories in both male and female wards were improved.

Income and expenditure gradually rose, but were kept in balance through the use of special appeals. A League of Hospital Friends had been formed and one of their fundraising ventures was to stage a mock operation outside the Market House in 1910. In 1913 the Goodrich and District Ladies Linen League was formed to supply linen required by the hospital. In 1904 the Committee of Management had suggested that the honorary medical officers should charge for small operations on outpatients and put the fee in the hospital charity box. There is no record of how popular this idea was.

It was also during the early 1900s that the assistant nurses caused some problems. Over a period of four years Miss Lucas, a trained staff nurse, developed pleurisy, then scarlet fever and finally a poisoned hand. She then had extra leave to attend a dying sister-in-law before she finally resigned. A Miss Nash was employed as a temporary assistant nurse and a year later had established a nursing home in Ross for private patients providing a threat of competition.

Nevertheless, by the beginning of the First World War an assistant staff nurse was required and four years later two additional junior nurses were employed.

One of the nurse's duties was to remove bodies to the mortuary, but after complaints the matron was allowed to employ two men for this purpose. It was also agreed that the nursing staff could have the use of the tennis court, by permission of the tenant, for two days a week.

Early in the century non-nursing staff included a resident servant, a 17 year old cook, a second non-resident servant aged 13 who was described as 'a willing little worker but hardly up to it'. A charwomen, a gardener and a boy were employed part time.

In October 1915 Commander Hudson attended the committee on behalf of the War Office requesting the hospital to admit wounded soldiers. The government would pay maintenance at 2s a day per man. The matron said she could cope with the addition of a night nurse, and the committee agreed to make beds available for five wounded soldiers.

X-ray apparatus was provided early in 1916, donated by Mrs Foster in memory of her son Cedric Foster, a Lieutenant in the Grenadier Guards, who died of his wounds at Neuve Chapelle. Two years later central heating was installed. The post of stoker for the system's boiler was offered to a medically unfit soldier who had contracted malaria, but he turned the job down.

It was also in 1916 that all three doctors on the honorary staff, Dr Campbell, Dr Green and Dr Shepherd were called up and Dr William Paulson, a locum medical officer provided temporary medical help.

Wounded soldiers started to be admitted in 1916 and up to March 1919 a total of 159 were treated, with 54 operations being performed and only one death. Some remained in the hospital for 10 months and as the government was paying for them there was no incentive to move them on. Many helped in the grounds and improved the garden and tennis court.

In 1918, 234 inpatients were treated, 120 operations were performed and 287 casualties attended. Inappropriate cases were sometimes sent in. Dr Campbell of Drybrook sent in a case of diphtheria, which Dr Green refused to admit, and was duly supported by the committee. A patient sent for admission from outside the district was not looked upon as a charitable case, but would be referred to one of the honorary medical officers and, if necessary, admitted as a private patient. Several inpatients were discharged when there was little chance of further effective treatment. A man with a broken back who was permanently paralysed was discharged to the infirmary at the Ross Workhouse, whilst a 13 year old boy who had been in hospital for over a year and had clearly stopped making any progress was sent to a home.

1919 to the advent of the N.H.S.

After the First World War a large pavilion was obtained free from the Red Cross and erected in the hospital grounds, with the help of £74 donated by Mrs Foster, to be used as a retreat and recreation room by the nurses. In 1919 a room was made available for massage treatment of patients by a local masseuse, the start of physiotherapy in the hospital. The addition of a seven bedded children's ward was also planned in 1919, but awaited finance. In the same year the Ross War Hospital Supply Depot closed and the 130 workers donated their welfare funds of £800 to the project; their president just happened to be Mrs Foster. This provided the necessary finance and the ward was built onto the back of the hospital and opened in 1921.

Due to a lack of accommodation nurses had been sleeping in shelters in the grounds and now Jubilee Ward was used to accommodate them for the next seven years before it was divided into two private wards. In 1927 a hand-operated lift was donated and this was electrified two years later due once again to the generosity of Mrs Foster. She also helped to finance the upgrading of the X-ray apparatus. Several years later a new portable X-ray machine was purchased out of capital.

In 1934 the Building Committee raised nearly £700 following a general appeal and this allowed a small ward to be added for agitated patients whose presence in a large ward would be disturbing for others.

In January 1920 Mr Frederick Cooper, who had been president, vice-president and life governor, retired after 56 years of outstanding service as honorary secretary to the dispensary and hospital. He died six years later but not before donating a piece of land adjacent to the hospital. He was replaced by Mr H.A. Nuttall.

The hospital committee was modified in 1930 to consist of the president, vice-president, 15 governors or subscribers and the treasurer. To increase support, representatives were elected from Ross Trades Labour Council and from Ross Railwaymen's Union. One third of the members were to retire each year, according to seniority, but in practise were usually immediately re-elected.

The number of life governors created through making a donation of £10 was getting too large, so the Rules were changed so that such benefactors would only hold their post for one year. In order to encourage fundraising, for every £50 raised by a body of collectors the committee could elect one of their number to be a life governor. Five years after this decision was made, even this right was limited to a term of 10 years.

In September 1932 Mrs Foster died in her seventieth year. Her father, Ebenezer Jordon of Boston, U.S.A., had presented her with Brockhampton Court as a wedding present when she married Mr Arthur Foster who came from a Yorkshire milling family. She built All Saints' Church at Brockhampton in memory of her parents, was the first lady magistrate in Herefordshire and the greatest benefactor the Ross Cottage Hospital ever had.

The regular income rose in fits and starts to £1,573 by 1939. As with all the voluntary hospitals, fundraising was ever ongoing. Hospital Sunday parades were held at Walford and Goodrich, whilst a Hospital 50 Committee composed of 50 ladies contributed £500 over seven years. A Hospital Football Cup Committee provided a Challenge Cup which was played for amongst local teams, while the Levick Hospital Cup was awarded to the winner of a fishing competition organised by the Ross Angling Club. The Julian Fund was a challenge by a Mr F.L. Julian, of Cheltenham, to pay off a year's deficit by offering to contribute £25 if 11 other people would do likewise—the money was duly forthcoming. The Ross Hospital Carnival Committee was formed in 1923 to redress annual deficits and in its fifth year raised over £400.

Expenses also steadily rose. The average cost of a patient per week increased from £2 5s 10d in 1926 to £4 6s 1d in 1939. Expenditure during the inter-war period exceeded income by between £70 and £400 a year, partly caused by an annual book keeping charge of £200 for depreciation on the land, buildings and equipment. Deficits were covered by donations.

In spite of these minor deficits the capital investments continued to grow. The Farmers Red Cross Fund endowed a cot for £465, while legacies were left by Mrs Foster for £756, the Rev. S. Clarke for £900, Mr Gatfield for £1,332 and Mr A.G. Powell for £3,100. The total value of investments in 1938 was estimated at £17,987.

During 1939 the number of inpatients was 251 with an average length of stay of just over eight days. The numbers of outpatients and casualties was 500, while the number of operations performed rose to 214. X-ray examinations had rapidly increased to 139.

Since the National Health Insurance Act of 1911 the dispensary had not been needed and, rather belatedly in 1940, the enterprise's name was changed to the Ross Cottage Hospital.

In the same year, part of the X-ray room was converted into a ward large enough to take two patients to be used either as an isolation ward or for emergency cases. Six years later plans to build a new block for nurses' accommodation, costed at £6,000, were approved by the Ministry of Health. It would provide a bedroom and sitting room for the sister, a general sitting room and five other bedrooms. Unfortunately, with approaching nationalisation, there were so many bureaucratic hurdles to overcome that it was not built by the time the N.H.S. took over.

Aerial view of Ross Cottage Hospital taken in the 1980s

The income increased to £2,907 by 1947. Although subscriptions were declining, payments by patients, particularly private patients, had dramatically increased. In spite of increasing expenses the finances remained healthy up until 1946. But in the following year expenses climbed to £3,624 mainly due to a national rise in salaries and the weekly cost of inpatients rose to £7 6s 0d. The committee had accepted and welcomed the Rushcliffe Report on nurses' salaries as it recognised the skill and value of the nursing profession, even if it involved a substantial increase in expenses. The deficit of £700 was covered by a legacy of £250 and credit of £600 in the bank.

Alderman Thomas Blake, alias Theophilus, writing in 1872, had challenged the working men of Ross to support the establishment of a cottage hospital. If he could have seen the consequences after 76 years, on the eve of Nationalisation, he would have every reason to be well satisfied.

CHAPTER 6

Ledbury Cottage Hospital

In the latter part of the nineteenth century Ledbury had a population of just over 4,000. There was little industry apart from glovemaking. An almshouse, St Catherine's Hospital, provided accommodation for 12 males and 12 females, and the union workhouse at Belle Orchard accommodated 170 inmates. A charitable dispensary was established in 1824 to serve the poor in the parish and some 500 people attended each year.

On Wednesday 1st November 1871, at the Court House, Southend Street, Earl Somers of Eastnor Castle presided over a meeting of the clergy and gentry from Ledbury and surrounding district to consider establishing a cottage hospital in the town. The influential supporters included two major landowners—John Martin of Upper Hall who had been an M.P., and Osman Richardo of Bosberrow Place, chairman of the Ledbury Magisterial Bench and a previous M.P. for Worcester. Also present were Dr William Henry of Haffield and London, an eminent and much respected Fellow of the Royal Society who had been involved in scientific research, and Dr Miles Astman Wood, who was in practice in Ledbury. The meeting agreed that a cottage hospital should be provided in Ledbury.

A committee was formed consisting of a number of clergy and gentry with Earl Somers as chairman. It included Michael Biddulph of Ledbury Place, M.P. for the County of Hereford and a partner in the banking firm of Cocks, Biddulph & Co., a firm originally established by his ancestors and those of Lord Somers whose family name was Cocks. Over the next 15 months the committee agreed the Rules, canvassed for subscribers, found a suitable building and held a general meeting to confirm the arrangements and make appointments. Subscribers of 5s a year and donors of £1 were allowed to vote at the annual meeting and be eligible to serve on committees.

The site of the original cottage hospital as it is today.
The Railway Inn sign is still just visible high on the gable end

A well-built three storey house in Homend Street, which had previously been the Railway Inn, was rented as the first hospital building. On the ground floor there were two large rooms suitable for a dayroom and a boardroom, together with a kitchen and an adjacent pantry. Upstairs on the first floor a male and female ward were created accommodating two patients in each, an operating theatre and matron's room. Several other rooms were available on the second floor. The committee advertised in the *Ledbury Free Press and Herefordshire Advertiser* asking for donations of furniture, ironmongery, and crockery.

Earl Somers was elected patron, whilst Dr Henry was appointed president. The Committee of Management consisted of nine clergymen which ensured that the surrounding parishes were represented, and nine lay members including Mr Michael Biddulph, together with Mr Richardo as chairman. The secretary was Mr George Edward Masefield, a solicitor in the firm of Masefield and Sons, and the father of John Masefield, the subsequent poet laureate. The treasurer was Mr Edward J. Webb, a banker and solicitor in the firm Webb & Co. All four doctors in the town were elected honorary medical officers, whilst Miss Mary Ann Tolley, who had previously been a nurse at the Ledbury Union Workhouse, was appointed matron. The Ledbury Cottage Hospital was duly opened on Tuesday 18th February 1873.

1873-97	Miles Astman Wood, L.S.A., M.R.C.S.
1873-1910	John Henry Wood, M.B., M.R.C.S.
1873-5	George Stratton Symmons, M.R.C.S.
1873-77	Robert Tanner, L.S.A., M.D., M.R.C.S.
1875-1907	Miles Astman Wood jnr., F.R.C.S., L.R.C.P.
1877-?	William Griffin, M.R.C.S.
1878-?	John William Buckell, M.B., M.S.
1891-1892	Thomas Hill, L.S.A., M.R.C.S.
1892-1921	Arthur R. Green, M.R.C.S., L.R.C.P.
1898-1938	James McKean Harrison, M.B., B.Ch.
1902-3	W.W. Talbot, M.R.C.S., L.R.C.P.
1907-42	George Bartley McKean, M.B., B.S., F.R.C.S.
1914-48	Leslie B.C. Trotter, M.A., M.D., B.C.
1921-35	Thomas Arthur Jones, B.C., M.R.C.S., L.R.C.P.
1935-?	William Steadman, M.C., M.R.C.S., L.R.C.P.
1937-8	Dr. H.A. Picton, M.B., M.R.C.S., M.R.C.P.
1938-47	G.G. Airey, M.R.C.S., L.R.C.P.
1938-40	James G. Coghlan, M.B., B.Ch.
1940	Edward Alexander Marie Joachim Goldie, M.C., M.B., B.S., M.R.C.S., L.R.C.P.
1940	Langdale-Smith, M.B., B.Ch.
1947	John Nixon Groves, D.S.O., M.A., M.B., B.CH., M.R.C.S., L.R.C.P.

Table 11 Honorary Medical Staff, Ledbury Cottage Hospital.
The initial year given above is that in which it is known that each doctor had their first hospital appointment

The annual meeting was held in February or March each year, usually in the Old Market House, the Ledbury Church Rooms or the Feathers Hotel. In 1875 two nonconformist ministers who had been asked to raise money for the hospital were invited to attend the annual meeting by the secretary, which was against the Rules. This caused initial unpleasantness, though it was eventually agreed that they should be allowed to attend the annual meetings.

One of the earliest medical officers was Dr Robert Tanner, who also acted at the workhouse as well as serving the Ledbury Foresters as their secretary and treasurer. He resigned in 1877 when he was aged 40 because of poor health in order to seek the benefits of the climate in New Zealand. A testimonial fund raised £360, an indication of the affection for him and regret people felt at his leaving. He sailed with his son, John Tanner, aged 11, and a servant John

Bishop, but all three were drowned when their ship the *Avalanche* sank after being in collision with the *Forest* from Nova Scotia off Portland in the English Channel.

Mr Michael Biddulph decided to commemorate the coming of age of his eldest son, Mr John Michael Biddulph on November 19th 1890, by providing a new cottage hospital. He therefore purchased a portion of the Belle Orchard Estate opposite the original hospital from the Ledbury Building Society. The builder selected was Mr George Hill, of Ledbury who commenced work in the Spring of 1891. The wards were sited on the south and west sides to get the benefit of the sun. The matron's sitting room and the kitchen were in the front with a corridor running back, on one side of which was a large ward with four beds, and on the other side the scullery, larder and toilets. At the back, the operating theatre was situated between two small wards of three and two beds. Upstairs there were two bedrooms and a storeroom. A mortuary was placed immediately underneath the operating room. A separate laundry was situated in the back garden where a lawn was planned. There was an additional apartment for a parish nurse on the north side which had its own entrance, and consisted of a living room downstairs with kitchen, scullery, larder and a toilet and a bedroom upstairs. The total cost of land and buildings was around £3,000.

Top: Michael Biddulph
Lower: His son John Michael Biddulph

The new hospital was officially opened on Tuesday 29th December 1891 by Lady Elizabeth Biddulph in the presence of her husband and son. She expressed the hope that for many years the hospital would be a comfort and blessing for Ledbury, describing how over the last 14 years, with the help of a ladies committee drawn from amongst her personal friends, she had raised subscriptions for a district nurse, who had, amongst other duties, attended hundreds of death beds.

Not to neglect an opportunity, the chairman, Rev. Maddison Green explained that the income to run the old hospital was £230 p.a. and as more would be required, he hoped the public would respond — £39 was collected at the door. Because of dampness caused by wet weather during the building, the new hospital did not open for business till June 1892, when it received the patients from the old hospital.

In 1898 it was decided that the committee had grown too large and it was agreed that the annual meeting would elect a Board of 23 governors who would then appoint a Management Committee of 13 to include a president, secretary and treasurer.

Most years there was a credit balance in the annual accounts. The income slowly increased to £268 in the year 1898, made up of subscriptions £106, donations £30, income from investments £45, charity boxes £5, church offertories £34, miscellaneous £19 and patient payments £29. There were charity collecting boxes at the Feathers Hotel, the New Inn, the White Hart, the Plough, the Ring of Bells and inside and outside the hospital. Income from church offertories from up to 13 parishes fluctuated from £15 to £40 p.a. There was no agreement about recognising a Hospital Sunday throughout the district, although church parades were held in Ledbury. There were a few fundraising activities such as concerts and street collections, which in 1875 raised a total of £70.

Some of the local firms and associations ran contributory schemes, which allowed their members privileges at the hospital. The Ross and Ledbury Railway Working Men's Association contributed £3 p.a. from a 1d a week fund.

Expenditure was £247 in 1899. The average cost per patient stay in that year was £4 16s 0d or 3s 7d per day. Agriculture was depressed in the late 1890s resulting in a drop in income, but successful special appeals managed to avoid the use of capital. Large donations over £20 and legacies were often recorded on boards hung in the hospital's hall, and which are still there. Mrs Russell of Woodlands endowed a bed to be called The Russell Bed and later also left a legacy of £150. In 1893 Mr George Hatton died leaving a legacy of £500. He was born in Ledbury and then went to Worcester, from where he travelled around with a horse and cart dealing in cider and salt. He never married, but returned to Ledbury 12 years prior to his death, living alone in a small cottage.

Board of donors in the hospital's hall

It appears that he kept his money in boxes scattered about the house and during a fire in the nearby Prince of Wales Tavern in Church Lane, he refused to leave his cottage until he had collected every box.

Initially there were four honorary medical officers appointed to the hospital from the town and district, and each week there would be two doctors on duty, one designated as a surgeon and the other as a physician. Most of the medical staff appeared regularly in either role.

One of the notable matrons was a Miss Bamber who arrived in 1897 from the Childrens' Hospital, Newcastle upon Tyne, having previously worked in infirmaries at Arbroath, Macclesfield and Cardiff. She managed to reduce expenditure by rigidly watching a patient's diet, which included only providing alcoholic drinks on the written request of a doctor. By the end of the century there was also an assistant nurse, usually a probationer.

The district served by the hospital included 22 surrounding parishes, and in its first year a matching 22 patients were admitted of which 20 were said to be surgical cases. There was only one death and he was already dying on admission. The numbers treated slowly increased over the years and the hospital was rarely empty. In 1899, admissions totalled 40, consisting of 19 surgical, 9 accident and 12 medical cases. Of these, 31 were cured, five were relieved, two died and two remained in hospital on December 31st. The average number of beds occupied was three and the average length of stay was 26 days.

Emergency surgery was required for obstructed groin hernias most years. In February 1874 a farmworker was feeding a chaff cutting machine when his left arm was dragged into the machine and so mutilated that his hand was virtually cut off. At the hospital Dr Symmons amputated the arm up to the elbow and the patient survived.

The hospital soon gained the loyalty of its potential patients and by December 1874 was being well supplied with gifts, especially on Christmas Day. On the early 1890s there was an influenza outbreak in Ledbury and two of the clergy opened a beef tea invalid kitchen at the cottage hospital.

1900 - 1918

In 1900 it had been agreed that the minimal weekly payments by patients towards their maintenance was to be 3s 6d for an adult, 2s for a child and 1 guinea for a private patient. The hospital was also able to charge the local authorities for work carried out on their behalf, and 50 tonsillectomies in children were performed in 1911 on this basis.

The early 1900s saw steady improvements being made to the hospital. Lady Biddulph realized the hospital had no bath and paid for one to be installed adjacent to the male ward. She also gave £100 to provide a private room for each nurse and contributed finance towards an increase in the number of male beds.

In 1906 a telephone was installed thanks to a donation by long serving governor Mr John Riley. Five years later Mr Spenser Bickam, a governor and committee member, gifted a mortuary chapel which was erected on the west side of the garden. Just before the First World War the operating theatre was upgraded following a special appeal.

A designated Hospital Sunday throughout the district was finally agreed on in 1907 with church services in the parishes and a parade organised in the town by the Foresters and Oddfellows which contributed £36 in 1918. Indeed, fundraising has been generally increasing prior to the war. The Ledbury Cycling Club presented the hospital with nine bedsteads and £11 raised from their dances, social evenings and an illuminated cyclist procession through the town. Money was raised by Cinderella Dances at the Plough Hotel and by the Snowflake Minstrels. Mr Henry Studt was a travelling fairman from South Wales who annually visited the market towns of Herefordshire including Ledbury,

Lady Elizabeth Biddulph

Kington and Leominster. His fairs were known for their 'swinging gondolas' and he had annual benefit nights for the local cottage hospital.

In 1910 the Ladies Linen League was formed with Lady Biddulph as its first president. By the end of the first year it had 90 members subscribing a total of over £8 and 260 items. Apart from providing most of the hospital's linen they organised an annual Pound Day, and raised money for specific projects such as the upgrading of the theatre.

For some years prior to 1904 a Miss Dora Bullock had annually had a house to house penny collection in the parish of Dymock. In that year Ledbury participated in the Cresswell Penny Fund organised by the General Hospital and the Ledbury secretaries, Misses N. and C. Smith, organised a monthly house to house collection, resulting in £19 being raised in the first year, half going to the Cottage Hospital and half to the General Hospital. After the first year the sums collected became smaller but Miss Bullock was still collecting in Dymock in 1918.

1873	Miss Mary Tolley
1884	Miss Stanton
	Miss Goodburn
1887	Miss Foster
1893	Miss Still
1903	Miss Bamber
1907	Miss Alice Lee Smith
1909	Miss C.M. Crawford
1910	Miss A.E. Cragg
1911	Miss Bramwell
1913	Miss Johnson
1918	Miss Holford
1922	Miss M.E. Richardson
1939	Miss B.M. Williams
1946	Miss M.J. Gore
1947	Miss S.M. Perch
1948	Miss Miriam I. Clarke

Table 12 Matrons at Ledbury Cottage Hospital

During the first 18 years of the twentieth century, eight matrons were appointed. Most came from large hospitals elsewhere in England, but the task of running a small cottage hospital with minimal staff must have been heartbreaking, especially when their popularity with management was dependent on them keeping expenses down. Patients in the private ward were an additional burden and no extra help was provided. Up until 1901, the matron had only one full time probationer nurse to help her, although she could employ a temporary nurse when the hospital was busy. After 1901 the appointment of a second nurse, either a probationer or a trained assistant, was intermittently allowed. The balance between adequate nursing and economy was always difficult. A ward maid was also provided.

During 1918 there were 65 inpatients treated of whom 36 were accident cases, 57 surgical and eight medical. The average number of beds occupied was just over three with a stay of 19 days. Only one patient was private. But the numbers of patients treated had drastically decreased during the war; for five years from 1911 inpatients had numbered between 100 and 171, of whom up to 10 had been private. Operations varied from 30 to 118 per year, the busier years partly due to a large number of profitable tonsillectomies.

1919 to the advent of the N.H.S.

In 1919 the rooms adjoining the hospital, which had initially accommodated the parish nurse and had more recently been occupied by the county council, were handed over to the hospital to provide extra bedrooms.

By 1922 electric light had been installed throughout the hospital. Two years later additions to the staff quarters were funded by the Grand Lodge Committee. A bath and lavatory for the women's ward and verandahs were gifted by Mr T.H. Hill in memory of his father Mr George Hill, the builder of the hospital. A few years later he helped the hospital again by replacing nine old fashioned beds with up to date ones. The building was modernised a year later with the installation of central heating. In the early thirties the Ladies Linen League under Mrs Trotter, who had been Secretary and Treasurer since 1920, provided wirelesses with headphones for each hospital bed.

In 1924 the medical staff had requested X-ray facilities in the hospital and an appeal was launched which raised £1,000 within two years. The old private ward was adapted to house the new X-ray apparatus and an X-ray fund was also established to help with maintenance and future improvements with the

Ledbury Cottage Hospital in 1923

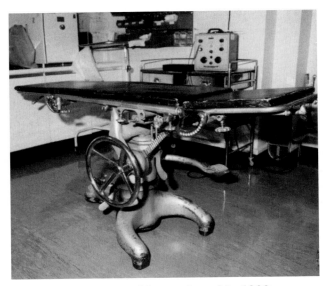

Operating table purchased in 1938

support of Ledbury's scouts and guides. A new private ward and an emergency ward was built, enabling the hospital to accommodate up to 12 patients. In the mid-thirties additional accommodation for the increasing number of nurses was built. Just before the Second World War modernisation continued with the purchase of a new portable X-ray machine and a modern operating table.

In 1937 the Rules were altered to allow patients to be looked after by their own general practitioner, even if he did not have an appointment with the hospital. At the same time letters of recommendation were discontinued as no patient had ever been turned away.

From 1919 onwards fundraising activities increased. Hospital Sunday church collections continued to contribute around £50. However, the event was often associated with a Hospital Sunday Parade through the town which attracted donations from individuals along with the staff of many Ledbury shops and firms, providing up to a further £150. In 1923 a Ledbury Carnival was held on August Bank Holiday in Ledbury Park, with the permission of Lord Biddulph, raising £250 for the hospital. It was repeated for several years, though with diminishing returns.

Hospital Balls were started in 1922 and the first one covered the then deficit by raising £191. Five years later the four doctors' wives organised a successful Ball and Children's Dance. A Bachelor's Ball was held in 1939 which 160 people attended raising £100, partly from to the sale of multicoloured golliwog mascots.

An annual Hospital Cup football competition was organised by a group of supporters and brought in around £20 p.a. which was increased one year to £56 due to a replay. An interesting project was the 'Mile of Pennies Scheme' when 690 yards of pennies produced £71.

Patient payments had steadily increased to £521 in 1939, partly due to charity patients having their weekly maintenance payments increased to 5s for adults and 3s 6d for children, but mainly due to more private patients being treated. The Cresswell Penny Fund had been replaced at the General Hospital by its own contributory scheme which the Cottage Hospital refused to join. However, Miss Dora Bullock continued to collect her pennies from Dymock providing just under £5 in 1927. By 1934 a Ledbury based contributory scheme had been established, independent of the hospital, in which its members and dependents under 16 were admitted free. Annual grants, initially £10, from the League of Mercy started in 1927.

Pound Day organised by the Ladies Linen League remained popular providing on one occasion 1,100 eggs which were preserved by the hospital for use over the following year.

There was an attempt to involve doctors from the surrounding district such as Colwall and Tarrington to encourage wider support. Some declined, others like Dr Picton of Tarrington only served for a year. The combination of commitments and distance involved was the likely reason.

The number of inpatients treated during the inter-war years increased, reaching 512 in 1939, as did the number of people being X-rayed. Most of the inpatients were either surgical or accident cases. In 1938, as a sign of the times, 102 road accident cases were dealt with.

Early in the war some beds were made available for possible war casualties, but only a few servicemen were admitted and like most small cottage hospitals, the hospital was soon released from this obligation by the Ministry of Health.

Immediately after the war there were victory celebrations around the district, and Colwall's Wings for Victory week, for example, raised £65 for the hospital. Individual donations also continued to be made and one of the most heart-warming was when three little girls gave their Christmas earnings. The hospital still

*Mr Charles Masefield
the last chairman*

attracted legacies from unusual sources and when Mr William Barrell of Tarrington, a roadman with the county council for 38 years, died in 1941 he left a legacy of £1,000. In addition payments by patients reached nearly £900 p.a. But nationally agreed increases in salaries after the war meant expenditure soared, whilst many sources of income declined—the Ladies Linen League, for example, found difficulty in obtaining linen due to inadequate post-war supplies and consequently suspended their activity in 1946.

The last Annual Meeting was held on 27th March 1948 when the Chairman, Mr Charles Masefield presented the 74th report. He closed by explaining how his family had served the hospital since its beginning. His father was the first secretary and treasurer and then his uncle Basil carried on till he took over. This was typical of many families who served the Ledbury Cottage Hospital over 75 years and its success was due to the widespread support it attracted from people in all walks of life throughout the district.

CHAPTER 7

Victoria Cottage Hospital, Kington

In 1880 local government in Kington was the responsibility of a Board of 24 Commissioners formed under the Kington Improvement Act of 1829. The town was linked to Leominster, Eardisley and New Radnor by railway and so to the main network beyond. The town essentially served an agricultural district and had extensive corn mills and malthouses, though it also supported an iron foundry and nail manufacturers. Its population was just over 2.000.

In the latter half of the nineteenth century there was little provision in the town for the sick. There were no almshouses, and the Kington Union Workhouse had been built in 1837 at Kingswood, a quarter of a mile south of the town to house 150 paupers, mainly the aged and infirm. But the union served 19 parishes in Herefordshire and 13 in Radnorshire, covering a total population of over 12,000.

On 26th February 1887 a public meeting was held in the recently built Board Schools to consider how best to commemorate Queen Victoria's Jubilee. Many of the landed gentry, professional people and doctors were present along with eight clergymen and a large number of ladies. The Chairman was Mr Stephen Robinson of Lynhales, Lyonshall, a breeder of Hereford Pedigree Cattle and a keen huntsman who had been high sheriff of the county in 1871.

Amid scenes of enthusiasm, it was rapidly decided that a cottage hospital would be a fitting memorial for the Jubilee, benefiting in the main the 'hard-working' poor within eight or nine miles of the town who became injured or sick.

There had clearly been previous discussions because annual subscriptions of £70 and donations of £622 had already been promised. Who these early leaders were is uncertain but they probably came from the gentry. The two doctors in the town, Dr William Cuthbert and Dr Richard Billiard agreed to offer their services to the hospital, which it was decided would be called The

Victoria Cottage Hospital. Lady Ormathwaite, who was present and well known for taking a great interest in the poor, was appointed patroness. She had been born Lady Katherine Somerset, the daughter of the duke of Beaufort, and lived with her husband Lord Ormathwaite at Eywood, near Kington. He had extensive estates in Radnorshire, had been M.P. for that county and was at present its lord lieutenant. He was subsequently appointed a trustee for the hospital.

Mr Anthony Temple

In subsequent meetings, usually held at the Oxford Arms Hotel, the Rules were decided on. Annual subscribers of one guinea or over and lump sum benefactors of £10 or over were to be governors, could vote at the annual meeting and be eligible to be elected onto committees. For every 10s 6d contributed, annual subscribers could recommend one inpatient a year for up to a three week stay. The Committee of Management was to consist of a president, 12 governors, the honorary medical officers and the honorary secretary and treasurer to be

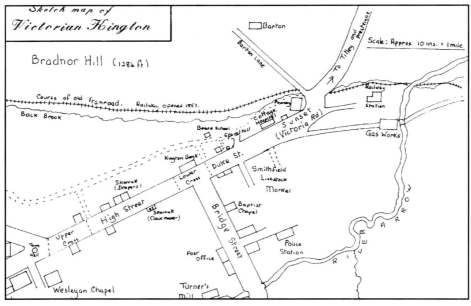

The Victoria Cottage Hospital in its early days

elected annually. Representatives were also appointed from 15 parishes in the area, one of their roles being to raise subscriptions and donations.

The Victoria Cottage Hospital was built on Cook's Hall Meadow, a piece of land on the north side of Sunset Road, now called Victoria Road, on the way to the railway station that had been given by Mr Temple, the hospital's first secretary and treasurer. The hospital was designed by the London architect Keynes Purchase and built by Henry Wishlade of Kington, grandson of the famous Kington builder who had built the Union Workhouse in 1837.

On the 21st June 1887, Queen Victoria's Jubilee, a large procession gathered, after services in the town's three churches and, led by the town's dignitaries, marched to Sunset Road where Mrs Stephen Robinson laid the foundation stone. The eventual green-painted, two storied building built mainly of brick provided accommodation for seven patients. On the ground floor there were two wards, one with three beds and one with a single bed, a sitting room, and a dispensary, while upstairs there was another ward with two beds, and domestic accommodation. It is uncertain where the operating theatre was initially located, but by 1900 a room upstairs was being used.

A mortuary, a coal and wood house was provided in the grounds which were surrounded by boundary walls and fences. No wash house was provided as it was intended to contract out any washing.

The first annual meeting was held on the 21st February 1888. Mr Richard Green of the Whittern, Lyonshall was appointed president, and included in the Management Committee were four clergymen and two magistrates—Mr Edward Greenly, a landowner at Titley Court, and Lt. Col. Richard Cox of Broxwood Court, Pembridge. The Victoria Cottage Hospital was ceremonially opened by Lady Ormathwaite on 19th July 1888.

Mr Richard Green

The committee decided that non-urgent patients had to attend between 11a.m. and 12 noon on a Tuesday but this proved too rigid and was revoked after two years. Each week patients who were recommended by governors for admission were checked as to their suitability and the weekly charge decided on.

The committee selected visitors for the month who would check how the hospital was functioning, speak to the patients and ensure they were being well looked after. In 1897 a Ladies Visiting Committee, which consisted of many of the wives and daughters of governors, took over this task.

There was no major additional building work up to 1900, though the outside was painted for £13 and an extra bed was squeezed into the male ward.

As with the other hospitals in the county, the income to initially run the hospital came mainly from charity. In 1888 annual subscriptions contributed £140, providing over half of the income and this pattern was to continue into the next century. Small donations were added to income but large donations and legacies were invested to provide dividends. In 1890 Hospital Sunday was started and all churches and chapels in the district were asked to contribute their offertories in the last week of November. In the first year £19 was collected from four churches. Almsboxes were also placed in churches and hotels. Fundraising entertainment became popular. Mr Henry Studt brought his travelling fair from South Wales, noted for its 'swinging gondolas', and laid on a benefit evening where the proceeds went to the hospital. He did this annually and was made a life governor, an honour bestowed on those who had given exceptional service to the hospital.

Patient payments varied between 3s 6d and 7s 6d per week. Paupers were occasionally admitted and the Board of Guardians was expected to pay for their maintenance. The first year for which annual accounts are available is 1900 when the income was £240 and expenditure £245. Associated with the hospital a group of supporters formed a Committee of Cinderella Dances which raised funds to finance patients convalescence by the seaside.

Initially the medical staff were confined to the doctors who were in practice in Kington and this usually meant there were two doctors available. Mr Horace

Medical Staff	
1888	William Hawkins Cuthbert, L.S.A.
1888	Richard Billiald, L.R.C.P.
1888	Shirley Woolmer Arundel, L.S.A., M.R.C.S.
1892	Henry Pope, B.A., M.B., Ch.B.
1895	James Chute, M.A., Ch.B.
1899	William Ainslie, M.B., Ch.B.
1906	Richard Harding, L.R.C.P. (Edin.), L.F.P.S.
1909	Gilbert Winter Dryland, B.A., M.B., B.C., M.R.C.S., L.R.C.P.
1915	Lazenby, M.B., B.S.
1916	Arthur Augustus Picketts, B.A., M.B., Ch.B., M.R.C.P., M.R.C.S.
1920	Ernest A. Milner, M.D.
1922	Francis Lionel Picketts, B.A., M.B., Ch.B., M.R.C.P., M.R.C.S.
1926	Ronald R. Walker, M.A., M.D., M.R.C.S., L.R.C.P.
1933	W. Logan Jack, M.B., Ch.B., B.S.
1938	Richard Jobson, M.B., Ch.B.
1944	George Donaldson Edie Tullis, M.B., Ch.B.
1947	Brian Raymond Mitchell, B.M., B.Ch., M.R.C.S., L.R.C.P.

Dental Surgeons	
1888	Arthur Levason, L.D.S., M.D.S.
1888	Peyton Levason, L.D.S., M.D.S.
1930	Ernest Arthur Gwynne Hooper, Reg. Dentist Act 1921
1941	F.S. Bromley, L.D.S., R.C.S.(Eng.)

Consultants	
1899	Horace K. Debenham, L.S.A., M.R.C.S.
1913	William Ainslie, M.B., Ch.B., M.D., F.R.C.S.
1933	Bernard Scholefield M.A., M.D., F.R.C.S., M.Ch.
1947	Richard Wood-Power, B.A., M.B., B.Ch., F.R.C.S., D.P.H.

Table 13 Honorary Medical and Dental Staff at Victoria Cottage Hospital. The year indicates that in which each doctor is first known to have held a hospital appointment

K. Debenham, who lived in Presteigne, was appointed honorary consultant surgeon which meant he was available for advice. There is little information about him accept that he owned the first car registered in Presteigne in 1906. Mr William Ainslie, more usually associated with the General Hospital, became an honorary medical officer in 1899 as he started in practice in Kington having gained experience as an assistant in a large colliery practice in South Shields. There were honorary dental surgeons from the start—initially Mr Arthur Levason and Mr Peyton Levason from Hereford attended the outpatient department once a month. The first matron, Miss Florence Drury had been appointed without pay but had free board and a £3 uniform allowance. Her cousin stayed with her for a short time and was charged 14s a week for board. After a year in post Miss Drury was offered another matron's

1888	June	Miss Florence Drury
1890	August	Miss Edmondson
1891	April	Miss Eva Marfell
1894	Dec.	Miss Johnson
1897	October	Miss Forbes
1897	July	Miss Clay
1902	March	Miss Mary Robinson
1908	August	Miss Feodora Austen
1913	February	Miss Annie E. Hulbert
1914	August	Miss Maud Vilmet-Scott
1915	June	Mrs Margaret Lazenby
1916	June	Miss H. Bacon
1916	August	Miss Alice M. Beedie
1919	March	Miss Eleanor Bounds
1921	March	Miss Mary Helen Bateman
1934	Sept.	Miss Ivy Freeth
1937	April	Miss S. Meredith
1939	June	Miss L.M. Crosbie
1945	January	Miss Levis

Table 14 Matrons at Victoria Cottage Hospital

post at £35 p.a., but she indicated she would like to stay if the committee could see their way to giving her a small salary. She was given £20 p.a.

The Rules were strict and the matron could not leave the hospital for the day or go beyond call without permission from the medical officers. No personal visitors were allowed in the morning. She was allowed a month's leave each year but this was dependent on a substitute being found, most commonly from either the Hereford Nursing Institution, the General Hospital or the Worcester City and County Institution for Nurses.

Up until the end of the century six matrons were appointed and all but one stayed less than four years. It was obviously a very stressful post and after 1894 candidates over 35 years of age were sought. Nurse Forbes asked to be allowed to do some district nursing when not fully occupied. This was not accepted, but she was allowed occasionally to attend special cases within a mile radius of the hospital with permission of the medical officers. Dr Richard Billiald resigned after 11 years following a disagreement with Nurse Forbes as she had allowed two of his patients to leave the hospital for five hours, and had given others roast beef and plum pudding on Christmas Day. Although she was exonerated by the committee, the doctor stated that he could not work with her.

When appointed the matrons were given a one month's trial. Nurse Clay had a second trial month as there were doubts whether she could manage the hospital, but when finally accepted she was allowed to engage a boy for an hour each morning, as occasionally happened down the years. One year later she was allowed £2 per annum for stimulants, likely to be alcoholic.

Initially the matron was the only permanent nurse during the day, although a night nurse was engaged for four nights a week. An additional skilled nurse could be engaged temporarily for a special case. Servants could be dismissed by the matron, but dismissal of a nurse had to be confirmed by the committee.

The first matron was allowed to employ a servant at £14 p.a. as well as a charwoman. Discipline was harsh. In 1897 the servant, Margaret Morris asked for a week's leave when she had 'only' been six months in post and was promptly dismissed. She must have been young, for it was decided that the next servant had to be over 25 years of age.

The number of patients admitted each year varied from 25 to 57. In 1900 the average stay was 32 days. Medicines were purchased from Mr Stanways, a chemist in the town, at a reduced price. In the first year an instrument cabinet, a fracture board and leg rest were bought, a Captain Kinglake donating £5 towards medical instruments.

In 1912 Mr Bernard Philpin resigned as chairman and was followed for the next nine years by Mr Stewart Robinson, the son of the first president. Mr Temple resigned as secretary in 1917 aged 82, and when he died two years later the whole town mourned the loss of a worthy figure and a staunch churchman. He left a gift of £1,000 to the charity commissioners for the benefit of the hospital.

There had been trouble with chimney smoke entering the wards and nurses' rooms from the beginning and in 1901 the chimney stacks were raised 3 feet, but with limited results. A few years later the chimney pots were also heightened. In 1905 an additional bedroom was built on for a probationer nurse at a cost of £99. Three years later Mrs Girvin equipped and refurnished a ward, subsequently called the Girvin Ward, in memory of her husband and later donated £150 towards improving the outpatient department.

Since 1906 the medical staff had been recommending a new operating theatre as patients had to be carried upstairs to a room which was lit by a skylight and gas lamps, but no action was taken by the committee. One stormy night during an emergency operation the skylight leaked rainwater which dripped into an open abdominal wound to the distress of all present, with prophesies of inevitable fatal infection. The patient in fact made an uneventful recovery but the incident pressurised the committee into action and a new theatre was provided downstairs.

The enlarged Victoria Cottage Hospital

In 1910 east and west single storey wings were added increasing the accommodation to some eight beds at a cost of £799. The kitchen was modernised with a new Eagle Range boiler and the sanitary arrangements improved. In 1911 the governors became concerned about the amount of wines and spirits being provided for the patients and decided that in future these would only be provided on the written instructions of a member of the medical staff. In 1915 a telephone system was installed.

The income increased to £407 in 1907, but decreased to £257 in 1916 during the war. In 1903 the finances had been helped by the Cresswell Penny Fund, of which the first local secretary was Mrs Dorothy Banks, the wife of William Hartland Banks of Hergest Croft, one of a family of landowners. The hospital received half of the collections in the town which consisted of just under £8 in the first year and £14 the following year. After this receipts slowly fell off. In 1911 Pound Day provided £16 as well as produce which was preserved or sold off by the hospital.

The poorer patients were now being charged between 5s and 10s a week. In 1915 elementary school children were charged 2s 6d for removal of tonsils and adenoids as long as they did not stay in hospital more than three days. More prosperous patients were also starting to use the hospital and were duly charged a realistic maintenance fee; in 1913 a major was charged 15s for a one day stay. As a result of all these efforts the income and expenditure were usually in balance and no persistent deficit developed until the First World War.

In 1906 Dr Harding was appointed as the first honorary anaesthetist. He lived at New Radnor and was the local medical officer of health. Three years later Dr Ainslie left to study surgery in Edinburgh, returning in 1912 to general practice in Hereford. A year later he was appointed an honorary consultant. In 1909 Dr Gilbert Winter Dryland, who had received his medical education at Cambridge and Guys Hospital, joined the staff. Within a year he was running several troops of boy scouts. In 1915 he was commissioned into the R.A.M.C., spending a year at Chester. On his return he became medical officer for the Red Cross Hospital situated at the infirmary of the workhouse at Kingswood, where his wife worked as a sister tending to convalescent wounded soldiers. He was also medical officer to the workhouse and the infectious disease hospital at Kingswood.

Two matrons were dismissed in the first decades of the nineteenth century. Miss Feodora Austen was accused by the railway stationmaster of refusing to

Kington Red Cross Hospital. Dr John Winter Dryland is in the front row, with Sister Dorothy Dryland second from the left in the row behind

treat an injured member of his staff, telling him to go to his own doctor, while Miss Annie Hulbert was dismissed for wrongly discharging a child.

In 1907 the work was increasing and Nurse Dash was engaged as a permanent assistant nurse. Thereafter either an assistant trained nurse was employed or a probationary nurse in training. Assistant Nurse Fern subsequently caught diphtheria and was granted three months' leave on the recommendation of Dr. Dryland. A year later she resigned her post complaining about the matron. The matron then refused to let the secretary interview Nurse Fern alone, the committee reinforced the request, and the matron resigned whilst Nurse Fern stayed on.

A probationary nurse, who was appointed in 1913, caught an infection from a male patient and died. On medical advice the hospital was closed for a short time and the men's ward, the matron's and late nurse's bedrooms were all disinfected.

The number of admissions increased to 67 in 1910 before reducing to 33 in 1916. In 1917 it was decided to temporarily close the hospital at the end of June as the number of admissions continued to decrease and financial support had diminished. The war had resulted in many men joining the army which was thought to have reduced the number of accidents requiring admission. It was hoped that subscriptions would continue so that the buildings and contents could be maintained allowing the hospital to reopen as soon as possible. Annual Meetings continued to be held.

1919 to the advent of the N.H.S.

The hospital remained closed till August 1919, but the investments had been kept intact and subscriptions had continued. Economies were still necessary and central heating was judged to be too expensive and instead three gas fires were installed along with an anthracite stove in a corridor. However, over the next few years partial central heating with radiators was introduced and a stoker was employed at 5s a week. Between 1932 and 1934 electric light was introduced by stages being partly paid for by the proceeds of a pantomime. Attempts by the matron to get electric light on the balcony was refused on the grounds of extravagance! When the hospital was reopened the rule forbidding smoking in the wards was removed.

The hospital needed to attract more patients, particularly from the neighbouring villages. So, soon after the hospital reopened, a letter was sent to all the doctors in the surrounding district 'cordially welcoming any doctor who has sent in a case, to visit his patient whenever and as often as he likes, when they will give the most courteous consideration to any wishes, advice or suggestions he may make.' Unsurprisingly it did not achieve its aim. Instead the hospital tried to appoint more honorary staff from outside Kington whilst, at another level, representatives from the railwaymen, the farmers union, and finally a member from Presteigne were invited to join the committee which grew to 17 members.

On reopening great efforts were made to increase charitable giving, such sources still providing 65 per cent of the income. Even so, during the inter-war years subscriptions fell slightly, though dividends increased due to large donations and legacies. There was also a bed endowed by several governors in memory of Mr and Mrs Stewart Robinson for £1,000. Shortly after the war a Ladies Linen League was started with Miss Craigie as honorary secretary. A silver cup, known as the Kington Hospital Football Challenge Cup, was competed for annually by local teams and the total amount raised by 1936 was £198. In the same year Pound Day provided 2,394 eggs for preserving, mainly collected by school children.

As the years passed there formed an especially enthusiastic group of fundraisers. Soon after the war Mrs West, the proprietor of a ladies outfitters and known as 'madame', was the leader in organising hospital balls, flag days and whist drives. From 1930 Miss Banks, the daughter of Mrs Dorothy Banks, organised successful annual hospital balls. From 1933 Miss Watkins produced annual pantomime parties raising £45 to £55 which went towards the installation of electricity and a new operating table.

Meanwhile payments by charity patients were raised in 1923 to between 5s and 21s depending on their income, whilst dental cases were charged 3s 6d if they required the use of the theatre. The selling of services to local authorities in Herefordshire and Radnorshire increased. Maintenance fees for private patients fluctuated between 2 guineas and 6 guineas, reduced if they had to share a ward. In 1928 the charge for a private midwifery case was 4½ guineas plus the cost of an extra nurse.

Kington continued to support the Cresswell Penny Fund which raised £18 in 1920. Workmens' collections from the Kington railwaymen and the employees of two firms, amounted to £23 in 1920 and earned them concessions if they required admission to the hospital. One of these firms was owned by Mr Earnest Deacon, a well-known builder, engineer and coal merchant in Victoria Road. The other firm was run by Mr W.A. Owen, Kington's first resident bus proprietor.

1935 the cottage hospital set up its own contributory scheme. Men and woman over 21 years of age, or a man and his wife with children under 16, earning less than £3 per week paid 3d per week. Single persons between 16 and 21 years contributed 1d. This entitled them to hospital treatment in Kington, or if referred elsewhere they received a payment of 21s per week. Following the introduction of this scheme, it was decided that letters of recommendation were no longer required.

The accounts for the year 1936 show that income had risen to £748, made up of subscriptions £137, dividends £107, donations £38, fundraising £187, payments for selling services £191, contributory schemes £87 and miscellaneous £1. Charitable contributions accounted for 43 per cent. Expenditure came to £719, made up of provisions and household expenses at £273, salaries £259, medicines £95 and miscellaneous £92. Over the inter-war years there were no serious crises.

Dr Dryland fell ill in 1921 and was successfully operated

Dr W. Logan Jack

on in his own hospital. In 1932 he and Dr Jack offered to place their X-ray apparatus at the disposal of the hospital and this was accepted though, as the X-ray plates were expensive, each patient would be charged a nominal sum of 10s 6d for its use. In June 1933 Dr W. Logan Jack, who had obtained his medical education in Adelaide, Australia, was taken into partnership by Dr Dryland as well as being appointed as an honorary medical officer to the hospital. He was later to marry Dr Dryland's daughter, Dorothy.

As late as 1939 the matron was being exploited. Four months after Miss Crosbie was appointed she asked for the committee's help as she had only had one half day off since being appointed. They agreed that she should have a half a day off each week, one whole day off a month and three to four consecutive days off every three months. The previous matron, now Mrs West, stood in for her during her days off, without remuneration. However Miss Crosbie was less successful when she asked to rejoin the Red Cross as an immobile member and was told that she could not leave the hospital for the two annual parades. She was obviously upset and challenged the committee by asking if they were satisfied with her work. Although one doctor had minor reservations, they confirmed that they were satisfied.

By the early 1920s two nurses were being employed mainly for day duty, usually an assistant nurse and a probationer nurse. Many of the probationers were young and inexperienced and there was a rapid turnover. A night nurse was employed and additional temporary nurses were taken on when necessary. When the hospital reopened after the war a cook and maid had also been appointed.

By 1935, the last inter-war year for which full statistics are available, the number of inpatients had reached 135, of which 22 were medical cases, 89 surgical and 24 dental with an average stay of 11 days. 28 major operations and 43 minor operations were performed. In the twenties there was an increase in operations for the removal of tonsils and adenoids, as well as in dental work for school children for which the local authority paid. An outpatient room was set up as a dental clinic.

Until 1922 patients were usually transferred to hospital in a cart when a large car was modified by having a detachable near side seat so it could be used as an ambulance. Dr Logan Jack subsequently formed a local division of the St John's Ambulance Brigade which was formally dedicated in 1937.

Over the years numerous building alterations were carried out which increased the beds available to 10, whilst the provision of a revolving summer house and a garden seat made the grounds more attractive.

In the late thirties private patients were allowed to use wireless receivers for a small fee to cover the cost of electricity at the discretion of the matron.

The hospital laid in an emergency supply of two tons of coal during the Second World War, and was asked if it could expand its facilities. Since this would mean taking over neighbouring properties, the idea was dropped. The arrival of the military on 48 acres of land at Hergest Court Farm south-west of Kington had little effect on the hospital, though it made a big impact socially. By 1944 two American hospitals were based there and when the hospital theatre's steriliser was out of action, one of the American hospitals kindly sterilised the cottage hospital's dressing drums. When the war was over a considerable amount of American equipment was given to the cottage hospital.

In 1943 there was some unpleasantness between the matron, Miss Crosbie, and Probationer Nurse Marshall who was asked to resign. Miss Crosbie also resigned, but was persuaded to withdraw her resignation. But the use of three

The Home Guard. Dr Logan Jack (on the left) and Major General W. Greenly

probationer nurses at any one time, coupled with a fairly rapid turnover partly due to low pay, was unsatisfactory. In December 1943, following requests from the doctors, the matron was given permission to appoint a state registered nurse.

From 1941 there was increasing anxiety over the hospital's financial position. Expenses were increasing dramatically. National negotiations over staff pay and conditions in 1943 meant the hospital lost control of its salary and wages bill, and the cost of living was also rising. The response was a massive fundraising exercise in Kington and the surrounding district, coupled with attempts to make realistic charges wherever possible. The Kington contributory scheme continued but was expanded to include those earning less than £6 a week. If a contributor was admitted to another hospital a capitation fee of £3 would be paid irrespective of the length of stay. Charity patient charges were geared to their income or size of their smallholdings and ranged between 5s 6d a week to 3 guineas. Private patients maintenance charges ranged from 5 to 8 guineas per week, and charges to local authorities were increased to 10s a day.

The hospital staff, with Dr Dryland on the left and Dr Jack on the right

Expensive drugs were carefully monitored by the committee. All patients were to be charged for penicillin at 5s an injection, even though it only cost the hospital 2s 9d. The honorary medical staff agreed to only charge fees when hospital maintenance was over 3 guineas.

Several groups including a Help the Hospital Committee raised over £1,000 by appeals. Other traditional events continued, including pound days, flag days, golf competitions, and theatrical shows including one called The Cuckoo in The Nest. Legacies continued to come in, the largest being for £2,412. In spite of all this income, by 1947 the current account was in a deficit and money was transferred from capital. By the following year the remaining investments of £2,400 were realised to pay outstanding accounts.

In 1946 there were 182 inpatients, consisting of 153 surgical cases, 23 medical cases and 6 dental cases. As this indicates, the hospital dealt mainly with surgical problems and of 149 operations 41 were classified as major.

In November 1947 the Kington Welfare Committee was established to raise funds which the hospital could retain after the introduction of the N.H.S. These would benefit the patients and staff for purposes not covered by the N.H.S. Events included the annual hospital ball and the hospital football cup.

As the day approached when the N.H.S. would take over the hospital, there was anxiety that the hospital might be converted into a convalescent home. At the last committee meeting on 1st July, 1948 Captain Lionel Green, the chairman of the new Herefordshire Hospital Management Committee, attended and reassured the members that the hospital would continue as before.

CHAPTER 8

Leominster Cottage Hospital

In 1900 Leominster was a Municipal Borough with a Mayor and Corporation and a population of 5,826. There were good road communications and the town was on the Hereford - Shrewsbury railway with a side branch to Kington and another through Bromyard to Worcester. The town had an iron and brass foundry, corn mills, a woolstapling industry, several brewers and brickmakers. But there were limited facilities for looking after the poor and sick. In Bargates there was an almshouse for four widows and which had an endowed income of £20 p.a., whilst an orphans home in Ryelands Road provided facilities for up to 40 destitute children under 10 years of age. The union workhouse was in the old priory buildings with accommodation for 141 inmates and served a population of 13,580 across 25 parishes. There was also a charitable dispensary in the town and a trained nurse provided by the Nursing Society.

The movement to obtain a cottage hospital for Leominster was somewhat unusual. In August 1891 the Lord Hill Lodge of Oddfellows formed a committee in conjunction with the Foresters to organise a Hospital Sunday Church Parade to collect money for both the General Infirmary and the Victoria Eye and Ear Hospital in Hereford. The chairman of the committee was Mr John Benjamin Dowding, newly elected treasurer of the Lodge of Oddfellows. Two secretaries were also appointed, Mr George Page from the Foresters who was a town councillor and Mr George Collard from the Oddfellows who served the Town Corporation as an elective auditor. The parade took place on Sunday 15th September, when 800 people including the mayor, Councillor James Page, marched through the town behind the band of the 1st Herefordshire Rifle Volunteers. Other friendly societies which joined the march included Hearts of Oak, Hampton Friendly Society, Herefordshire Friendly Society and the

Rechabites. Numbers swelled to 1,500 people for the service and £21 was collected.

In view of its success, it was decided to make Hospital Sunday an annual event and to put the proceeds towards a fund to finance a cottage hospital in Leominster. The joint committee became the Leominster and District Cottage Hospital Committee, identifying the Friendly Societies with the movement to provide Leominster with its hospital. Previous attempts to provide a hospital had failed as many of the doctors felt that the local dispensary and the trained nurse were adequate, while the public had shown no interest.

Mr George Collard

Support came from many of the local gentry, as well as Mr Henry Studt of Swansea who visited the May Fair in 1894 with his 'swinging gondolas' and raised £50. In the following year he organised a Grand Fête on behalf of the hospital fund which raised £168, indeed over several years he raised a total of £360. (Mr Henry Studt died in 1922. Although his fair annually contributed to the cottage hospitals in Kington and Ledbury he had been particularly supportive and generous to Leominster giving large sums to the building fund.) A Shilling Fund was advertised in the *Leominster News* and produced 2,000 shillings (£100).

By 1897 the clergy, initially lukewarm sympathisers became enthusiastic supporters and Rev. Edward Charles, vicar of Leominster was to play an active role in the committee, which by then had an enlarged representation. By the end of 1897 a total of £1,185 had been raised, sufficient to establish a cottage hospital. In

Mr Henry Studt

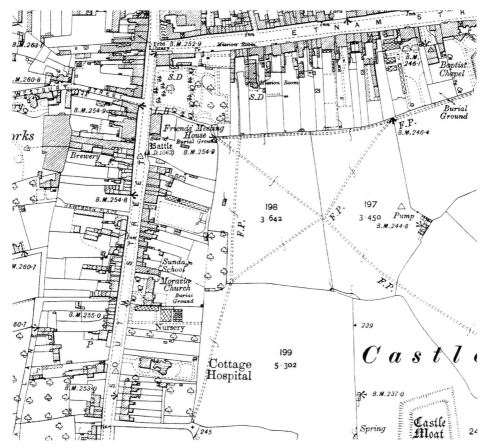

Site of the Cottage Hospital

January 1898, a site in South Street that included three allotments was purchased for £230. By this time the committee had 18 members and after some controversy it was agreed that five of their number would act as a Committee of Management and be trustees for the property and funds till the first Annual Meeting was held. Dr F. Hart-Smith, senior medical practitioner in the town, Alderman Richard Bright, Councillor Andrew Duncan, Mr John Dowding and Councillor George Page were chosen as the initial members of the committee.

Mr E.G. Davies of Hereford was selected as the architect for the project and in September a tender for £1,300 for the building work was accepted after the initial plans had been modified to restrict the cost. The site ran from east to west and the building was to be in two blocks joined by a corridor. The hospital

The Cottage Hospital c.1900

was placed diagonally on the site so that the front faced south-east, while the nurses' home faced west and was set back from South Street. The hospital was single storied while the nurses' home was two storied. Each ward would accommodate two patients.

On Thursday 24th November 1898 the foundation stone was laid by Miss Woods of Ryelands, a landowner well-known for her generosity and good works, before a large crowd including the mayor, dignitaries and all involved in the project. The evening ended with a concert which raised £40.

The committee decided not to provide a mortuary as they felt this was the town council's responsibility. Dr Hart-Smith drew up the Rules which established that the hospital was to essentially provide treatment for the poor who could not obtain this at home, but it did not place any restriction on the length of stay. No tickets of admission were required, only a medical certificate indicating the nature of the disease and its duration. However, subscribers could refer suitable patients with a medical certificate.

The hospital was opened on Thursday 27th July 1899 by Lady Annie Rankin following a procession to the site. Here she was presented with a gold key by Mr John Watkins, the builder, and duly opened the door. The whole town was decorated with flags and bunting, and sports in the afternoon attracted some 5,000 people. Other entertainment included a company of variety artists and a grand balloon ascent to 3,000 feet followed by a parachute jump. Fortunately the hospital's services were not required.

A massive procession of dignatories and friendly societies approaches the hospital from South Street for the opening ceremony

The committee appointed Miss Ellen Harrington of University College Hospital, London, to be Nurse Matron. She had 29 years of experience crowned by a mark of Queen Victoria's esteem when she was presented with the badge of the order of St Catherine, a badge only ever given to nine nurses. Also appointed were a probationer nurse, Miss Holland, who would receive her board and uniform, and a servant, Miss Annie Hall of Leominster. The first patient was admitted on 10th September.

At the first Annual General Meeting the officials were elected. Sir James Rankin was the first president; Mr John Dowding was elected honorary secretary and Mr Richard Bright honorary treasurer. Ten members were elected to the Hospital Management Committee including all the five members on the previous committee. One member also came from each of the villages of Stoke Prior, Kimbolton and Kingsland, hopefully to stimulate district support. The Management Committee consisted of the elected members plus the above officers, the vice-presidents and the four medical officers in the town. The chairman of the annual meeting was usually a member of the gentry or a person of distinction often not directly associated with the hospital.

The title of vice-president was given to supporters who had contributed in a major way to the hospital either by giving of their services or generous donations. They were elected every year and their number usually included the previous year's mayor. The Committee appointed visitors every month to inspect the hospital and question the patients.

Within two years of opening some long stay patients were blocking beds and the Rules were modified to ensure that no patient could be admitted unless the medical officer felt that speedy benefit was likely. It was stressed that cases of incurable disease, mental disorder, infection and midwifery were not admissible. But every patient had the right to be attended by their own doctor. In 1905, as a result of these changes, Dr Hart-Smith was able to report that the average stay over the previous three years had been reduced from 21 days to 17 days.

In 1901 the hospital purchased a strip of land adjacent to the hospital's northern boundary partly to protect the hospital from intrusive buildings and partly to build a mortuary which had become essential. The town council was granted access to it in return for a contribution towards its upkeep.

There was no purpose-built theatre in the original building and operations were carried out in a ward in the presence of other patients. A fund was therefore opened to build a theatre and received the support of Sir Frederick Cawley, M.P., who had bought Berrington Hall in 1900, Sir James Rankin and the mayor. By June 1912 plans were approved for building a heated theatre on the north side of the hospital at a cost of £200. These changes and better use of the wards allowed up to 12 inpatients to be accommodated. A hut used as an office in the cattle market was bought to be used as an chalet in the grounds.

In the early years income generally showed a small surplus over expenditure. Annual subscriptions and patient payments stayed relatively static until the start of the First World War, whilst small amounts of income came from the Cresswell Penny Fund and from charity boxes. By 1912 Hospital Sunday was being organised throughout 33 parishes and around £100 annually was contributed. Other fundraising activities included an annual football competition, the prize for the winning side being a silver Charity Football Cup provided by Councillor Bright, and a Ladies Linen League.

With the advent of the war both income and expenses dramatically increased, partly due to providing for wounded soldiers at the government's expense.

During the early 1900s the number of honorary medical officers fluctuated between four and eight, and their relationship with the committee seems to have been difficult. In 1911 six of them signed a letter stating that they would not attend any patient in the hospital unless they had the option of charging the

1899	F. Hart-Smith, M.B., B.S., F.R.C.S.
1899	Gerald Steel, J.P., L.S.A., L.M.S.S.A.
1899	Martin Scales, L.R.C.P., L.R.C.S.
1899	Octavius Edwards, L.R.C.P., M.R.C.S.
1909	George J. Cressy, L.R.C.P., L.R.C.S.
1909	Charles A. Robinson, B.A., M.B., C.M.
1911	Gordon Wilson Thomas, M.B., B.S., F.R.C.S.
1914	George F. Eady, L.M.S.S.A.
1922	Harold Victor Lamb, F.R.C.S., M.R.C.S., L.R.C.P.
1922	William James Niblick, M.B., B.Ch., F.R.C.S., M.S.
1922	Harford Edwards, M.R.C.S., L.R.C.P.
1922	H.D. McCall, B.A., M.R.C.S., L.R.C.P.
1925	Henry Wallace Johnston, M.B., B.S., M.R.C.S., L.R.C.P.
1928	William Edward Kingdon, M.B., B.S., M.R.C.S., L.R.C.P.
1928	Alfred Thomas Lock Lingdon, M.R.C.S., L.R.C.P.
1928	Donald James McLaren, M.B., B.Ch.
1929	Robert Gordon Ffolliott Thompson, B.A., M.B., Ch.B.
1930	T.F. Everitt, B.A., M.R.C.S., L.R.C.P.
1931	Douglas Cyril Vaughan, M.R.C.S., L.R.C.P.
1934	A.H. Driver, M.B., Ch.B.
1939	G.H. James, M.R.C.S., L.R.C.P.
1939	Geoffrey McIvor Housden, M.B., B.Ch., L.R.C.P., F.R.C.S.
1941	John Hutton jnr., M.B., Ch.B.
1944	A.H. Zair, M.A., M.B., B.Ch., M.R.C.S., L.R.C.P.
1947	Richard Holden Davidson, B.A., M.R.C.S., L.R.C.P.
1948	Huw Owen Williams, M.R.C.S., L.R.C.P.

Specialists

1927	A.H.A. Richardson, M.R.C.S., L.R.C.P., D.O.M.S.
1948	Geoffrey McIvor Housden, M.B., B.Ch., L.R.C.P., F.R.C.S.
1948	Richard Wood Power, B.A., M.B., B.Ch., F,R,C.S., D.P.H.
1948	Bernard Scholefield, M.A., M.D., F.R.C.S., M.Ch.

Dental Surgeon

1899	Alfred George Hudson, L.D.S.
1925	Philip I. Lewis, L.D.S.
1940	Charles Housden, L.D.S., R.C.S.
1946	George Mills Titterington, Reg. Dental Act 1921
1947	Horace Banfield Dumughn, L.D.S., R.C.S.

Table 15 Honorary medical staff of Leominster Cottage Hospital / Leominster District Hospital. The date indicates the year when each doctor is first known to have a hospital appointment

patient whatever they considered adequate. The committee did not object to prosperous patients being charged a medical fee, but they were unanimously opposed to leaving the level of charges to the doctors alone. A deputation met the doctors and it was agreed that in cases where the committee charged a maintenance fee the medical staff would be entitled to charge a fee.

1899	Miss Ellen Harrington
1911	Miss Margaret Templeton
1912	Miss Ethel Frances Tew
1921	Miss Richardson
1922	Miss Graham-Lynn
1923	Miss Charlotte M. Rees
1926	Miss Sharpe
1927	Miss Barton
1929	Miss Elsie Harris

Table 16 Matrons of Leominster Cottage Hospital / Leominster District Hospital

Miss Harrington, the matron, retired in 1910, a sad loss to the committee because she had constantly modified the menu to keep costs down. The next matron, Miss Margaret Templeton, was a disaster and only lasted a year. She displayed a lack of tact and judgement in dealing with the subscribers, even accusing one of being drunk, following which he cancelled his subscription. Two nurses and a servant left because of her attitude. She had also stated her age as 43 on appointment, but her birth certificate proved her to be 51. It was suggested that a younger matron might be capable of more activity and energy and she was asked to retire.

Initially there was a probationer nurse as assistant and in 1913 a second probationer assistant post was created. The probationers' training lasted two years and, if proficient, they were provided with a certificate, following which they usually left as the hospital was not prepared to increase their salary to a level required for a trained nurse. There was therefore a rapid turnover in staff. A servant, Rose, stayed for five years and was then offered an increased wage to stay on longer, but she declined.

At the beginning of the war, at the matron's request, it was agreed that some beds should be offered to Red Cross Nursing Association.

During 1900, there were 40 inpatients, of which 18 were accident cases and 15 were emergencies, 28 of the admissions coming from outside Leominster. Seven out of ten fractures occurred in children, and about half the patients were operated on. By 1917 inpatients had nearly doubled to 79 with a daily bed occupancy of 6.8. From 1915 onwards relays of wounded soldiers occupied many of the beds and were encouraged to look after the garden during their convalescence. Occasionally a pauper or an incurable patient was admitted in error, and once this was discovered they were rapidly sent home or moved to the workhouse. A case of appendicectomy with scarlet fever was moved post-operatively to the isolation hospital at Ebnal on the outskirts of Leominster.

1919 to the advent of the N.H.S.

Mr Dowding resigned in November 1924 after 25 years as honorary secretary. Six months later he was asked to resign as a trustee for he had been declared bankrupt and was found to have been falsifying public accounts, though fortunately not the hospital's, and was sent to prison for four years. He had held most public offices in the town including that of mayor and until his arrest he had been looked upon as one of Leominster's most respected and distinguished citizens. One of his successors was asked to resign as secretary, though only due to poor performance.

In 1928 the Hon. Robert Devereux of Hampton Court, who two years later became Viscount Hereford, was elected president, a post he held till the hospital was nationalised, and also became chairman of the Hospital Committee, a post he held till 1946.

In order to encourage support for the hospital, representatives of the Friendly Societies, the Railway Unions, the Trades Council and farmers were invited to join the committee. It thus grew unwieldy and in 1924 an executive committee of six members was formed to deal with routine matters. Four years

Aerial view of Leominster Cottage Hospital. The Red Cross hut is the squarish building with a pitched roof towards the top right of the hospital grounds, with the garage and mortuary to its right. Southgate Villas face the road towards the top of the photo

later Dr Lamb challenged the necessity of having this committee, which he felt was duplicating the work of the main committee. After much debate the executive committee was dissolved, but bureaucracy won in the end because three other committees—finance, house and medical—were formed.

The inter-war years brought an expansion of facilities and patient accommodation. In 1919 the Red Cross had considerable sums of money left over from donations given to them during the war and were keen to help local hospitals. They initially provided a large hut together with £600 for the hospital. The hut proved to be too big for the grounds but a portion of adjoining garden was purchased so providing additional space once again to the north of the hospital. The hut was subsequently developed to provide an infant welfare centre, an after care clinic, a tuberculosis dispensary and an orthopaedic clinic. A dental chair was also provided.

The Red Cross contributed a further grant of £1,500 to be spent on the new facilities and it was hoped to double this by a public appeal. A further shelter was provided to house the ambulance which used to bring children to the site.

In 1923 electricity was installed in the main hospital (it had already been provided to the new hut) including the theatre, for which Lord Crawley of Berrington Hall contributed £50. Two years later wireless was installed. In the same year the Red Cross gave No.1 Southgate Villa, adjacent to the north of the hospital, for future expansion; No.2 Southgate Villa had previously been given to the hospital. Both these properties were rented out to help provide income.

Since 1922 there had been heated discussions about the necessity of providing X-ray facilities, with the then president, Mr Wright, challenging the need. A sub-committee eventually concluded that X-ray facilities were desirable and an appeal fund was established which, by 1929, had reached £1,565. The running costs would come from charging those patients who could afford it.

A major expansion took place to provide space for the X-ray facilities and additional accommodation for staff. The new building comprised a two storey wing built onto the north of the hospital with, on the ground floor, an X-ray room, a developing room and a third room which could be used as a waiting room or an emergency ward, and, on the first floor, three bedrooms and a sitting room for staff. The total cost was £1,348. Dr Lamb was appointed as honorary radiologist after some disagreement with his colleagues who were reluctant to accept one of their number being designated as a specialist. The matron became an assistant radiographer as in other hospitals.

In 1930 there was concern about the need for more patient accommodation. It was claimed that the cottage hospitals in Ledbury, Ross and Kington had one bed for every 250 of the population, whilst Leominster had only one bed per 450. Plans for a new ward were agreed but don't appear to have been implemented.

In 1932 an appeal was made for funds to redecorate the operating theatre and provide a sterilising room with the necessary equipment. A hospital garden fête was held and raised £306, covering the cost.

Pressure on bed spaces must have remained, for in the mid-thirties ambitious plans were made for rebuilding the south side of the hospital to provide more patient and staff accommodation, but it was not till 1937 that there was agreement and building went ahead. The work involved extensive alterations with the addition of a southern wing. As part of the development a new women's ward was built, the old one becoming a male ward. The old male ward was reduced in size and was allocated for children or private patients. The existing private ward was reduced in size to provide access to the female ward. Sanitary arrangements were provided for each ward, and central heating was installed in addition to fireplaces in the wards. A new wireless system was also installed in the wards and staff quarters by the *News Chronicle's* Wireless for Hospitals Fund appeal. In addition a two storey wing was built onto the southern end of the nurses' home providing a matron's room, a storeroom and coal house on the ground floor and two bedrooms upstairs. As a result of this work the hospital ended up with accommodation for 16 patients. Lady Hereford opened the new extensions in May 1938 with considerable ceremony which included a guard of honour formed by the hospital nurses.

During this period there were arguments with the town council and rural district council about a public mortuary. The doctors were concerned that the hospital mortuary, which annually catered for some 10 cases from the hospital and four from elsewhere, was visible to the patients, staff and the public and wanted it moved elsewhere. Finally, in desperation, in May 1939 the authorities were told that public use of the mortuary would cease on 31st December 1940. Leominster Town Council finally agreed to a public mortuary but the war delayed any action.

In 1935 income totalled £1,662, including subscriptions of £222, dividends at £254 and patient payments of £795. The increase in patient payments were due to both an increase in charges and in numbers of private patients.

Local authorities were charged for patients for whom they were responsible and also paid rent for use of the clinic in the hut. Extra income came from renting out the houses and from providing private nurses in patients' homes. In 1925 the United Services granted the hospital £30 annually to maintain a bed free of charge for local ex-servicemen and their dependents.

In 1924 all local receipts from the Cresswell Penny Fund which had been shared between the cottage hospital and the General Hospital in Hereford, were directed to the General Hospital to provide more inpatient and outpatient tickets for patients in the Leominster district. This move was criticised as the

Fundraising in 1919

cottage hospital felt it could provide many of the services in Leominster. Perhaps it was not surprising that when the General Hospital later introduced their new contributory scheme Leominster declined to join. In 1933 the General Hospital refused to pay for their contributors admitted to the cottage hospital on the grounds that they could have been transported to Hereford.

Fundraising continued, and events included having a tent at the annual show where contributors were encouraged to throw money into a sheet, band concerts and a British Air Pageant at Leominster. Regular Hospital Fêtes raised large sums varying between £208 and £400.

There were also two particular generous characters in the inter-war years. Mr Sidney Bridge came to Leominster as a painter and decorator in 1887, when he was 29, but made his wealth by buying old properties and renovating them himself. He usually wore old clothes, lived frugally, and was an impressive Methodist preacher and a generous benefactor. In 1923 he donated £100 to the cottage hospital followed by £2,000 a few years later while on his death he bequeathed £10,000. Mr Edward Stanley Holland was surveyor to the Leominster Corporation and was caught cheating his employers. Given the choice of emigrating or prosecution he went to America. There he made a fortune as an engineer building bridges and regularly sent donations to the cottage hospital ranging from £100 to £500 as well as gifts of linen. On his death in 1936 he also bequeathed £2,000. Further money came to the hospital from his relatives when they died.

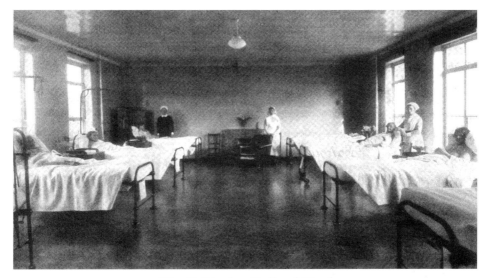

The E. Stanley Holland Ward

An annual Pound and Egg Day was held and one year 11,842 eggs were provided for preserving. The Ladies Linen League lost support in the late 1920s but was rejuvenated under the chairmanship of Mrs Clowes of Burton Court.

The numbers of doctors on the staff seemed to fluctuate and included some from the surrounding district, such as Dr Johnston from Bodenham. After another argument with management, who wished the doctors to be on a monthly rota to attend all poor patients, and not just their own, they agreed on a weekly rota.

Dr Martin Scales retired after 23 years of service, one of the pioneers of the hospital movement in Leominster. In 1930 a father and son were appointed, Dr Ernest Everett, the father, being interested in surgery. They both contributed much to management and when they left Leominster after nine years, they sold their surgical instruments to the hospital for £100. They were replaced by Dr Geoffrey Housden who took over most of the surgery. A year later his brother was appointed honorary dental surgeon.

At one stage a complaint was made by a local garage that the medical officers were informing one particular garage when a patient was involved in a motor accident. To counter charges of favouritism the committee ruled that that no member of staff was to inform any garage in these circumstances. More seriously, at the annual meeting in 1931, Mr Gregory, a subscriber, asked if the Rule relating to medical fees was strictly adhered to and whether the medical staff made a payment for the benefits they received. This was reported unfavourably in the press and a special meeting was held with Mr Gregory present. It was resolved that the Rules allowed that when the hospital made a maintenance charge the doctor could charge a fee in proportion to that charge. It was also noted that the medical staff often gave their services free and therefore did not have to subscribe to the hospital's funds. A letter was sent to the press detailing the outcome.

After the war Miss Tew, the matron, retired following 10 years of service; she had taken a special interest in looking after the wounded soldiers. There then followed five matrons over the next seven years who did not distinguish themselves. Miss Richardson from Llandrindod Hospital had a row with her assistant and left; Miss Graham-Lynn from London felt she was being criticised and departed. After three years of Miss Rees from Workington, who had trouble controlling her staff, the committee felt a change of matron was in the best interests of the hospital. Miss Sharpe from Sutton wanted a testimonial so she could find a more lucrative post and although she had her salary increased by £10 with emoluments, she resigned. Finally, Miss Barton had five complaints relating to patient care made by the medical officers and was forced to resign. In 1929, to everyone's relief, Miss Elsie Harris arrived and was to remain admired and respected till the hospital was nationalised. Shortly after being appointed she was sent on a radiographers course.

After the war an assistant nurse, soon to become a fully trained staff nurse, was appointed as well as a probationer. There appeared to be constant quarrelling between the staff, resulting in the Rev. Elder, a governor on the committee threatening to dismiss them all, but the threat was not carried out. On a happier note an orchard adjacent to the south of the hospital was rented in order to provide an outdoor retreat for the nursing staff.

As pressures grew, the matron was informed that she was not permitted to engage in private home nursing herself, but could allow her staff to do so when convenient for the hospital as it would provide additional income.

In 1923 there had been a ward maid and a cook general, subsequently increased with the appointment of an assistant cook, a kitchen maid and a gardener whose duties included stoking and bringing in coal and wood. During the inter-war years salaries increased two or three fold and there was constant readjustment of remuneration to attract and retain staff.

In 1935 inpatients had increased to 294 with an average bed occupancy of eight and an average stay of 10 days. The majority of the cases remained surgical—in 1923 11 appendicectomies were performed and 83 anaesthetics given. During the inter-war years the hospital also started to accept cases of complicated midwifery. In 1924 a motor ambulance was in use and run by the St John's Ambulance Brigade while the previous horse drawn ambulance which the duchess of Bedford had given to the hospital in 1914 was sold for £2 10s.

In 1934 a patient was admitted for drainage of a large abscess over the left orbit relating to a previous gunshot wound which had resulted in the loss of his left eye. Postoperatively he became confused and violent and was transferred to the Leominster Public Assistance Institute where he died after a few hours. The Guardians of the P.A.I. made critical remarks about the cottage hospital which were repeated in the local press and some subscribers threatened to withdraw their support. A public inquiry was held and concluded that the case should initially have been sent to another hospital with better facilities to control agitated patients, but that proper care and attention had been given to the patient whilst at the cottage hospital, and it was agreed that he had been fit to be moved.

There were also complaints about the food and the committee admitted on one occasion it was not up to standard and agreed to more variation. A lady had offered to provide margarine for the patients, but the matron informed her that she only gave butter. The first sign of patient power appeared when each patient was encouraged to sign a paper on discharge indicating whether they were satisfied with their treatment or if not to complain in writing. There is no record of the results.

Perhaps because of such complaints, Dr Housden insisted that stretcher poles should be made available to lift cases on and off the operating table and recommended that written permission should be sought before any operation or anaesthetic was administered, procedures that soon became routine.

Early in the Second World War, the Ministry of Health asked small hospitals to try and identify additional accommodation for the treatment of wounded servicemen. Hampton Court, the home of the hospital's president, was made available and it opened in May 1942 as the Hampton Court Convalescent Hospital with the cottage hospital being responsible for staffing and running it. The matron was therefore appointed matron superintendent to Hampton Court Convalescent Hospital and took on the added responsibility of supervising the nursing services there, being rewarded by a small increase in her salary. Miss Trotter, previously assistant matron at the City of York Mental Hospital, became the resident sister in the hospital with the support of two other sisters.

With several of the medical staff involved in the war, Dr Housden, Dr James and Dr Thompson did most of the work until Dr James was commissioned into the R.A.F. Assistants to the general practitioners were allowed to perform minor operations, but if an anaesthetic was involved then a principal member of the honorary staff had to be in attendance. A dentist from Worcester once extracted a tooth at the hospital without permission and then applied for honorary status. This was refused as he did not hold a registered dental diploma.

Air raid precautions included shuttering the windows of the operating theatre, sterilising room and X-ray department, building protective blast walls outside the front door and acquiring a stirrup pump. The blast walls were only removed in June 1945.

In 1943 the name of the cottage hospital had been changed to the Leominster and District Hospital, one year before the last detailed report. This shows that total income amounted to £3,752. Subscriptions and fundraising income had steadily decreased while payments for patient services and by local authorities had increased, amounting to £1,966. Several firms also made annual contributions so that their workers could get rapid and subsidised treatment.

Large legacies continued to be left to the hospital, including a house which was sold for over £1,000. In 1944 the investments totalled £10,530 with the value of the hospital buildings and equipment estimated at £4,698.

As the war continued, there was a constant struggle to retain and appoint staff due to rapidly increasing salaries, restrictions on hours of work and resignations. Several senior sisters were recruited into Queen Alexandra's Imperial Nursing Service. To try and ease the situation, the matron agreed to take an untrained auxiliary nurse for a short period of training and was also given authority to take on temporary staff if necessary. In 1942 Sister Baynam, who had been a sister for six years, was promoted to became the first assistant matron, a post she held for a further four years before leaving to get married. During the war domestic staff were even more difficult to replace partly owing to higher wages being paid to munition workers.

When the county council was trying to agree a policy under which all midwifery cases, for which they had a degree of responsibility, would be kept in hospital for 14 days, Leominster proudly said their average was 21 days as they only admitted complicated cases—11 Caesarian sections had been performed in just over three years.

When there were complaints from the patients that they were required to retire at 8p.m., even in the summer, the matron was told to use her discretion.

In 1946, a new X-ray plant was installed at a cost of £1,900 along with a modern anaesthetic machine and diathermy unit.

The Friendly Societies and town councillors played the major role in establishing Leominster Cottage Hospital and they continued to support it over the years. Its long term success was due to the widespread support it attracted from throughout Leominster district.

CHAPTER 9

The Victoria Eye and Ear Hospital

The first specialist hospital treating eye and ear diseases in Hereford was established in July 1882 by Mr Francis Woodley Lindsay, an eye surgeon, and supported by a few private subscribers. He soon gained the support of the Rev. John Venn, a great philanthropist, who subsequently became a trustee of the future hospital. His other great supporter was Mr Mackay John Graham Scobie, who was educated at the Cathedral School, practised as a solicitor in the town and was a member of the city council. The hospital was initially housed in a leased building in Commercial Road in front of the Baptist Church and called the Herefordshire and South Wales Eye and Ear Institution.

It was soon obvious that the building was unable to cope with the demand, demand which also generated expenses of £193 in the first 15 months, an amount beyond the capacity of its private subscribers. In October 1883 Mr Scobie, who had become Mayor of Hereford at the age of 30 and had already made his mark by being the main instigator in establishing the Thursday half day closing, convened a public meeting at the Guildhall to seek support to turn the institution into a charitable voluntary hospital.

The meeting achieved his aim, a provisional committee was elected and appeals for subscribers and donors were made. The hospital was duly reopened as a charitable institution on 1st January 1884. The hospital was to be governed, according to the Rules, by subscribers of 10s 6d p.a. or donors of 10 guineas or over who would be eligible to vote at annual meetings and to be elected onto the Committee of Management. In return for the above amounts, subscribers also received tickets of recommendation to refer two patients to the hospital per year, and in addition could buy extra tickets at 5s each.

The hospital was to serve a wide area which included not only Herefordshire but neighbouring counties and South Wales, and was to treat

Herefordshire and South Wales Eye and Ear Institution, 1883

without charge the needy poor who were referred with tickets of recommendation. The majority of patients were treated as outpatients. The committee usually met monthly to receive reports from the nurse and officers, read the visitors book, appoint visitors and confirm tenders for supplies. The names of familiar Hereford businesses appeared, such as Pullings, now Tanners, for spirits and Mr Rowberry for meat.

At the annual meeting in March 1887 it was once again accepted that the premises were too small and unsuitable to meet the increasing demand—some 60 patients were awaiting admission while the six beds were always occupied. It was decided that a new purpose-built hospital would be a fitting memorial to Queen Victoria's Jubilee.

A suitable site was found in Eign Street, opposite the Eignbrook Chapel, which along with the surrounding property was purchased by Mr John Mackay, a wealthy benefactor, with the purpose of securing it for the hospital. He then sold them the part of the site required for the new building. Three sets of plans for the new hospital were judged by Mr Henry Currie, vice-president of the Royal Institute of British Architects and those of E.H. Lingen Barker of Hereford were chosen. The successful builder was Messrs Stephen & Bastow of Bristol who employed local labour. The foundation stone was laid by the Countess of Chesterfield on December 4th 1888, and a sealed bottle containing documents and coins was buried nearby.

The two storey building provided beds for 14 patients in two large and two small wards as well as all the supportive accommodation including a dinner lift. The cost of the land and buildings came to around £3,400, all but £700 of which was raised from benefactors. The wards were furnished by the trade unions and the Friendly Societies of Hereford, the Victoria Tile Works and many individual supporters.

The hospital was opened on 20th August 1889 by Lady Bailey, whose husband, Sir Joseph Russell Bailey, owned the Glenusk estates, lived in Hay Castle and was M.P. for Hereford. On the opening day, the Mayor and Corporation of Hereford, city magistrates, Committee of Management, chairman and vice-chairman of the county council, the high sheriff and mayors or chairmen or commissioners of Leominster, Abergavenny, Ross, Monmouth, Brecon and Pontypool walked from the Guildhall to the hospital, now to be named The Victoria Eye and Ear Hospital with permission of the queen. In

Mr John Mackay, 1822-1906

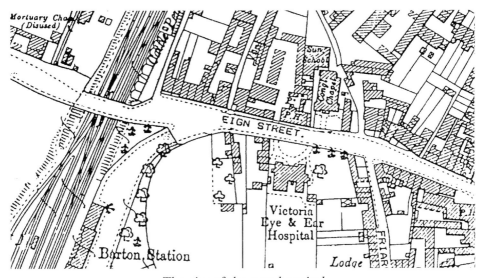

The site of the new hospital

171

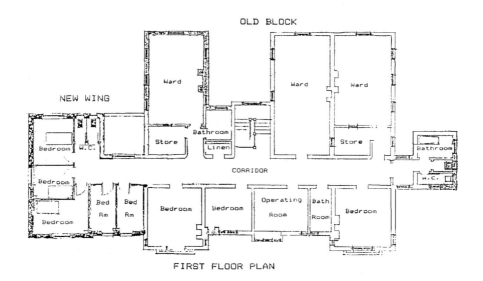

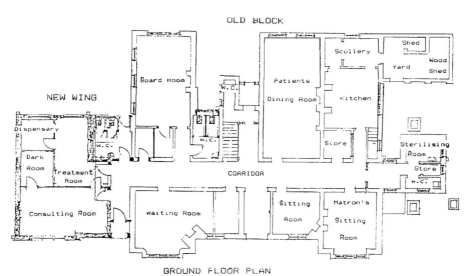

Hospital plans, 1938.
The Old Block shows the general layout of the original hospital. The three
bedrooms on the first floor of the Old Block were subsequently used for a
store room, a bathroom and a private ward. The New Wing was built in 1938

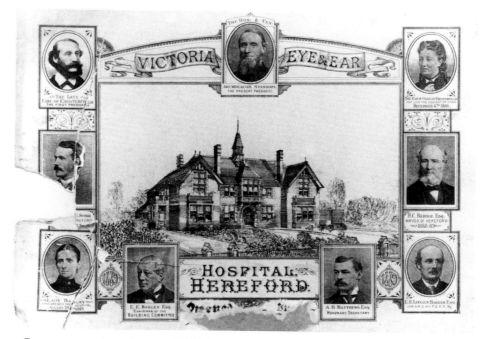

*Commemorative picture of 1889 on the opening of the Victoria Eye and Ear
Hospital, showing an artist's impression of the building
and personalities involved*

the evening the grounds were illuminated by thousands of fairy lights including
an inscription reading 'Success to the Eye and Ear Hospital'.

In the same year the Rules were changed and only subscribers of one
guinea p.a. or donors of 21 guineas would become governors and be entitled
to vote at annual meetings, whilst the title of life governor and vice-president
would only be awarded to donors of £21 and £50 respectively. Rules
concerning tickets of recommendation were also altered. Clergymen were to
receive one ticket for each guinea collected in an offertory. However, the ulti-
mate authority to decide on the suitability of a patient for admission remained
with the surgeon. Most of the patients were seen and treated as outpatients on
Wednesday and Saturday mornings. The hospital was usually closed for two
weeks each September for cleaning.

In 1899 the hospital became incorporated under the Companies Act giving it
legal status and allowing it to own property and the Committee of Management
became the Board of Management, under the chairmanship of Mr Scobie. By
1899 the number of subscribers had reached 300, not only from Herefordshire but
from surrounding counties and South Wales, and there were 15 life governors.

During the 1890s further land was acquired from Mr Mackay on either side of the hospital, from the railway on the west to Friars Street on the east and initially rented out to provide income. But in 1897 several severely injured patients could not be admitted because there was no room and it was decided to enlarge the hospital. The ground floor common room was expanded and a new ward built over it costing £119 which allowed a total of 20 patients to be accommodated. A grand piano was purchased and gardens were laid out with a summer house and garden seats.

To raise money collections were made in churches and there were negotiations to obtain a share of the offertories from Harvest Thanksgiving and Hospital Sunday. Contribution boxes were placed in hotels, public institutions, railway stations and tradesmen's shops, though fundraising events were limited. Many gifts were received including a piano. The accounts were generally kept in balance.

In 1892 the possibility of appointing a chemist was discussed but Mr Lindsay, the surgeon wanted to retain control of the drugs and their quality himself so no action was taken. Two years later he accepted the help of a dispenser, Miss Frances Hunter, who would also help him in his private practice. She had been trained as a nurse and served in several hospitals before having dispensing training at the Middlesex College of Pharmacy in London.

Miss Jones, the first nurse, stayed on as housekeeper and nurse when the original institution became a voluntary hospital in 1884, but resigned later that year. She was followed by Mrs Fanny Meredith who had worked at the County and City Asylum at Burghill. For a time

1882	Miss Mary Jones
1884	Mrs Fanny Meredith
1905	Miss S.C. Lewis
1922	Miss Margaret Daisy Gwilt

Table 17 Matrons at the Victoria Eye and Ear Hospital

she had a daughter staying with her and she was allowed to engage a servant. After seven years she was granted a raise on her original salary of £20 p.a. In addition a part-time laundress was employed, and a charwoman twice a week.

In 1884, 768 patients were treated, of whom just 58 were inpatients, and 61 operations were performed. They came from 106 parishes in Herefordshire, Gloucestershire, Monmouthshire, Shropshire, Breconshire and Glamorganshire.

Fifteen years later 1,385 patients were seen, the vast majority with eye rather than ear problems. The number of beds occupied each week varied between 15 and 20. Most operations were carried out under a local anaesthetic such as cocaine; general anaesthetics using chloroform or ether were only used under exceptional circumstances.

The hospital was always stressing that delays in treatment could be fatal for the restoration of sight or deafness, and encouraged early attendance if damage had been caused from stone breaking or hedging. Advanced age was no bar to treatment and they cited the case of an 86 year old man who had his sight restored after 30 years of blindness. A number of volunteer ladies relieved the boredom of the patients by reading or playing music.

In 1900 Mr George Cresswell (*for picture see p.10*) joined the Management Committee. Col. Scobie, now an active member of the Herefordshire Regiment Volunteers, continued as chairman, apart from 1915 to 1916 when he was on active service (*for picture see p.12*).

From the hospital's beginning, the appointed visitors had been very active and were regularly reporting defects in the fabric which resulted in many improvements. The matron also used the visitors to feed her own complaints through to management. They advised outdoor amusements such as croquet, hopefully for patients whose sight had been restored, and bright pictures for indoors. The patients, however, never seemed to complain. The nearest they came to this was when one patient stated that 'the Matron had poured a chemist shop into my inside, assuring me it would cure my streaming cold.' The victim promised to let the visitor know the result.

An aerial view taken in the 1950s showing the Eye Hospital with the New Wing, built in 1938, on the left, and the surgeon's house on the top right. The photograph clearly shows the path between the hospital and the surgeon's house that was to be the source of several problems

An area of land in Edgar Street was left to the hospital by Mrs Martha Edwards. It was initially rented out but in 1910 part of the land was sold to the Great Western Railway Co. for £2,100 under a compulsory purchase order. Another part was bought by the city council.

Meanwhile, the land on either side of the hospital continued to be rented out. In 1913 a surgeon's house was built at a cost of £1,646 on the western side adjacent to the railway and Mr Lindsay became resident there. In 1918 the land adjacent to Friars Street was rented to Mr A. Wallis, a cycle and motor engineer who was to become a long term tenant. A request was received from the managers of the Lord Scudamore School for a footpath through the hospital grounds to Eign Street. Many of the governors were involved in both institutions and so had a conflict of interest. After much agonising the request was rejected on the grounds that it would compromise the privacy of the hospital. However, six years later after pressure from the city council the repeated request was agreed to.

The income during this period fluctuated. Some years there was a reduction in the amount received from subscriptions and offertories but this was compensated by interest from investments. Workers in the South Wales coal mines together with railwaymen were regular subscribers to the hospital as their work often resulted in injuries to their eyes. A colliery in South Wales even offered to send a truck of coal to the hospital at a much reduced cost and this was accepted.

In 1911 the honorary chaplain must have become a little forgetful as he had to be asked to visit the hospital. He retired within a few months. A cook and a

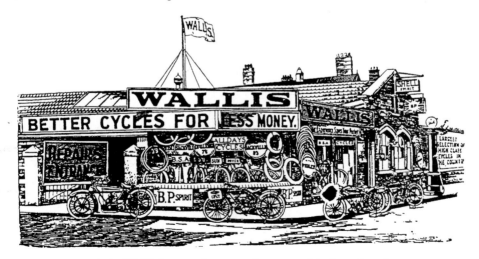

A.A. Wallis's premises, as shown on his letterhead

housemaid were employed as well as a gardener to look after the grounds, one of whom's less pleasant tasks was to keep the outside toilet clean.

The numbers of patients attending increased every year up until 1913 when 2,167 patients attended. In 1915 there was anxiety that certain patients from South Wales were appearing with tickets of recommendation when they could afford to pay for treatment, while others might be attending whilst on strike. In all such cases the surgeon had the power to refuse them non-urgent treatment. By 1918 the numbers attending had decreased to 1,910.

1919 to the advent of the N.H.S.

Col. Scobie remained Chairman of the Committee until 1929 when he retired, the year before his death. He had a distinguished career in public service, was a brilliant part-time soldier ending up commanding the 1st Battalion the Herefordshire Regiment and had served the Victoria Eye Hospital for over 45 years. The following year Major Amphlett Capel became chairman and was to remain so for 18 years. He had also served with the Herefordshire Regiment during the war and afterwards became the coroner for Hereford city. In fact, during the inter-war years many familiar names appear as members of the Board, including Lt. Col. J.H. Sleeman, who organised the contributory scheme at the General Hospital, Mr Frederick Bulmer of Bulmer's Cider, Major Stewart Robinson, who also served on the committee at the Victoria Cottage Hospital, Kington and Mr Francis Hawkins, a county alderman and farmer whose father gave his name to Hawkins Ward at the General Hospital.

By 1923, as ever fewer ear conditions were being seen, an extraordinary meeting of governors was held which resolved that the reference to ear in the title of the hospital should be omitted, and the hospital was renamed the Victoria Eye Hospital.

In 1922, the retirement of the surgeon Mr Lindsay created the opportunity for the General Hospital to broach the subject of working more closely together and even having a joint Board. It was agreed that the two hospitals should co-operate in treating patients but the Victoria Hospital did not wish to lose its identity and merge with the larger hospital with a likely loss of income from duplicate subscribers. They therefore jointly appointed an ophthalmic surgeon, Mr Hugh Woodward Barnes, but it was not until 1925 that they reached agreement on how to share his services—he would be based at the Eye Hospital but would attend the General Hospital and see outpatients twice a week, one being a market day. When patients were referred to the Victoria by the General Hospital that hospital would finance them at the rate of 7s 6d a day. In effect, ophthalmic work at the General Hospital steadily lessened and in 1934 outpatient services at the General Hospital ceased, with all ophthalmic work, both inpatient and outpatient being provided at the Victoria Hospital.

In due course the county council wished to start a monthly school eye clinic at the hospital, and this was accepted at 7s 6d a session.

In the 1920s it was agreed that the Victoria Eye Hospital would share receipts from major fundraising events in the city with the General Hospital. They duly received a fifth share of the receipts from the Alexandra Rose Day and from the Hereford Carnivals in the thirties, though their share from the May Fair charitable donations was a quarter.

Regular donations were received for some years from the Hereford Society for Aiding the Industrious, from the Tredegar Medical Aid Society and from income from the Stanley Holland Estate. The proceeds of a comic football match organised by the Cotterell Arms and Plough Inn on Coronation Day in 1937 provided the sum of £2 16s 2d.

Additional sources of income were always sought. Many of the patients were insured with the Hospital Savings Association who paid the hospital 6s a day and 5s for each new operation. Several firms including Messrs Painter Bros. organised contributory schemes amongst their workforce and paid

The Bulmer Family.
Percy Bulmer, the founder of H.P. Bulmer Ltd is at the back, right, his brother
Fred at the back, left, and their parents, the Rev. Charles Bulmer and his wife
Mary are seated

similar sums when a worker was treated. However, H.P. Bulmers decided that they had referred so few cases that a contributory scheme was unnecessary.

The government paid for certain services to war pensioners while Herefordshire County Council paid £15 p.a. in place of the contribution from the Board of Guardians to cover paupers. Private patients were charged between 3 and 6 guineas a week and outpatients were encouraged to make donations towards their treatment.

When the General Hospital proposed a county-wide contributory scheme, this was rejected by the Victoria Hospital in view of the specialist nature of its work, and the fact that it was coping with all the work there was to be done and was receiving sufficient income for this purpose. No other hospital in Herefordshire's history could boast of such a success story.

But there were two minor irritations. The scholars of Lord Scudamore's School had been throwing waste paper into the hospital grounds and the Director of Education had to apologise. There had also been excess noise at night from nearby railway engines emitting steam and after protests the railway company agreed to amend their practices.

A further irritant proved to be the wording on the tickets of recommendation — 'Not to be used for begging purposes' — which was considered offensive and therefore changed to 'This ticket does not entitle the holder to free hospital treatment except in necessitous cases.' However, the L.M.S. Railway Fund objected to the word 'necessitous' and wanted the alternative wording 'A proper person to receive treatment at the above Charitable Institution.' They were told they could issue their own vouchers.

During the inter-war years many improvements were made. In 1924 electricity was installed. A year later a telephone was provided, but an extension to the surgeon's house had to wait another 10 years and an internal extension to the matron's bedroom a further three. The heating was upgraded but this did not include central heating which was thought too expensive. A wireless set was also made available and in 1928 it was relayed to three wards.

Mr Wallis was constantly seeking permission to expand his neighbouring garage and in 1928 the hospital eventually agreed to let him install a petrol pump and underground tank adjacent to the hospital buildings.

In 1929 part of the back of the hospital was reconstructed and a ground floor lavatory was turned into a sterilising room whilst the first floor toilet facilities were extended. In 1937 a major extension was planned to improve the accommodation. The ground floor would be modified to provide a consultant room, dark room, dispensary and lavatories. The theatre was upgraded whilst the first floor would provide an additional private ward and five bedrooms for two nurses and three maids. The cost was £2,227, half of which was raised by dona-

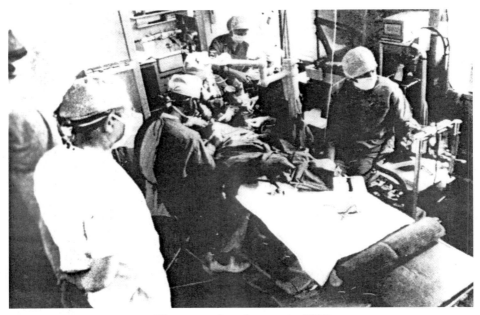

The operating theatre in 1938

tions with the help of the *Hereford Times*. The new wing was opened on the 2nd May 1938 by Lady Hereford, the wife of the president.

In the late 1930s, common operations performed were those for cataracts and correction of squints. The hospital was particularly appreciated by the railwayworkers and miners who were especially liable to injuries of the eye.

The charge for correcting a squint was 10 guineas. Venereal disease effected the eye but most of these cases required isolation and were referred to the Birmingham and Midlands Eye Hospital. The exception was Ophthalmia Neonatorum in babies and the county council paid for their treatment at the Victoria Eye Hospital.

More up to date equipment was appearing and a Gullstrand's slit lamp which projected a narrow intense beam of light into the eye to help in its examination together with an ophthalmic magnet to help in removing foreign bodies from the eye, were purchased. A new anaesthetic machine was also provided.

A list of local chemists interested in supplying spectacles was placed in the hospital's waiting room. In 1937 the Herefordshire Optical Association asked that the list should indicate the cheapest pair available which at that time was a pair of nickel frames with spherical lenses costing 5s.

Over the years the hospital also received its share of complaints. A claim of negligence was made by a clergyman from Much Birch on behalf of a lady,

The Viscountess Hereford and hospital officials
at the opening of the extension on 1st May 1938.
Sitting (from left): Mr C.A. Benn, vice-chairman; Major E. Amphlett Capel,
chairman; Viscountess Hereford; Viscount Hereford, president;
Miss M.D. Gwilt, matron; Mr. S.C. Herbert, secretary.
Standing (front row): Dr H. Woodward Barnes, surgeon; Mr J.H.T.
Nicholson, architect; Mrs H.H. Downes, Mayoress of Hereford;
Mr F.E. Bayley, builder; Mr G.D. Best, Board member.
Standing (back rows): Mr W.T. Bayley, builder; Rev. G.B.E. Riddell, Board
member; Mr E.L.G. Sciven, architect; Mr R. Bentley-Taylor, Board member;
Capt. C. Cope, Board member; Mr J.J. Bayley, builder;
Mr G.A. Hall, Board member

probably because he had given her a ticket of recommendation. She had a painful back in hospital and the surgeon had applied a plaster. When she went home the relatives took the plaster off and applied liniment to her back but she developed bed sores. The Board interviewed the surgeon and matron and no negligence was accepted as the relatives had interfered with the treatment. Another complaint stated that the matron had performed a minor operation, but it turned out that she had simply removed a foreign body from a patient's eye.

Nevertheless, following this complaint a register of all casualties attending the hospital was kept.

In 1938 an Emergency Committee consisting of the chairman, vice-chairman and Mr Bentley-Taylor was formed to deal with urgent matters in the event of war. Requests from the Ministry of Health that the hospital should be used as a first aid post were turned down as it would interfere with the hospital's work. When the Army announced that an army camp of 1,400 men would open in Hereford on 1st July 1939, the hospital agreed to offer a service—and rapidly produced a list of charges!

In 1939 the hospital was protected against possible air raids with blinds for the theatre and new plate glass for the front door. Trenches were dug in the grounds and 10,000 sandbags were used to protect vital parts of the hospital since it was designated as a facility for the initial treatment of casualties with eye injuries. The sandbags at the rear of the outpatient department slowly collapsed to be followed by those elsewhere but they were not replaced. At the end of the war the 107th U.S. Hospital at Kington generously gave laboratory equipment, the U.S. Military Police donated books and the Red Cross a large amount of bed linen.

The railings alongside the footpath across the hospital ground for the use of pupils from Lord Scudamore School had been taken down following a 'Salvage of Iron Railings' drive on behalf of the war effort. This had been followed by some vandalism and the hospital gave notice to terminate the agreement regarding the path, but the city council saved the day by erecting a chestnut paling. There was further trouble when the gates at either end of the path were not kept locked as agreed, and the Director of Education was reprimanded. (The path is still there, though its position was modified in 1979 to pass to the west of a new theatre.)

H.P. Bulmers changed their minds and instituted a monthly collection amongst their workforce in aid of the hospital. Legacies continued, the largest being £3,600 from a Miss M.T. Turner.

In 1947 the total income was £2,881 with the expenditure £185 less. 5,306 outpatients were seen, about half being new patients, while there were 321 inpatients having 132 operations.

In the 65th and final annual report the chairman stated that the principles and ideals which inspired the foundation of the hospital were still firm and strong. The report felt that the people of Herefordshire, the surrounding counties and South Wales had every reason to be satisfied with their specialist hospital.

After 26 years as matron, Miss Gwilt retired on 5th July 1948, the day the hospital came under the N.H.S.

CHAPTER 10

Madhouse to Mental Hospital — Hereford Lunatic Asylums

In the eighteenth century lunatics were considered as people who could not look after themselves and were not the responsibility of doctors. Pauper lunatics tended to be treated as vagrants and end up in gaol or the workhouse, whilst there were private 'madhouses' for those whose relatives could afford the cost. However, these had a very bad reputation for incarcerating the sane for the benefit of their relatives. This led to the 1774 Act for Regulating Private Madhouses under which justices of the peace were to licence private asylums and appoint two justices and a physician to inspect them. In effect they had little power and there were no regular visits.

By the 1770s there was a perceived need for a lunatic asylum in Hereford in spite of there then being only four charitable asylums in the whole of England. In January 1777 the governors of the Hereford General Infirmary therefore opened a fund to establish an asylum for the reception and cure of lunatics. There must have been a lack of interest because it was not until 1792, when £1,200 had been collected, that the governors set up a committee, consisting of the medical staff and the treasurer, Mr Joseph Perrin, to organise the project.

The committee commissioned John Nash to draw up plans for a two storey asylum in the grounds of the infirmary to accommodate 20 lunatics. Nash subsequently became famous for designing Regent Street and Marble Arch in London, and locally he also designed Hereford Gaol. The builder was Mr Knight and the cost was £1,297. But the building work was clearly not up to scratch, for £63 was held against outstanding defects. A few years later a legacy of £100 was used to build a washhouse, brewhouse and cellar in the courtyard.

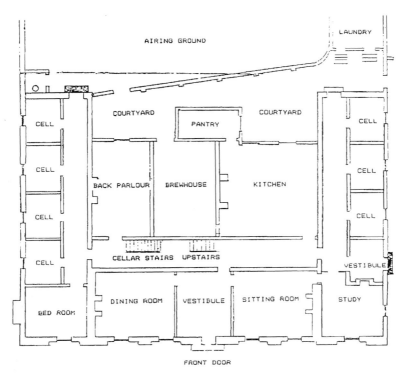

The Lunatic Asylum of 1820, showing the ground floor plan with the resident superintendent's quarters at the front. Upstairs there were 14 rooms for inmates and staff

Plans of the ground floor dated 1820 shows the generous quarters for the resident superintendent in contrast to the rooms, called cells, for the lunatics, indicating prevailing attitudes.

Originally it was intended that the asylum would be run under the control of the governors and their officers and it opened in 1799 under a supervisory committee with Dr Francis Campbell, Physician Extraordinary, as president. A manager, Mr David Davies, was employed but the asylum did not prosper. It was then decided to contract private management as the governors felt that the function of an asylum was incompatible with that of the infirmary. In 1801 it was therefore rented out to two of the medical staff, though this was immediately revoked, for no obvious reason. It was then leased for 21 years, subject to renewal, to John Pateshall, a surgeon in the city, and thus became a private madhouse.

Although the asylum remained the property of the governors they had no say in its running and Mr Pateshall, known as the keeper, took in both pauper and private lunatics. Physicians looking after the lunatics were known as alienists, a derogatory term to indicate they were looking after people who were alienated from their reason.

Pauper lunatics were the responsibility of the Overseers of the Poor in each parish who, armed with a certificate of insanity from the parish medical officer, could request a justice of the peace to sign an order of admission to an asylum. The relevant parish paid for maintenance through their rates, a responsibility taken over by the Board of Guardians of the Poor Law Unions in 1834. A private lunatic could be admitted on the request of a near relative supported by certificates of insanity by two independent physicians and the family paid the maintenance. In an emergency, a single doctor could issue an 'urgent order' for admission.

Legislation in the 1820s and 30s increased the powers of the justices and introduced registers of inmates and admission procedures. The Visiting Committee of Justices and a physician were required to inspect the licensed asylum regularly several times a year and ensure the inmates were being cared for. A lunatic asylum book had to be kept in the building containing the justices reports. As a final sanction, they had powers to revoke the licence and close the establishment. In 1820 the visiting justices said that the exercise yard was too small. The governors were consulted and agreed with Mr Pateshall that he should enclose an area of the infirmary's land 37 yards long and 13 yards wide with a wall 14 feet high, at his own expense.

Mr Pateshall died in 1834 and the asylum was then leased to the surgeon Mr John Gilliland, with his brother Dr William Letta Gilliland as the resident medical superintendent. Dr William Gilliland was subsequently appointed as a physician to the infirmary in 1836, the same year that matters started to wrong with the asylum. Admission procedures and statutory registers were not being kept properly and there were more patients in residence than was permitted. Changes were made in systems and the asylum was enlarged to accommodate 36 patients. Complaints then arose that patients were being ill-treated, such as being ducked in a bath of cold water for misbehaving. The relatives of a private patient found him neglected and bruised. The visiting justices compiled a condemnatory report and Dr Gilliland's licence was withdrawn. It was then discovered that licences had been issued by the county justices when the asylum was within the city. Dr Gilliland therefore applied to the city magistrates and after a quick inspection they issued a new licence. The county justices appealed to the Lord Chancellor and a select committee was appointed to investigate. They met in 1839 and whilst criticising the past licensing procedures and the conditions at the asylum, they allowed Dr Gilliland to keep his new licence.

Since 1808 counties had been encouraged to provide their own asylums, if necessary by combining with neighbouring counties and boroughs. In 1845 Parliamentary legislation made it the duty of each county to provide an asylum for lunatics and they established a Board of Commissioners to regulate the running of the asylums. The asylum at the General Hospital was thought too small and unsuitable for this purpose, as were two other small madhouses in Herefordshire that little is known about—one at Peterchurch and another at Portland House, Whitchurch. Greater safeguards were also introduced against wrongful detention.

Meanwhile, repairs costing £62 became necessary at the existing Hereford asylum and the governors of the infirmary wanted to increase the rent to £50 p.a. Dr Gilliland refused to pay, tenders were sought unsuccessfully for a new management contract, and Dr Gilliland's reduced tender was accepted. It was resolved, however, that as soon as the county asylum was open the present asylum would be closed.

As the asylum was self supporting, the Lunatic Asylum Fund, now standing at over £1,000 and controlled by the governors, had not been needed. The governors therefore agreed that the fund should be used to assist patients, other than paupers who were the responsibility of the proposed new county asylum, to be sent to other public or private asylums. In October 1850 there were still 35 patients in the asylum, of whom 30 were paupers and five private patients. The last admission was in January 1852 and the last patient was discharged in January 1853. The building was demolished a few years later.

Meanwhile, in response to the 1845 Act, negotiations had been taking place between the justices of the counties of Monmouth, Hereford, Brecon, Radnor together with the City of Hereford resulting in an agreement reached in September 1847 to form a union with the purpose of erecting a joint lunatic asylum at Abergavenny. There was widespread opposition to this plan and a petition was drawn up and sent to Parliament supported by 14 of the parishes that would have to bear the cost. It was claimed that there was spare capacity for looking after lunatics in the county, and that the duration of stay was shorter in the private licensed establishments and therefore cheaper. But the petition was lost.

The Abergavenny asylum was to be controlled by a Committee of Visitors made up of justices from the various authorities in proportion to their populations, Herefordshire providing 10 and the city three. The asylum itself was built just north of Abergavenny at a cost of £37,000, Herefordshire's share being £11,700 and the city's £1,200. It opened on 1st December 1851 with accommodation for 254 patients. Subsequently it was enlarged and by 1864 had 480 inmates.

Despite this, the Commissioners in Lunacy agreed that there was over-crowding and an increasing demand for further accommodation, and so the Committee of Visitors agreed to dissolve their union in order that Herefordshire and the city could build their own asylum. By July 1867 a committee of justices drawn from the two authorities had chosen a site for their asylum at Burghill, three miles north of Hereford, and building began in 1868.

The Hereford County and City Asylum

The building of Hereford County and City Asylum at Burghill was completed in 1872 at a cost of £87,873 and covered 10 acres. A further 100 acres comprised gardens, a farm and several cottages. The buildings faced south-east and were divided into a male and female block each accommodating 200 people in four secure wards, two each on the ground floor and on the first floor. The term 'wards' was used to include a complex of dormitories, single rooms and wide corridors. There were also numerous bathrooms and day rooms. Facilities for the staff were found on the second floor and scattered elsewhere in the buildings.

In the male block there was also a workshop and brewhouse. (The men got more food than the women and ³/₄ pint of beer compared to ¹/₂ pint. An extra allowance was awarded to those who worked in the hospital, garden or farm.) The female block contained a laundry. Each block also had several exercise yards sometimes called airing courts. The spacious general dining and recreation hall was adjacent to the kitchen and wards. Above it there was a chapel which could hold 250 people.

Lighting was by gas near the ceiling with the gas taps in the corridors, being inaccessible to patients, the supply coming from gas works in the grounds. The heating was partly by open fires and partly by hot water pipes which served the chapel, dining room and some of the wards. The water supply came from wells in the grounds.

The primary purpose of the asylum was to treat the insane and return them home, not just to securely hide them away. In the event it provided this service mainly to paupers referred from the Guardians of the Poor Law Unions, as very few private patients were admitted.

The management was by a Committee of Visitors appointed by the justices of the county and city, again in proportion to their population. The first chairman was the Rev. Archer Clive who had been the rector of a living in Solihull for 16 years before he inherited a large estate at Whiffield from his father, and become the local squire and a magistrate. He had previously been the chairman of the asylum at Abergavenny. Over the years many notable people who already served

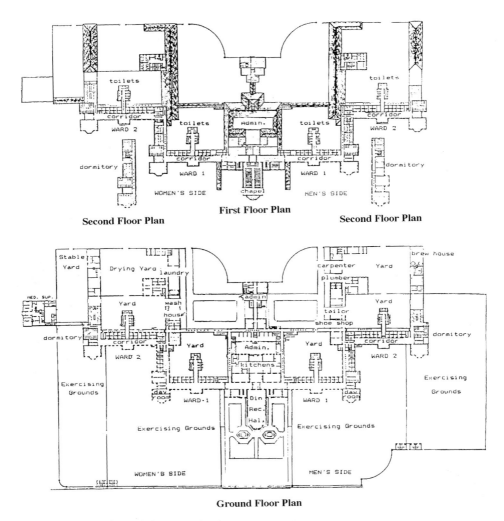

Plan of the Hereford County and City Asylum in 1872

on the committees of one or other of the county's hospitals, also served on the Committee of Visitors. In 1888 the responsibility for asylums was transferred from the justices direct to the county and city councils.

The whole committee met every quarter and each month three or four members would meet as a House Committee prior to visiting each ward and department and seeing all the patients. Any criticisms were written into a visitors' book which formed part of the annual report. The committee's most important appointment was that of the medical superintendent who acted as

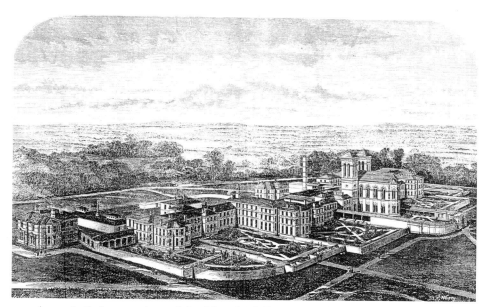

An artist's impression of the Hereford County and City Asylum in 1872

director and physician to the hospital, being responsible to them for the running of the establishment. The first superintendent was Dr T. Algernon Chapman who had served for seven years as an assistant medical officer at the Joint County Asylum at Abergavenny. He proved to be an outstanding choice and created a friendly atmosphere; under his supervision, remarkably, there were no suicides. He was a keen entomologist and was an active member of the Woolhope Naturalists Field Club. He retired, aged 56 in 1897, with melancholia. Every year there was an unannounced visit from the Commissioners in Lunacy who made a detailed report having inspected every department and seen all the visitors and staff. They were particularly interested in any deaths, coroner's reports, suicides, and patients under restraint or in bed during the day, dismissals of staff and turnover of patients. Restraint of a patient had to be recorded in a register and could consist of isolation in a single room, medical sedation, or physical restraint by wrapping an excited patient in a blanket or a straight jacket, or by the use of a special padded cell. However, putting a troublesome patient who was not physically ill to bed during the day was an easy option which did not have to be reported. On one visit the Commissioners found 27 patients in bed out of 382 inpatients.

In 1890 the previous division of responsibility, based on the proportionate populations of the county and the city, was causing disagreement and Viscount Llandaff, a privy councillor and recent secretary of state, was asked to adjudi-

Chairmen of the Committee of Visitors	
1872	Rev. Archer Clive, of Whitfield
1878	Rev. B.L.S. Stanhope, of Byford Rectory
1890	Rev. George H. Davenport, of Foxley
1899	Mr John T. Southall, of Ross
1906	Alderman A.P. Turner, of The Leen, Pembridge
1924	Mr H. Gosling, of Leominster
1931	Mr Thomas J. Hawkins, of Thinghill Court

Medical Superintendents	
1872	Dr T. Algernon Chapman, M.D.
1897	Dr C.S. Morrison, L.R.C.P., L.R.C.S., L.F.P.S.(Glas.)
1815	Dr Thomas Chivers Graves, M.B., B.S., B.Sc., F.R.C.S., L.R.C.P.
1919	Dr John Grimmond Smith, M.D.
1931	Dr G.W.T. Flemming, M.R.C.S., L.R.C.P., D.P.M.
1937	Dr Thomas E. Burrows, B.A., M.R.C.S., L.R.C.P., D.P.M.

Chaplains	
1872	Rev. C. Bulmer, M.A., rector of Credenhill
1888	Rev. Compton Reade, M.A.
1910	Rev. Charles H. Taylor, M.A.
1923	Rev. Thomas O. Charteris, vicar of Burghill
1934	Rev. William H. Goddard-Fenwick, rector of Credenhill
1944	Rev. Edward G. Benson, M.A., vicar of Burghill

*Table 18 Chairmen, medical superintendents and chaplains
to the asylum and later hospital*

cate. He ruled that the proportion of cost borne should be dependent upon the accommodation actually required by each of the county and city. At that time it was 79 per cent to 21 per cent, and this figure was to be reviewed every three years. In 1872 the charge was 12s per pauper per week, which had dropped to 9s 4d per week by 1899, indicating an increased numbers of inmates. Paupers from without the county, private patients and patients boarded out from other asylums were charged more. Over a third of the patients left within a year.

In 1899 there were 367 inpatients, of whom 71 had been admitted that year. 26 were said to have been cured, six relieved and there were 33 deaths. The average age of the males was 42 and that of the females 50. With overcrowding, increasing numbers of patients were being boarded out at considerable expense and two years later plans had been laid to increase the accommodation of the asylum by 150 beds and modernise the facilities at a cost of £40,000. As an interim measure the committee tried to get chronic harmless lunatics transferred to the workhouses, but met a lot of resistance.

The farm was run as a separate business, selling pork, beef, veal, milk, vegetables, fruit and cider to the asylum worth around £812 p.a., out of a total income of some £2,000. Usually there was a small profit which went to the asylum.

In 1873 there was a head male attendant and nine male colleagues, a head female attendant and 11 female colleagues, at a ratio of one member of staff for every 8.5 male inmates and 8 female inmates. The salaries for the male staff were often nearly twice that for female staff.

Other staff consisted of a housekeeper, cook, laundress, housemaid, kitchen maid, porter, baker, engineer and stoker. There were also four artisans, a bailiff in charge of the house and garden, a gardener, cowman, wagoner and various farm staff. The Rev. Charles Henry Bulmer, rector of Credenhill was appointed chaplain in 1872 and as well as being responsible for conducting services he visited all the patients weekly and was responsible for entertainment, including supervising a band, and for looking after a library of 205 dilapidated books. He organised dancing or other forms of entertainment twice weekly in the dining hall, and encouraged patients to walk in the airing courts which were exposed to the weather but secure. Walking parties of up to 20 patients were also regularly taken round the grounds and beyond to help ease the sense of seclusion and isolation from the world. Charles enjoyed growing roses and fruit trees, particularly apples, in the rectory gardens, and it was his son, Henry, who later established the cider firm H.P. Bulmer.

Pauper patients were referred by the Union Workhouses, private patients by relatives and gaol patients by the authorities, but they all had to be certified as insane. In 1890 the Lunacy Act tightened this procedure. A reception order had to be issued by a J.P. and relatives could no longer do this on their own. In addition, two medical certificates had to be provided. In 1872 there appeared to be three reasons for admission—moral causes which included anxiety, disappointment, reverse of fortune, loss of or desertion by a spouse; physical causes which included hereditary factors, head injuries, and every sort of physical illness; and unknown causes which covered the remaining 42 per cent.

1900 - 1918

Dr Morrison, who had succeed Dr Chapman, fell ill in July 1915 and he died later that year aged 56. During his 18 years in office the asylum's death rate was the lowest of any in England. Earlier that year Dr T.A. Graves had been appointed as a junior assistant medical officer and he was now appointed acting superintendent for six months, after which his appointment was confirmed. Two years later he was called to serve in the armed forces and Dr John Grimmond Smith, assistant medical officer at Hills End Asylum, St Albans, was appointed to act as his locum, taking the job on a permanent basis not long after the end of the First World War.

By the end of 1900 the new buildings were complete. The female side included a two storied building to accommodate 100 patients while the male side was single storey and housed 50 patients. The wards were large, with four rows of beds. Electric light was installed throughout the asylum, powered by three dynamos in the basement. The excess steam was used to heat the asylum via hot water boilers and radiators. The kitchen was enlarged and new gas cookers provided. The chapel and dining hall were extended, and the latter provided with a stage. A telephone system was installed.

In 1914 it was recognised that there was an increase in tuberculosis in the asylum and verandas were built onto each ward accommodating sick patients

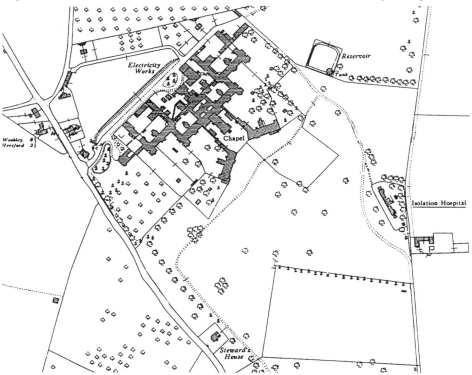

The general layout of the Hereford County and City Mental Hospital in 1920, also showing the site of the isolation hospital

so they could be nursed in fresh air. Six cottages were built for attendants and their families. Up to 1911 a cottage had been kept vacant to act as an isolation hospital, but an isolation hospital was then built in the grounds to accommodate six patients together with domestic quarters for the staff. It was not used for four years until there was an outbreak of scarlet fever.

There was continuous difficulty in keeping male attendants, with the majority leaving within a year of appointment. As an incentive to stay, uniforms were provided and they were allowed more time off. Extra income could be earned when someone escaped—if an attendant had to search for an escaped inmate outside the hospital he was awarded 3s 6d a day and an additional 1.5d per mile for using a bicycle. When war came male attendants were excused military duties which made the posts more attractive. At the same time the committee agreed to take 80 patients from Cardiff Mental Hospital, freeing accommodation there for wounded soldiers.

In March 1915 there were 531 inmates, consisting of 513 pauper patients from Herefordshire and 18 private patients. A further 13 patients were boarded out. Patients were now classified as suffering from congenital or infantile deficiency, acquired epilepsy, general paralysis of the insane, mania, melancholia, dementia and delusional insanity.

1919 - 1939

In 1919 the status of the insane and asylums was improving, and reflecting this the name of the asylum was changed to the Hereford County and City Mental Hospital. Over the next 20 years it was increasingly unofficially referred to as the Burghill Mental Hospital. The term attendant was changed to nurse, the insane referred to as mentally defective and an inmate became a patient.

Dr John Grimmond Smith retired after 12 years and was followed by Dr G.W.H. Flemming and then Dr Thomas Burrows, aged 30, a former senior assistant medical officer in the hospital. He was one of the youngest physicians to hold such a position and was regarded as a pioneer in involving patients' families in treatment as he believed their support was vital for long term success.

As the years progressed, more staff cottages were built and services modernised. In 1920 a new sewage system was connected to the main. A few years later the private gas works required costly repairs and mains gas was installed.

The hospital tractor ran into the front gates of the hospital which had to be replaced. The tractor came into the news again a few years later when there was a complaint to the superintendent that, while travelling up Eign Street in Hereford with a load of coal, it had frightened a horse causing it to bolt and cause damage. The tractor driver was able to convince his superiors that he was not on the public road at the time and that the rider had lost control while waving at some girls!

In a typical year, such as 1931, the farm supplied the hospital with 14,359 gallons of milk, 42,100 lbs of beef, 15,594 lbs of mutton, 4,867 lbs of pork and 2,313 eggs. In March 1939 it was awarded the Harry Lane Challenge Cup for bacon pigs for the third year running and the cup became the property of the hospital. In most years the hospital was in credit in part thanks to the profits from the farm.

Wages and conditions of service became a constant battleground. The workers were represented by the National Asylum Workers Union whilst management was advised by the Mental Hospitals Association. Nurses' hours of work reduced to 60 and then 56 a week, they were allowed two days off a week and granted 14 days annual holiday twice a year, changes which resulted in some 22 additional nurses having to be appointed. In addition a uniform was to be provided and certain nurses were to be allowed to sleep out. Regular staff dances were allowed in the patients' dining room.

Over the years there were several unfortunate incidents. A cider barrel was found in a male nurse's room and he was threatened with dismissal unless he repented and improved. He managed to convince the authorities that he had done so, a sign that the regime was getting more gentle. Prior to 1919 one nurse had been sacked for hitting a patient. Between the wars a second nurse was asked to resign for rough handling of patients but before she could leave, she died of a spreading infection. Another nurse died of influenza and a sister was admitted to the Nieuport Sanatorium with tuberculosis.

The hospital was like a closed community as many patients spent a large part of their life there. The total staff in 1939 serving this community numbered 143, which included an increased artisan staff then amounting to a baker, two tailors, a shoemaker, a switchboard attendant, an electrical engineer, a fitter, a stoker, two carpenters, two masons and bricklayers and a painter. They once started work at 6 a.m. with a stop for breakfast but their hours were reduced by introducing a 7.30 a.m. start after breakfast had been taken in their own time.

In 1930 the Mental Treatment Act tried to make admission to mental hospitals more acceptable by introducing two new categories of patients and hopefully removing some of the stigma of being certified. Voluntary patients were those accepted for treatment who could leave at any time, and temporary patients were those incapable of expressing themselves at the time of admission and who required required two medical recommendations, but they were not certified. Their condition was reviewed within a month but if they became able to express their wishes these had to be honoured.

Aerial view of Holme Lacy Hospital

In 1939 it was agreed that the bodies of any patients who died that were unclaimed by relatives would be offered to the anatomy schools as long as the schools paid for any expenses. On a more upbeat note, there was difficulty in attracting professional entertainment and a cinema projector was installed. The hospital band was reformed. During the visit of Queen Mary to Hereford in 1937, when she laid the foundation stone for the County Hospital, 60 patients were taken there by buses and another 30 were given parole. As war approached the Committee was told that in an emergency they should be prepared to receive 170 civilian casualties from Birmingham.

In 1932 it had been agreed with the county council that Holme Lacy House should become a hospital for psychiatric women under the management of Burghill Mental Hospital. For several centuries Holme Lacy House was the home of the Scudamore family until they sold it in 1909. The last private owner was Mr Noel Wills of Wills Tobacco Company, who's widow presented it to the

195

county council in 1930. The property included a farm, but this was to be managed by the county council. The cost of modifying the building, including attending to the drains, changing the heating from oil to coal and modernising the electrical installations came to £19,000, covered by a loan. It was planned to provide accommodation for 107 women patients, of whom 83 were to be private and 24 rate aided, and the new hospital opened in June 1935.

For the first few years the hospital ran at a loss, but had moved into surplus by 1939. By December that year there were 81 women inpatients, of whom 57 were private. The majority of the patients were voluntary and not certified and attendant relaxation in supervision may have been the cause of a significant suicide rate, mainly through drowning in the River Wye or in one of the several lakes in the grounds. One certified patient escaped and was not recaptured for 14 days, so ensuring her legal discharge as the law then deemed her capable of leading her own life. The case of one patient who went missing in midwinter in and was only found several weeks later in a shallow pond, resulted in a very critical article in the *Hereford Times*.

1940 to the advent of the N.H.S.

During the war, a hospital home guard was formed at Burghill, though no member of the essential staff was allowed to join. In April 1940 the War Office converted the mental hospital at Talgarth in Wales into a military hospital, relinquished their claim to beds at Burghill for civilian casualties, and in June transferred 143 mental patients and 18 nurses from Talgarth to Burghill. By December there were 780 patients in Burghill and Holme Lacy Hospitals including 456 county and city patients, 11 private patients, 12 service patients, 3 out of county patients, 90 contracted boarders from Burnwood and Derby, 141 Talgarth patients and 67 patients in Holme Lacy. Two months later the Talgarth patients were moved elsewhere.

In June 1944 the accidental explosion at the munitions factory at Rotherwas, described in chapter 3, broke 76 panes of glass in the hospital in spite of it being three miles away.

Since before the war there had been plans to build a nurses' home, but this was finally abandoned in 1946 when arrangements were made to board out 50 nurses in Redhill Hostel, south of the river, in Hereford. It proved popular with many nurses as it gave them respite from the hospital environment. However, several of the senior nurses for whom Burghill Mental Hospital had been their home for 15 to 20 years were allowed to stay on site in the 29 cottages and two farm houses used for staff accommodation.

A lady house physician had been provided at Holme Lacy Hospital, but this post was abandoned in 1946 because doctors at this grade lacked experience in

Aerial view of Burghill Mental Hospital in the 1980s

mental problems. The following year they were equally unfortunate with the assistant medical officer at Holme Lacy who could not get on with the nursing staff and refused to resign until there had been a formal inquiry.

Psychiatric services continued to expand and an outpatient clinic was started at Leominster. Dr Jean Lloyd from Ross was employed to anaesthetise patients in Burghill for electroconvulsive treatment (E.C.T.), then being used to relieve certain types of depression. Male nurses had their uniform changed from a suit to a white coat, flannel trousers and cap. Up until 1945 the hospital had employed Mr Sessarrego to wind all the hospital clocks but thereafter this duty was devolved onto other members of staff.

During the war there were staff shortages at all levels, particularly amongst male nurses as so many men had been called up to serve in the forces. Overtime became necessary and 67.5 hours on duty spread over a six day week became common.

In 1944 the chaplain retired due to ill health and Rev. Benson, vicar of Burghill was appointed at a salary of £100 p.a. However, the bishop of Hereford refused to issue a licence till his terms of appointment had been reviewed. The committee initially refused to compromise but finally increased his salary to £120 p.a. In addition a Roman Catholic priest and a Free Church minister attended with expenses of £20 p.a.

By 1944 some patients suffering from depression were being offered an operation at the County Hospital called prefrontal leucotomoy, in which connection between parts of the brain were divided. The visiting neurosurgeon was paid £25 for up to four cases.

The care of mental patients had changed from being mainly custodial towards more active treatment with new drugs, electroconvulsive therapy and occasionally surgery. The in-patient accommodation was still in the country-side, but all this was going to change in the following 50 years.

CHAPTER 11

The Struggle Against Infectious Diseases

By the end of the nineteenth century local authorities were responsible for controlling and treating infectious diseases. Cholera was never seen in Herefordshire and smallpox only appeared in minor outbreaks up to 1930, but scarlet fever and diphtheria presented problems as did occasional cases of typhoid fever and meningitis. By the early 1900s tuberculosis was also an increasing threat. All these diseases became notifiable to the local medical officer of health.

Each local authority had to find means of isolating and treating these diseases and they did this in one of three ways. One option, known as 'hospitalisation of cottages' was to isolate patients in their own home and provide resident nurses. But this was expensive and not very effective, being rarely used after the 1920s. The second was to transfer patients to isolation hospitals run by other authorities on payment of maintenance and medical fees. Long term contracts became popular with payments to retain a certain number of beds coupled with maintenance fees for patients who were actually admitted. As demand was intermittent and outbreaks usually limited to only a few districts at a time, there were usually no problems concerning admissions. The third option was for a local authority to establish its own isolation hospitals. This was the route followed in Herefordshire, where eight isolation hospitals were established.

Under legislation enacted in 1929 the county council had to rationalise its provision, resulting in four of the hospitals being closed. Attempts to have one central hospital for both the city and county to treat scarlet fever and diphtheria resulted in a running battle from 1920 onwards—agreement could not be reached over a joint committee controlling a central isolation hospital. On the advent of the National Health Service, both the city and county still had their own infectious disease hospital plus a smallpox hospital. The county also provided a tuberculosis sanatorium serving both authorities.

Tupsley Hospital

The Public Health Act of 1875 and subsequent acts made the City Council responsible for controlling infectious diseases and organising treatment for infected persons within the city. The council's Sanitary Committee initially relied on temporary tents situated off Gorsty Lane, in Tupsley, to act as an isolation hospital. They subsequently purchased a prefabricated iron hospital with 12 beds and erected it on the Tupsley site, opening it on 10th May 1893. This was lined with wood and fitted with 'every known convenience', having a ward at either end with nursing and catering facilities in between. There were also apartments for the matron, and equipment and space was provided to disinfect bedding and clothes. It became variously known as the City or Tupsley Infectious Disease or Isolation Hospital.

Tupsley Hospital was administered by the medical officer of health for the city who reported to the Sanitary Committee. He was expected to visit regularly, even when no patients were present, to check on the staff and the state of

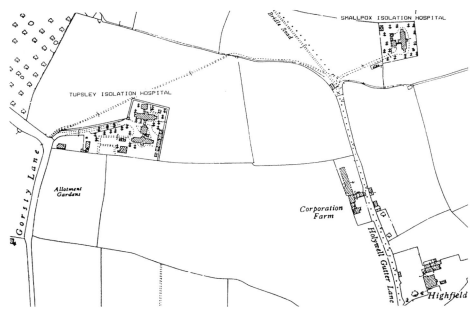

The Tupsley Hospital site off Gorsty Lane,
and the smallpox hospital in Gutter Lane

Tupsley Hospital photographed in 1898.
Notice the carriage in front of the buildings on the left

readiness. Mr Edgar Morris from the General Infirmary was appointed to look after the patients and he served for the first 13 years of the hospital's life.

The first resident staff were John and Beatrice Maillard of Leeds. Mr Maillard acted as master but in practice was the porter and his duties included assisting the medical officer and nurse, transporting patients in the horse drawn ambulance, disinfecting houses in the city and bringing clothes into the hospital for disinfection. His wife was housekeeper and matron as she had some nursing experience. One of them always had to be at the hospital.

There were strict rules for patients. To be admitted they required a medical certificate signed by a doctor. No patient could leave the hospital without a change of clothing unless the clothing used in convalescence had been disinfected. Heavy penalties for disobedience could be enforced by the Sanitary Committee, and its successor in 1910 the Health Committee.

By 1896 more accommodation was required for patients and a further wing, identical to the first, was opened in March 1898 providing another 12 beds. Staff accommodation was increased by erecting a separate iron building with four bedrooms, a bathroom and living room, and a porter's lodge.

In 1902 the Local Government Board, a government agency that liaised with local authorities to ensure that government policies were carried out, recommended that cases of smallpox, which were very infectious, should not be nursed in the same building as other infectious diseases but at least quarter of a mile away. Another prefabricated building was therefore erected at the edge of the

The opening of the second wing in 1898.
Sitting (from left): Alfred Gurney; The Mayor H.C. Beddoe; C. Witts.
Standing: H.T. Williams; James Mitchell; Henry Rogers, Chairman of the
Sanitary Committee; Thomas Turner, surgeon at the General Hospital;
the matron; Alderman Llanwarne, clerk to the Hereford Board of Guardians;
Dr Fitsimons, medical officer of Tupsley Hospital; W. Humphrys, porter

Tupsley site, off Gutter Lane (now Holywell Gutter Lane). It could accommodate 12 patients, but in practice it was only furnished for six and was closed when not in use. A smaller building with two bedrooms was built nearby for staff.

The income to run the hospital came mainly from the rates. Initially patients were charged 7s a week for maintenance and £56 was collected from this source in 1893. In the same year £7 was collected for disinfecting bedding and clothes at the hospital. In 1914 it was decided not to charge for patients who were resident in the city, whilst the army was charged 2 guineas a week if one of their soldiers required admission. Extra staff were hired during outbreaks of scarlet fever or diphtheria; during an outbreak of the latter in 1896 seven nurses and three domestics were temporarily employed. Over the following 13 years the numbers of admissions varied between 12 and 70 each year, due mainly due to outbreaks of scarlet fever or diphtheria. Some of the admissions were made by the medical officer of health, but he encountered the wrath of the General Hospital's medical staff when he removed a patient with typhoid without their permission.

In 1921 the earth closets were replaced by water closets, and the drains were relaid and connected to the main sewers. In the same year electric bells were installed connecting the wards with the matron's room. Initially there were inadequate facilities for carrying out operations and so a second-hand operating table was procured. In 1926 the wards used for treating patients with scarlet fever were heated by hot pipes running from a coke furnace, supplemented in cold weather by tortoise stoves and this system was soon extended to the rest of the hospital. In the 1930s it was agreed that the hospital was inadequate both in its structure and accommodation, but plans to replace it were overtaken by the war.

Miss C. Budinger, who had been appointed temporary matron in 1915, had her appointment made permanent in 1919. Nine years later her nurses made a whole series of complaints against her—that she refused to let them talk to the doctors about the patients, that she discussed them with the patients; that she kept them short of blankets and soap and finally that she wandered about in a red dressing gown which they thought unsuitable. An inquiry supported the matron and several nurses resigned. She herself resigned due to ill-health in 1931, aged 59, and died five months later.

In 1935 a van was purchased for £200 and the porter was told to pass his driving test, for one of his duties was to disinfect houses and bedding in the city of those admitted to the hospital. On one occasion he even disinfected two wards at the General Hospital.

The numbers of patients in the hospital varied between six and 24, as outbreaks of infectious diseases gradually declined. In 1923 there were three cases of smallpox and then none till a single case in 1928 and again the following year. The numbers of patients with scarlet fever admitted varied from 12 to 43 per year and diphtheria from six to 25 per year. The occasional case of typhoid fever continued to be admitted.

Visiting hours were restricted to between 3 and 4 p.m. on Thursdays and Sundays, and to two visitors aged over 16. There must have been some political snooping going on for in 1928 councillors not on the Health Committee were forbidden to visit the hospital without permission.

There is a story told by Jim Thomas who was admitted to the hospital with scarlet fever when 11 years old. 'The ambulance was drawn by a black horse and the man who was the driver, Vaughan, was a lovely chap. He carried me on his back into hospital because I was as nutty as a fruit cake because of the delirium.' Jim developed obstruction to his breathing and had to have a temporary tube inserted into his windpipe by Mr Ian MacGregor. Some years later Mr MacGregor met him and said 'You are lucky to be alive. If I did to you now what I did to you then, I would have been struck of the medical register. But if I hadn't operated, you would have been dead.'

The Second World War resulted in windows being blacked out and small brick built shelters appearing in the grounds. After the war a member of the women's land army helped with the grounds.

Like all hospitals there were repeated salary rises during this period, accompanied by increased charges. Nurses with infectious disease training proved increasingly difficult to recruit and in the autumn of 1947 there was such a shortage of nurses that some patients had to be nursed at home.

The numbers of inpatients at any one time during this period varied between three and 19, and were mainly suffering from scarlet fever or diphtheria. Smallpox had disappeared, scarlet fever was becoming less common and diphtheria was being controlled by prophylactic inoculation. The day of the infectious diseases hospital was passing.

Folly House

At the beginning of the war the Ministry of Health had requisitioned Folly House in Folly Lane, Hereford and given it to the county council to act as additional accommodation for cases of infectious disease. In November 1940 the city council agreed to take it over as a reserve facility for their cases of scarlet fever cases or scabies.

1941 was the busiest year for Folly House. In the first few months the average number of patients was nine with a staff of five, they then coped with an outbreak of scabies when 11 cases were in the hospital at one time. After 1941 it was used very intermittently for scarlet fever and dysentery, and also for the occasional case of meningitis, of which nine such cases were nursed at Folly House. It closed at the end of 1944, as most such cases could then be provided for in the new County Hospital.

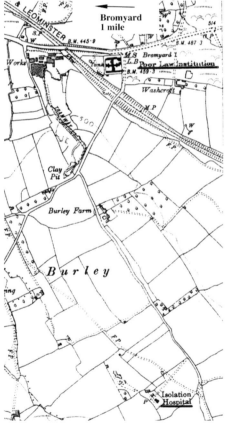

The site of Bromyard Isolation Hospital at Burley, and the Workhouse

Bromyard Isolation Hospital

In 1893 there was an outbreak of smallpox in the workhouse in Bromyard which resulted in the death of Mr Taylor from Sheep Street who had been employed to disinfect the building. Under pressure from both the medical officer for health and the Local Government Board, Bromyard Rural Sanitary Authority established an isolation hospital at Burley 1.5 miles south-east of the town and about half a mile from the workhouse. Called Humble Bee Cottage, it cost £260 and came with five acres of land. A two storey hospital was built for £1,200 adjacent to the cottage with two wards accommodating two beds each on either side of a central nurses' room, behind which was a kitchen and bathroom. Upstairs there were two rooms for convalescent patients. Although four patients were usually accommodated it could cope with eight.

Humble Bee Cottage itself was used as an isolation hospital until the building opened in 1896. It subsequently accommodated the caretaker and when necessary one nurse. The yearly expenses of running the hospital varied between £100 and £200.

In its first 10 years only five to 10 cases were admitted each year, mainly with scarlet fever, and the hospital was often empty. In 1906 there were outbreaks of scarlet fever in Pencombe, Little Cowarne and Ocle Pychard with 22 admissions. Over the next few years the numbers fluctuated, though increasing numbers of cases of diphtheria were admitted. After 1916 admissions decreased and for several years it was empty. However, in 1925 admissions totalled 14.

In 1928 the Joint Committee formed from both Bromyard Rural and Urban districts and which administered the hospital considered closing it, but in 1934

Humble Bee Cottage on the left, and the isolation hospital on the right

Hereford Rural District Council agreed to rent it as the smallpox isolation hospital for the county and be responsible for its repairs.

When the caretaker retired in 1942 her replacement was designated a warden. In the absence of any smallpox cases the hospital continued to be used mainly for scarlet fever and diphtheria cases until nationalised in 1948. There was always a degree of informality about such hospitals and even now patients can recall hens wandering about the wards.

Leominster Borough Isolation Hospital

In 1897 Leominster Town Council leased a house and grounds at Ebnal, off the Kingsland road, with the intention of establishing an isolation hospital. It proved unsuitable and in 1902 a small wood and corrugated iron building was erected adjacent to it at a cost of £280 with three wards accommodating five patients. The original house became the caretaker's cottage.

It was opened in a hurry early in 1903 to accommodate a case of smallpox from the workhouse. There was no permanent nurse and when temporary nurses were employed they lived in the caretaker's house, indeed on one occasion a case of scarlet fever was even nursed by the caretaker in her house. Dr Octavius Edwards, from Leominster was paid a retainer of £10 p.a. to attend the patients.

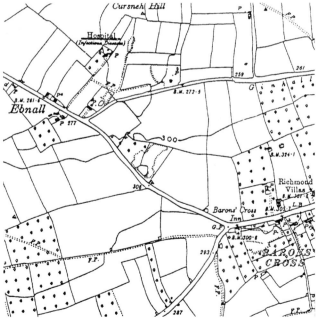

It was often empty but continued to function till 1930 mainly for sporadic cases of scarlet fever and diphtheria. In November 1930, when surveyed by the medical officer of health, it accommodated 10 patients suffering from diphtheria, there being an outbreak in the town, being looked after by two trained but temporary nurses. There was no toilet, no disinfecting room or telephone. The drains

Site of Leominster Borough Isolation Hospital

206

emptied into a cesspit in the grounds. On the positive side, a motor ambulance was available. Unsurprisingly, the building was considered entirely unsuitable for infectious disease cases.

In December it was evacuated and the patients transferred to the building vacated by the Abbeydore Public Assistance Institute which had recently closed—presumably the only suitable facility that could then be found. Four nurses and support staff were provided. By March 1931 an agreement was reached with Hereford Rural District Council for infectious disease cases from Leominster Borough to be admitted to their hospital at Stretton Sugwas. The old hospital has since been demolished but the caretaker's house remains.

Leominster and Wigmore Rural District Isolation Hospital

The stimulus to establish an isolation hospital in the Leominster and Wigmore Rural District followed a case of smallpox at Leintwardine in January 1903. After inspecting 12 sites the council established their isolation hospital at Birtley, 1.5 miles north of Lingen. The inhabitants of Lingen objected strongly to having an isolation hospital on their doorstep, partly because of its inadequate facilities and partly because it was near two busy roads along which cattle were regularly driven. Their pleas were ignored.

The hospital, built of wood and corrugated iron, contained two wards each accommodating two patients,

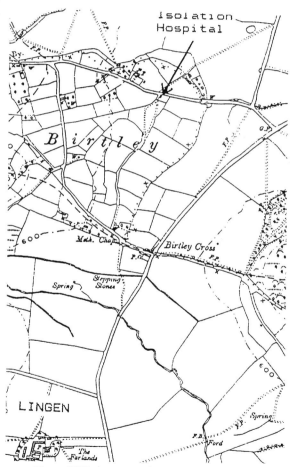

Site of Wigmore and Leominster Rural District Isolation Hospital at Birtley

a day room, two bedrooms for a caretaker and nurse, a small kitchen, larder and outbuildings. There was no indoor sanitation or heating and it was lit by oil lamps. Water had to be brought in. It was opened in 1903 mainly as a smallpox hospital and certainly two such cases were admitted in 1927. The first medical officer was Dr Bower.

When it was inspected in 1930 little seemed to have changed and on the day of inspection the drains were completely choked. The only ambulance consisted of an old cab for which no horse or harness was available. It was soon closed and arrangements made with Hereford Rural District Council to admit future patients to their hospital at Stretton Sugwas. The old hospital was sold for £60 and subsequently upgraded first with wood and then with brick walls to become an idyllic cottage.

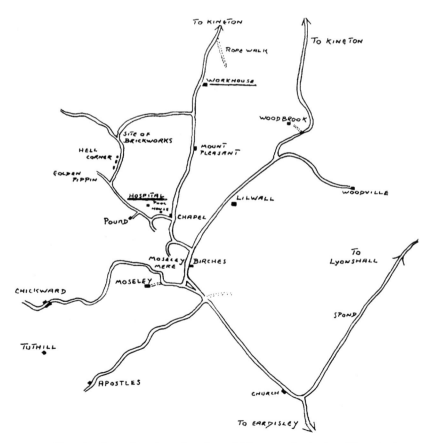

Sketch plan showing the site of Kington Isolation Hospital

Kington Isolation Hospital above, and its kitchen below

Kington Isolation Hospital

In 1906 the Kington Rural and Urban District Councils formed a joint Kington Isolation Hospital Committee. An outbreak of scarlet fever the following year stimulated the committee into leasing a small private house, called Ivy Cottage, at £20 p.a. at Kingswood, near the workhouse. It was a two storey, four roomed house and one of the rooms on the first floor was used as a two bedded ward.

A caretaker and his wife lived in the house and nursed any cases of scarlet fever or diphtheria, although only one type of infection could be treated at a time. During 1909 some 50 cases of scarlet fever were admitted. The caretaker resigned in November 1932, and as the lease expired early the following year, the hospital was closed on 3rd December. A contract was signed with Hereford Rural District Council for them to retain three beds at Stretton Sugwas Hospital for infectious disease cases from the two Kington districts, for a retaining fee of £15 per bed p.a. plus maintenance when they were occupied.

Drybrook and Camp Meadow Isolation Hospitals, Ross

In 1913 members of Ross Rural District Council decided that they required an isolation hospital mainly for the cases of scarlet fever and diphtheria that had appeared in their district. They arranged with a Mrs Greenway who was a tenant of a cottage at Drybrook in the Forest of Dean, Gloucestershire, six miles south-east of Ross, that she would provide a room for two patients and nurse them. As only one room was available it was only possible to treat one

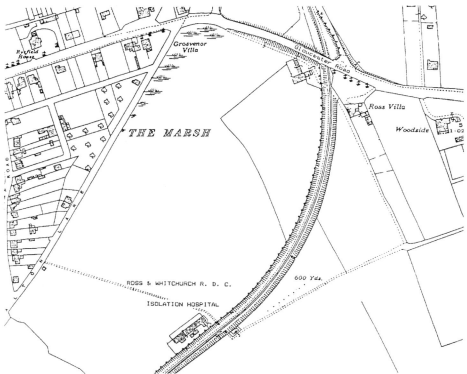

Plan showing the site of the isolation hospital at Camp Meadow, Ross

type of infection at a time. She was paid a retention fee, initially of 3s 6d a week, and a maintenance charge per patient. If the Urban District Council wished to admit a patient they were charged a daily rate for each patient. The hospital, so called, admitted 21 patients between 1919 and 1924 and was often empty. Mrs Geenway's lease was terminated in 1927.

Following the closure the council initially leased and subsequently bought for £100 the old golf club house at Camp Meadow on the Alton Estate from the trustees of Mr Thomas Blake for use as their isolation hospital. They spent £600 in repairs and upgrading the plumbing, heating, cooking and toilet facilities and installing a telephone. The accommodation included two four bedded wards and caretaker's quarters. One of the wards was divided into two to cope with mixed infections.

The Camp Meadow Isolation Hospital opened in 1927 and was inspected each month by a council member. Cases from the Urban District were charged at 4 guineas a week for the first case dropping to 2 guineas if more than two of their cases were in at the same time. Mrs Slater was employed as the resident caretaker and nurse at a retaining fee of 15s a week. In 1932 Nurse Beatrice Haines was appointed as matron and Mrs Slater was kept on as housekeeper. An assistant nurse was occasionally employed as was necessary in November 1934 when there was an outbreak of diphtheria at Gorseley, east of Ross— during two weeks 16 cases were admitted.

The hospital continued to function until January 1936 when an agreement was reached with Hereford Rural District Council that their hospital at Stretton Sugwas would admit local cases of infectious disease. However, it was reopened in the summer for cases of uncomplicated tuberculosis. Around five patients every three months were admitted with an average stay of 63 days. It closed for tuberculosis cases in October 1939 and during the war was used as an isolation hospital for evacuee children suffering from infectious diseases such as whooping cough or measles.

Stretton Sugwas Isolation Hospital

For 10 years prior to 1904 there had been discussion led by Hereford Rural District Council about combining with other authorities to provide a central isolation hospital for infectious diseases, but only Weobley District joined the project.

The hospital was built on 3.5 acres of land between Burghill and Credenhill purchased from Guy's Hospital.

Four separate brick buildings were built, the main one consisting of a central area with a nurses' duty room, and a ward on either side each providing four beds. A small building called a discharge block could be used either as an observation ward, for isolating virulent cases, for convalescence or as a predischarge ward. A third building contained a mortuary, a wash house, a disinfecting room and a coal house. Finally there was a separate administration block with a kitchen, sitting room and four bedrooms. An 80 feet deep well with a wind-mill pump provided a good supply of water, and sewage went to a septic tank.

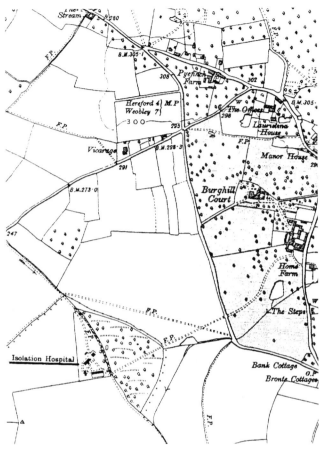

Plan showing the site of the isolation hospital at Stretton Sugwas

An Isolation Hospital sub-committee of seven members was formed, drawn from both councils (Weobley had contracted for two beds) oversaw the hospital's work. The sub-committee duly appointed Dr Herbert Jones, the medical officer of health who had played a major part in setting up the hospital, as non-resident medical superintendent at a salary of £20 p.a., to both administer the hospital and treat the patients. A resident caretaker, Mrs Hyde was appointed to act as housekeeper and cover any nursing duties. Her son Walter was employed as porter.

The hospital was duly opened on 21st September 1904 before a large gathering including the mayor of Hereford and dignitaries from Hereford and Weobley. The hospital was initially created to admit cases of smallpox and scarlet fever, but it was soon agreed that the medical superintendent could use his discretion and admit cases of diphtheria or typhoid fever.

Stretton Sugwas Isolation Hospital. The large building in front of the windpump is the main hospital, with the administrative block in the house to the left

In 1907 the hospital was connected to the telephone system. Over the next two years the link was extended to the caretaker's house, the wards and laundry. In 1917 heating in the wards was improved when new open fire grates in the wards and tortoise stoves were installed.

Most of the expenditure was covered by the rates. Patients were expected to pay towards their maintenance according to their means but this income played a minor roll. Gradually other councils began to appreciate the poor state of their own isolation hospitals, choosing to close them and, like Weobley, contract for beds at Stretton Sugwas.

The medical superintendent would normally treat the patients unless their own medical practitioner wished to attend, calling in specialist medical help as and when necessary. In 1909 Mr Edgar Morris operated on a girl with an infected ear, who was in hospital with scarlet fever, and charged a fee of 3 guineas.

In 1910 Mrs Hyde became ill. Miss A.C. Brennan from The County and City Asylum at Burghill was appointed as a permanent nurse at a salary of £35 p.a. plus rations. She was expected also to act as health visitor and be prepared to help out in other isolation hospitals. With such wide ranging duties it is perhaps not surprising that she only stayed two years. Numerous temporary nurses were employed to help during busy spells. Even so, the average cost of nursing in the three years up to 1920 only came to £55 p.a.

Two further storage tanks for water were provided in 1926, and electricity was installed five years later. With increasing numbers of patients being treated due to taking more people from an ever wider area, a timber pavilion to house 13 beds was added in 1928. Five years later a further pavilion consisting of eight cubicles and two nurses' bedrooms was formally opened by Lord Somers in the presence of the mayors of Hereford and Leominster. A year later the Ministry of Health expressed dissatisfaction with the previous timber pavilion but it was never rebuilt due to the approaching war.

In July 1939 the government advised Hereford Rural District Council that they would be responsible for admitting infectious diseases amongst evacuees, many of whom were children, as well as locally based troops. As these were already arriving a sectional building was urgently purchased from Dore Rural District Council and subsequently known as Dore Ward. A more permanent four roomed building was also built. These additions meant that the hospital could now accommodate 43 patients.

The government thereupon wanted to postpone the expansion, as they had requisitioned Folly House in Hereford instead, and when they heard everything was already in place were reluctant to pay for it. The Hospital Committee were outraged that they should be criticised and hampered when they had met the emergency situation in such a decisive way. They remained outraged for two years.

In March 1922 Dr J.R. Bulman was appointed medical superintendent for the hospital at a retaining fee of £20 p.a. plus 2 guineas for every patient admitted. Dr Ian MacGregor, retained as an E.N.T. advisor at £20 p.a., was also paid 10 guineas per operation, whilst the anaesthetist received 2 guineas. There was a succession of matrons, often only offered temporary appointments as the future of the hospital was being discussed. By the late thirties the supportive nursing staff included a sister, a staff nurse and two probationers.

The hospital was rarely empty during this period, having initially around 5 to 11 inpatients at any one time increasing to around 12 to 23 in the 1930s. The greatest number of scarlet fever inpatients at any one time was 19 and in diphtheria cases it was nine. By October 1939 11 evacuees had already been admitted and treated. But thanks to forward planning, the hospital was never full.

In 1941 a new temporary house was erected for the porter, but it was not until the end of the war that a coal fired boiler and radiators were provided to heat Dore Ward. The same year there were improvements to the sanitary arrangements and a separate bathroom was provided for each ward.

In 1941 the Ministry finally agreed to pay for the additional emergency buildings erected two years previously and for the maintenance of evacuees admitted there. The charges to other authorities for maintenance of their patients rose to 11s 3d per day in 1945 and the total cost of the hospital in its last year as a municipal establishment was £4,995.

The matron, Miss Hacking died in April 1942 after being in the post for 14 years. At this time the nursing staff had expanded to eight nurses—the matron, a sister, a staff nurse, three assistant nurses and two probationers. In 1947 three ward orderlies were also appointed. The domestic staff consisted of a cook, a housemaid, a kitchen maid and two porters.

In 1941 there was a minor outbreak of diphtheria with 22 affected patients in hospital at any one time. Two years later it was scarlet fever with 30 affected patients in hospital. The greatest number in hospital at any one time was 35 patients, and in its 44 years of service no patient was ever turned away.

Nieuport Sanatorium: The Galloping Consumption

In the early part of the twentieth century the spread of tuberculosis was becoming increasingly recognised. When it was associated with rapid progress and loss of weight it was often referred to as the 'Galloping Consumption'. Many cases involved young children under five years of age. From 1908 Public Health Acts placed responsibilities on county councils for the notification of cases of tuberculosis and the provision of facilities for treating them.

Initially Hereford County Council provided inpatient care by contracting for beds in neighbouring counties, and by 1917 were paying £91 p.a. for each of 24 beds in the King Edward VII Memorial Sanatorium at Knightwick in Worcestershire and for 10 beds at Graham Lodge Sanatorium near Stroud in Gloucestershire.

Nieuport Sanatorium

In 1917 they bought the Nieuport Estate at Almeley for £47,500 with the help of a government grant and a loan, to provide a sanatorium for T.B. cases. The property consisted of Nieuport House with stables, cottages, outbuildings and 55 acres of land. Old Castle Farm was part of the property but this was subsequently managed by the Small Holdings Committee of the county council. The house occupies the site of an ancient manor house once the residence of Sir John Oldcastle, Baron Cobham, a leader of the Lollards, who was burnt in chains as a heretic on 25th December 1417.

The county council spent £9,500 to convert the house and stables into a sanatorium with 62 beds—18 for men, 16 for women and 28 for children, though three-fifths of the cost was met by central government grant. A sub-committee of up to 12 members was appointed to supervise the administration of the sanatorium and grounds. For many years Miss Maud Armitage, a member of the county council for the ward of Holmer in Hereford City, was chairman. The sanatorium opened on 29th January 1923 with Dr George Basil Doyne Adams as resident medical superintendent, responsible both for its administration and for providing medical care for the patients. He also had additional commitments in the county attending six tuberculosis dispensaries. His salary was £500 p.a. and he was provided with a clerk.

On opening, the first patients to be admitted were those who had previously been accommodated outside the county. It rapidly filled up and the average annual bed occupancy varied between 50 and 54. The turnover was slow and the duration of stay could vary from 100 to 200 days. Tuberculosis was a killing disease and up to 10 patients might die in any one year.

Most of the patients had tuberculosis of the lungs which was judged curable. Rest, good food and fresh air was the staple management till antituberculous drugs such as Streptomycin became available in 1947. Up to 10 extra patients were often accommodated in huts or shelters in the grounds partly for isolation and partly as fresh air treatment.

Many of the children, who had been in contact with relatives or friends with proven tuberculosis were admitted for observation because they were ill and malnourished but without proof of tuberculosis. Advanced terminal cases of tuberculosis which were not considered curable were if possible not admitted. It was not till 1940 that the new County Hospital provided a unit for such cases.

In the late 1930s a popular treatment for a tuberculous lung was to collapse it by filling the chest cavity with air allowing the lung to rest and heal. This procedure was duly carried out at the sanatorium after they purchased the necessary equipment. Surgery was sometimes necessary for dealing with complications and for this patients would be referred either to the Hereford

General Hospital or to specialist centres such as the Robert Jones and Agnes Hunt Orthopaedic Hospital in Oswestry. In 1934 there was an outbreak of diphtheria; admissions were stopped and 22 children were evacuated and their block used for isolation.

From its opening the children had enjoyed outdoor schooling and a full time teacher was employed. Entertainment was provided by the wireless, with individual headphones and a loudspeaker in the day room, a cinema, a sanatorium magazine and snooker. Regular religious services were held and light work in the garden allowed for fit patients.

The estate generated its own electricity though this soon proved inadequate and a new electric light plant was located in the mortuary. In 1935 a house was built for Dr Adams in the grounds at a cost of £920. Part of the stables were used to house the hospital's one ton Morris motor ambulance, whilst a pony, mower and cart were purchased to cut the extensive lawns. In the 1930s Dr William Ainslie used to bring his mobile X-ray equipment at a cost of 5 guineas, though by the end of the decade X-ray facilities were established on site.

The expense of running the sanatorium for the first 10 years varied between £5,725 and £7,790 p.a., with an average cost of a patient per week varying between £2 and £2 11s 3d. By 1947 annual expenditure had reached £10,000. The county and city councils covered any deficit for patients from their areas, whilst authorities responsible for patients admitted from outside the county were charged according to their contract. At one time nine beds were let to the London County Council. Patients or their relatives were also encouraged to make a contribution depending on their means and this produced £20 to £114 p.a.

Separate accounts were kept for the extensive garden and farm which sold its produce, which included pigs and turkeys, to the sanatorium. The turnover was around £400 p.a.

When Dr Adams resigned in 1942, Dr Vincent Rorison Philip was appointed in his stead. The matrons included Dr Adams' wife who acted as matron till Sister Shanks was appointed in 1942. There were 10 other nursing staff, consisting of a home and ward sister, two staff nurses, two assistant nurses, four inexperienced nurses and one probationer. In 1947 a nursing review advised that 15 nurses were required. Nursing tuberculosis cases was dangerous and over the years three nurses became infected.

The domestic staff were constantly changing and consisted of a cook and four maids. A storeman, engineer and gardeners were also employed. During the war there was no cook for a time and the matron took over. Staff shortages continued after the war, though the cause then was considered to be due to the isolation of the sanatorium and the lack of amenities for the staff such as heating and comfortable chairs in their bedrooms.

By the time the N.H.S. took over, effective drugs were winning the battle against tuberculosis and outpatient care was increasingly used.

CHAPTER 12

The County Hospital

Following the Local Government Act of 1929, Herefordshire County Council took over responsibility from the former Board of Guardians for managing the Hereford Union Workhouse. The workhouse, situated in Union Walk, was promptly renamed the Public Assistance Institute (P.A.I.).

In 1935 the P.A.I. accommodated around 200 inmates, most of whom were aged and infirm paupers. There were also wards for children, non-complicated midwifery and the sick as well as casual wards for tramps and temporary residents. In the grounds there was an isolation block, together with a piggery and extensive gardens where many of the fitter inmates worked. The staff included a master and matron, two staff nurses, six assistant nurses and 18 others. A medical officer and chaplain were in attendance. Around this time two additional male nurses were appointed to cope with 'dirty male cases'.

From 1933 consideration had been given to building a municipal hospital, as the standard of care for the sick in the institute was causing anxiety. Plans were drawn up for a new hospital that would provide the range of services for which the council was responsible—the chronic sick, midwifery, advanced tuberculosis and venereal disease.

Two years later it was agreed, with support from the Ministry of Health, that the hospital should be built on a site the council owned between the institute and the bus station. Additional land at the back of the institute and the proposed new hospital, required for building a nurses' home, was bought for £200 from the Trustees of Johnson's Hospital—six almshouses built in 1863 to provide a home for widows of men who had died in other almshouses in the city. After discussions with the governors of the General Hospital it was agreed that acute cases would not be admitted nor major surgery performed to avoid duplication and competition.

219

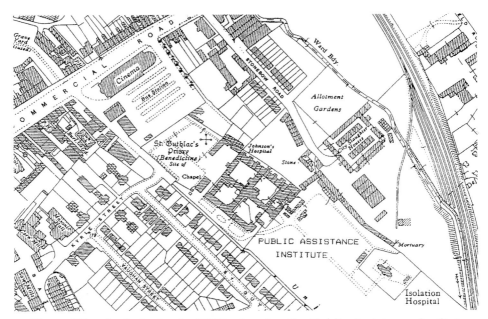

Plan of Hereford city in the 1930s showing the Public Assistance Institute with its Isolation Hospital and Johnson's Hospital

A three storey block was planned to provide accommodation for 115 patients, including advanced cases of tuberculosis. No X-ray department was to be provided because of doubts about its necessity; the main functions of the institute would remain unchanged.

Both the city council and the Hereford Trades Council expressed their concern at having a hospital in the centre of the city that included wards for tuberculosis cases. The county council's Public Health Committee, responsible for planning the new hospital, insisted that best advice, medically and architecturally, had been obtained and the risks were minimal. However, anxieties continued to be voiced over the next few years.

The Ministry of Health approved the plans in May 1936 and the following year Messrs S.W. Bowers & Co. were given the contract to build the hospital at a cost of £68,836 which would be financed by a loan. It was to be called the Herefordshire County Council Hospital, more commonly the County Hospital.

Arrangements for Queen Mary to visit Hereford on the 29th July 1937 and lay the foundation stone of the hospital were planned well ahead. This was just as well as the route and welcome was altered by the city council to allow the mayor and corporation to show her more of the city before arriving at the site of the ceremony.

The War Years

In April 1939 the Ministry of Health proposed that in the event of war the still to be completed hospital, which was considered to be in a relatively safe area, should become part of the Emergency Medical Service (E.M.S.) and have its accommodation increased by 336 beds with the erection of 10 wooden and corrugated iron hutted wards. Officers quarters, a modern operating theatre and X-ray facilities would also be required for which the government would bear the extra cost.

Captain Lionel Havelock Green

It was pointed out that the Royal Ordnance Munitions Factory lay just across the River Wye in Rotherwas and was a possible enemy target. Also, concern was expressed at the annual loss of £200 of produce grown on the land where the huts were to be erected. Nevertheless, by June the Ministry had confirmed their intentions, allowing the county council to run the expanded establishment, whilst participating in policy decisions, the appointment of senior medical staff and controlling the use of the huts, including providing most of their staff. A new management sub-committee, The Hospital Management Committee (H.M.C.), was established with Capt. Lionel Green of the Whittern, Lyonshall, as chairman. As time progressed this committee tended to report to the full county council via the council's medical officer of health.

The Ministry's intervention dramatically altered the whole project. Under the previous plans the institute would have continued to function, but now its accommodation was to provide support facilities for the huts and new hospital. The provision of a modern theatre and an X-ray department meant that the new hospital would have the potential for treating acute cases including major surgery which, if developed, would compete with the services at the General Hospital.

Aerial view of the County Hospital. In the distance on the top left is the bus station, then the New Block with the nurses' home to the right. The old P.A.I. is on the near side of the New Block with the huts in the foreground. The isolation hospital is to the right of the huts

In May 1940 it was agreed that a medical superintendent would be appointed who would combine the duties of hospital administrator and senior medical officer. Dr Walter Ogilvie Reed was duly appointed and in November moved into quarters prepared for him in the institute. Early administrative appointments included a clerk and steward at a salary of £220 p.a. and a clerk for the matron. Within two years the clerical staff had increased to five.

Early in 1943 the Hospital Management Committee wished to establish outpatient facilities to follow up and treat their inpatients, to see patients referred by their practitioner for X-ray or physiotherapy and to treat minor injuries to their staff. The representatives of the General Hospital opposed this as it would duplicate services and was contrary to the original agreement. The committee agreed to refer the disagreement to the medical inspectors from the Ministry who were surveying hospital services. Meanwhile the county council ordered the committee to go ahead and provide outpatient facilities to all county residents.

A meeting was held in December with the medical inspectors. They advised that the separation of acute and chronic cases between the two hospitals was undesirable both for patients and nurse training and recommended that there should be co-operation in the nursing services, in the division of services and that there should be a common consultant staff. The County Hospital was on the way to becoming a general hospital, although many of the recommendations had to await the appearance of the National Health Service in 1948.

The first of the huts, then simply numbered 1 to 10, were admitting patients by August 1940 and the rest were open by the end of the year. The pathway between the fronts of the huts was roofed over but the sides were open. Heating to the huts was provided by open stoves and initially only one telephone was provided for every two huts. A paltry two sandbags were allowed per hut and alarm bells were available in every second hut and two along the covered way. A portable X-ray unit and a temporary operating theatre was provided in one of the huts until the main facilities were available in the new building. The huts were built to last 10 years, but are still being fully used in the late 1990s.

While the Ministry had priority in the use of the huts, the numbers of service personnel admitted fluctuated wildly and they were often available for civilian purposes. In September 1941 seven of the huts were temporarily occupied by Herefordshire patients and Huts 9 and 10 were used for nursing accommodation. Other huts were used for physiotherapy, rehabilitation, as accommodation for sick nurses and occasionally one was available for dances and Christmas parties.

The number of inmates in the institute had decreased to around 100 by the autumn of 1940 and most were then transferred to institutes in Weobley,

The wooden and corrugated hutted wards, each measuring 144ft by 24ft

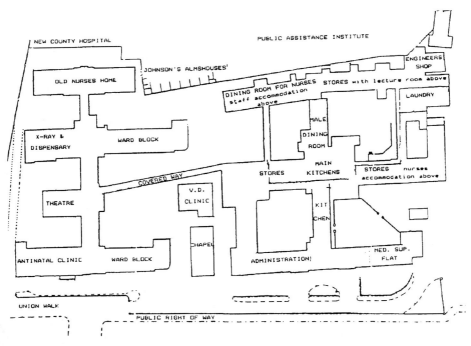

Ground floor plans of the upgraded P.A.I. and the new County Hospital block

Leominster and Ross. The casual wards were the last to close in April 1941. A few old workhouse patients were allowed to remain. One of these was Mr Skuse who used to run errands to the town for his favourite staff and, having read their newspapers, returned with his pockets bulging with precious cigarettes. When he finally died several thousand pounds were found under his mattress. Another inmate, Bert, had a small greenhouse and loved to hand out flowers and luscious tomatoes to the nurses.

The staff of the institute were either retrained and offered alternative posts or were given notice to terminate their employment. Unfortunately the master, Mr F.W. Thomas, took his own life. His wife who had been the matron initially became the laundry superintendent and subsequently was put in charge of the kitchens, becoming the domestic matron, before she retired and remarried in 1942. The engineer, gardener and stokers were kept on.

The institute contained 69 bedrooms and sitting rooms and required considerable modification. The central boiler house was sited there as were the main kitchens. The alterations included the creation of a superintendent's house, a sitting room and bedroom for a senior medical officer, bed-sitting rooms for the junior medical officers and a common dining room. Offices and storage facilities were made available for a military registrar and up to 11 of his staff. Residential accommodation was provided for nurses and maids, along with shared dining rooms, sitting rooms, recreation rooms and a lecture hall. There were offices for the clerks, a laundry and general storage rooms.

During the initial upheavals there was a lack of midwifery accommodation and it was decided to keep open one of the old midwifery wards until the new ward opened in June. The General Hospital also agreed to provide temporary facilities for 12 non-complicated cases among non-destitute county residents whose homes were unsuitable for childbirth. Complicated midwifery had been dealt with at the General Hospital since they built their new unit in 1931 under an agreement with the county council.

The new part of the hospital, subsequently called the '1930 block', opened in stages between January and September 1941. The modern operating theatre on the ground floor opened first, initially to serve the patients in the huts, with the room opposite being used as an anaesthetic room. At the same time an adjacent ward opened to temporarily accommodate E.M.S. surgical patients.

The ward which subsequently housed male patients and children with E.N.T. problems, was named after the famous Shakespearian actor David Garrick who was born in 1717 at the Angel Inn, at the junction of Maylord Street and

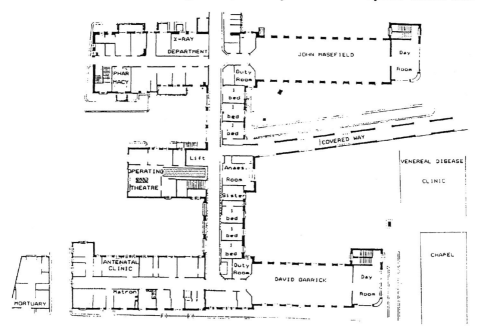

Ground floor plan of the 1930 Block

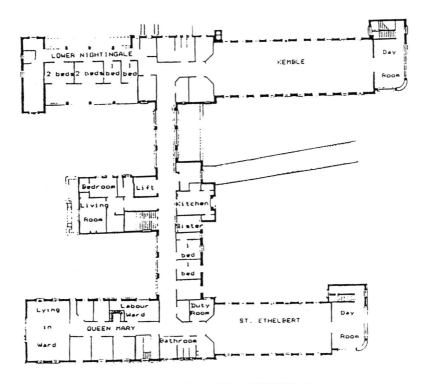

First floor plan of the 1930 Block

Widemarsh Street. The next ward to open was called John Masefield Ward, (male surgical), after the Poet Laureate who was born in Ledbury in 1878. Also on the ground floor was the midwifery clinic, a venereal disease clinic and the pharmacy. The provision of the X-ray department allowed the county council to close their local dispensaries for tuberculosis and let the patients attend the hospital dispensary where X-rays could be taken on the first visit.

On the first floor Kemble Ward, (male medical), was named after St John Kemble who was martyred for his faith on Widemarsh Common in 1679 and whose hand is still preserved in St Francis Xavieur's Church in Broad Street. St Ethelbert Ward, (maternity), was named after King Ethelbert who was martyred near Moreton-on-Lugg in 792 and in whose name Hereford Cathedral was rebuilt. Queen Mary's Ward, (maternity), was named after the queen who laid the hospital's foundation stone. The midwifery wards opened in May and by June were sharing complicated cases with the General Hospital. Nightingale Ward, (tuberculosis & midwifery isolation), was on two floors and named after Florence Nightingale who did so much to enhance the training and status of nurses.

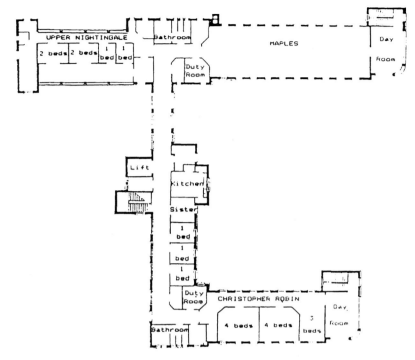

Second floor plan of the 1930 Block

On the second floor Maples Ward, (female surgical), was named after Dr E.W. Maples, the chairman of the planning committee which had promoted the idea of the hospital. His friends and colleagues had great difficulty in persuading him to allow his name to be used. The front ward was called Christopher Robin after A.A. Milne's mythical character in *Winnie the Pooh* and naturally accommodated children.

The nurses' home was on three floors and accommodated 30 nurses in single rooms and provided kitchens, laundry and storage facilities. The new hospital finally ended up with 140 beds, plus nominally 336 beds in the huts, though that number was never achieved.

The city's mortuary, which handled about 30 cases a year, was in a single room at the abattoir in Stonebow Road, adjacent to the new hospital, and it was agreed that the city council could share the planned mortuary at the hospital, which had three rooms and a lavatory, at a cost £25 p.a.

Air raid precautions were strictly enforced. Blackout fittings were required for 462 windows, doors and skylights, and on one occasion the medical super-intendent was summoned before the bench and the hospital was fined for allowing a light to be left showing. Air raid shelters were dug. There was a rota for volunteer fire watchers who had to climb a ladder onto the flat roof of the hospital from where they could view the entire complex.

After the huts were built there was was a drastic reduction in the land suitable for cultivation. However, there was still a piggery to use up any swill and supply food for the hospital, especially at Christmas, while the shrunken garden still required a pony and cart. Early in the war the head gardener, called Horace, was the oldest employee, a typical Herefordian, who in his spare time acted as a special constable and sang in a church choir. He requested four assistants but was awarded one. The pony was 30 years old and constantly featured in the hospital reports being prone to bolting, injury, canker of the feet and swelling of the stomach, requiring repeated convalescent rest periods. It was nearly sold several times before being reprieved. In 1943 a special committee was set up to consider its future and agreement was finally reached to it being sold for slaughter. The gardens were later used to grow soft fruit and accommodate bees.

After the war the Ministry reimbursed the council for the running costs of the huts, but most of the cost of maintaining the hospital came from the rates. Civilian patients or their relatives were expected to contribute up to 4 guineas a week towards maintenance depending on their means. Patients in the General

1930 Block	
Ground Floor wards	
John Masefield	25
David Garrick	20
First Floor wards	
Kemble	18
Nightingale (isolation)	6
Queen Mary	7
St Ethelbert	21
Second Floor wards	
Maples	22
Christopher Robin	24
Nightingale (sick staff)	6
TOTAL:	149
Hutted wards	
Hut 1 (outpatients & physiotherapy)	
Hut 2 Children s ward	26
Hut 3 Rehabilitation	
Hut 4 Male Medical	24
Hut 5 Female Medical	24
Huts 6, 7, & 8 Chronic sick wards	70
Huts 9 & 10 Nurses accommodation	40
TOTAL:	184
GRAND TOTAL:	333

Table 19 Accommodation in the County Hospital in 1945

Hospital's contributory scheme were charged a fee of 30s which was soon raised to £3. The L.M.S. Railway Fund also paid £3 per inpatient irrespective of the length of treatment.

Dr Ogilvie Reid, as medical superintendent, was in clinical control of the other medical officers which was the custom in municipal hospitals. He was also the tuberculosis officer for the hospital and as an E.N.T. specialist he also ran this service. His great reputation as a specialist resulted in the hospital becoming one of the top five E.N.T. centres outside London. But in March 1945 he returned to Birmingham, though continuing to attend the hospital on a weekly basis to provide an E.N.T. service. There were seven candidates interviewed for the vacant post of medical superintendent before Mr Pat Brown, aged 39, was appointed.

Mr Pat Brown,
Medical Superintendent

Doctors holding any of the three assistant medical appointments changed rapidly during the war and vacancies were often temporarily filled from the county's Health Department or the staff from the R.A.F. camp at Credenhill. No permanent appointments of visiting staff made during the war; Dr Ainslie and Mr Scholefield were appointed annually as county consultant obstetrician and deputy. The medical superintendent was authorised to seek specialist help when necessary, usually from the General Hospital or from Birmingham.

The pharmacist Mr Horace Clansey had been trained in Birmingham and before the war worked in a new acute 250 bedded hospital in Southend-on-Sea, which was rapidly evacuated because of the threat of bombing and invasion. At that time pharmacists were on a wartime list protecting them from being called up so he was glad to escape to rural Hereford. He started work in November 1940 in the P.A.I. at a salary of £200 p.a. and the following year moved into the pharmacy in the new block. His reprieve was only temporary, for he was called upon to join the services in 1943.

Miss Catherine Wheeler

In June 1940, Miss L.A. Worley Johnson was appointed from amongst 61 candidates as matron at a salary of £250 p.a. plus emoluments. She was in charge of nursing and the domestic side, apart from the huts, which were initially mainly staffed and run by the military. In July the following year, she tended her resignation due to the strain of running and organising the new hospital and was replaced by Miss Catherine Wheeler. The rest of the nursing staff had begun to be appointed in the autumn of 1940 by the superintendent and the matron, and a staffing establishment was agreed in 1941. However, these numbers were never reached partly because the hospital was never full and partly because there was great competition for female labour from the munitions factory. Even so, by July 1941 the new hospital had 34 permanent nurses consisting of 15 trained nurses and 19 probationers. The huts were staffed with 85 nurses from the Civil Nursing Reserve consisting of 20 trained nurses, 25 assistant nurses and 40 auxiliary nurses. By early autumn the training school for nurses was recognised by the General Nursing Council.

A great source of interest to the nurses was inspecting plasters on the limbs of wounded soldiers to see if the signature of Mr Wood Power, one of the surgeons from Hereford serving in northern France prior to Dunkirk, was inscribed. They remained disappointed.

A part-time masseuse trained in massage and electrical therapy initially functioned from Hut 2 where radiant heat baths and electrical therapy formed the nucleus of a physiotherapy department. She attended a course on occupational therapy and in 1944 the old isolation ward in the grounds was provided with an electrical supply and telephone to become an occupational therapy department. An occupational therapist was then appointed with the Ministry providing the equipment. Physiotherapists, who were more extensively trained and registered with the Chartered Society of Physiotherapists, were soon

Hutted wards	
Sisters	8
Staff Nurses	24
Assistant Nurses	25
Nursing Auxiliaries	37
TOTAL:	94

1930 Block, General Nursing	
Assistant Matron	1
Sister Tutor	1
Home Sister	1
X-ray and Theatre Sister	1
Night Sister	1
Ward Sisters	8
Staff Nurses	13
Night Charge Nurse	1
Probationers	46
TOTAL:	73

1930 Block, Midwifery	
Sister in Charge	1
Staff Midwives	4
Probationers	8
TOTAL:	13

Supportive Staff	
Masseuse	1
Almoner	1
Domestics	40
Laundry staff	11
Sewing Maids	3
Other Maids	36
Daily Cleaners	11
Porters	6
Gardeners	2
Engineers	2
Stokers	4

Table 20 Staff establishment in 1941

replacing masseuses, and by 1945 there were two part-time physiotherapists at the County.

Miss R. Phillips was appointed as almoner. Almoners were the future social workers and played an increasingly important role, their work including some 1,250 office interviews a year, giving advice to patients, collecting payments from and old age pensions for patients, attending to the provision of dentures and surgical appliances ordered by the medical staff and placing a number of single girls with babies in domestic employment. By 1945 there were two part-time almoners.

In January 1941 the Management Committee approached local churches to nominate chaplains, which they hoped would be honorary. The history of the General Hospital should have warned them that they would not get away so lightly and not surprisingly the Rev. Preb. C.E. Warner, the Rural Dean insisted that the Anglican Chaplain would be almost full time and should be offered a salary. The committee asked him to reconsider as the Free Churches and Roman Catholic Church were prepared to provide honorary chaplains. Eventually £150 was allocated on the proportion of three shares to the Church of England and one each to the others. The non-denominational chapel would be shared.

Admission to the hospital came from several sources. Wounded or sick servicemen and civilian evacuees were admitted, usually to the huts, on the authority of the Ministry. The wounded had already had their initial treatment elsewhere. Local civilian patients were admitted by referral from their general practitioner. Some elderly and infirm patients, who previously would have been referred to the P.A.I. could be admitted under the poor law. Suitable cases of tuberculosis would also be referred.

The first patients arrived in October 1940 and included 51 aged and infirm evacuees from London and 112 service personnel. There were few civilian evacuees after this while the convoys of wounded soldiers fluctuated wildly. At first there was a special train stationed in Hereford to transport the wounded and it was used after the evacuation of Dunkirk. Subsequently it was withdrawn and convoys were brought from the railhead at Worcester. In September 1943, 200 wounded soldiers were admitted from the Eighth Army in Italy and between May and August 1944 nine convoys arrived from Western Europe. By 1945 most of the huts were occupied by chronic sick. Further wounded arrived early that year causing a crisis necessitating the transfer of some of the chronic cases to convalescent homes, such as Brockhampton Manor, or even family homes. The last convoys appeared in May and included a large number of repatriated prisoners of war.

Operations were regularly performed. Some of these were carried out on the wounded, but many of the new recruits at the R.A.F. camp at Credenhill and the army barracks at Bradbury Lines, in Hereford, required operations to correct defects such as ruptures or varicose veins to make them fit for service. The operations were normally performed either by the hospital doctors or honorary staff from the General Hospital, though a few major procedures required a specialist from Birmingham.

Twice a week there were tuberculosis clinics. There were sporadic outbreaks of meningitis and these cases were admitted to the County Hospital where 'Iron lungs'—often called the Old Nuffield Lungs, as they were donated by Lord Nuffield—were available for those who were temporarily unable to breathe due to paralysed muscles.

By 1943 more accommodation was required to allow for childbirth in hospital as the number had increased by nearly a third in the previous year, resulting in 408 hospital deliveries, about a quarter of the deliveries in the county. Kemble Ward was made available by transferring the medical patients to the huts. In the following year county council policy decreed that all maternity patients should stay in hospital for 14 days, but due to accommodation problems this was rapidly relaxed to 10 days.

From its inception the Management Committee had arranged a rota of visitors from a list of volunteers who were to visit each month, interest themselves in the welfare of the patients and listen to any complaints. Most of the complaints were about the food. Many of the resident staff have memories of dried eggs, frozen Australian rabbit, whale meat steaks and snoek, a type of fish found off South Africa and in Australasia. To try and increase palatability the staff 'dug for victory' around the hospital buildings, whilst tomatoes were grown in Maples Ward.

The Post War Years
By the autumn of 1945 plans were formed to adapt the County Hospital to civilian needs. It was soon decided to make the County Hospital into a general hospital dealing with acute and chronic conditions; the General Hospital had by now accepted that the County would take on acute cases and there was increasing co-operation between the two.

In March 1946 the Ministry gave up any claim to the huts and the Management Committee were able to reorganise the use of the hospital buildings. Hut 1 was used for outpatient clinics, including antenatal and the physiotherapy department. Hut 2 became a children's ward and included orthopaedic cases while Hut 3 provided rehabilitation and a child guidance clinic. Huts 4 and 5 became acute male and female wards while Huts 6, 7 and 8, were used for chronic cases. Huts 9 and 10 were cubicalised and used for nurse accommodation.

On the ground floor of the 1930 block the antenatal clinic had been transferred leaving an admission room and a dental room. The remaining space was occupied by administration. David Garrick became a female medical ward and John Masefield a male ward. Early in 1947 there was anxiety that the male patients in John Masefield were too near the nurses' home so the patients and the name of the ward were swapped with David Garrick Ward. E.N.T. cases would be accommodated in the adult and children's wards.

On the first floor maternity accommodation was increased by using Kemble Ward for this purpose and Lower Nightingale for isolation cases. This provided 46 maternity beds. Another labour ward was provided by converting a large linen cupboard while a guest room was used as a preparation room with a sterilizer. On the second floor the only changes were in Upper Nightingale which was set aside for sick staff.

The old institute buildings provided mainly administrative facilities. However, the upper floor adjacent to the front drive was converted into a Public Health Laboratory which previously had been located in the council building in Bath Street. It was funded by the Medical Research Council. Quarters were also allocated to house the nursing school.

The first fully trained orthopaedic surgeon, Mr Brian Thomas was appointed in 1947 to work at both hospitals and at the Royal Orthopaedic Hospital in

Oswestry at a salary of £700p.a. Later that year Dr William H.J. Baker (Billy) was appointed clinical pathologist to the County Public Health Laboratory service with commitments to both hospitals.

By 1948 there were five resident officers. In 1945 Dr Peter Devlin was appointed senior resident medical officer and deputy medical superintendent. Dr Thomas F. Heavey was appointed as a house surgeon in 1946 and subsequently developed an interest in anaesthesia.

In January 1946 the number of nurses employed totalled 120 which included 43 from the civil nursing reserve. The numbers in this last category steadily decreased as they were replaced by permanent nurses. In a more liberal climate it was agreed that coloured nurses would be taken on and up to 12 male student nurses were also appointed. By 1948 the ancillary departments had expanded, resulting in the employment of two radiographers and three physiotherapists. There were 13 porters, five cooks and some 62 varied domestics. The total staff numbered 151.

Dr Peter Devlin who was appointed senior resident medical officer and deputy medical superintendent in September 1945

Unsurprisingly the cost of maintaining the hospital was rising, that per patient even more dramatically as the average bed occupancy had dropped, in part due to the ending of the war, and in part due to local reluctance to go to the County as opposed to the long-standing General. The average bed occupancy for the year to March 1947 was 173. Of these 143 were Herefordshire County Council cases, eight were from the city, three were from other local authorities and just 19 were still the responsibility of the Ministry. Prejudice against the County Hospital, because it had arisen from the old workhouse, was to continue for over the next two decades and perhaps accounts for so few patients being admitted from the city.

General Medicine
Dr Charles Walker, M.C., M.A., M.D., M.B., B.Ch.
Dr Odie Robey, F.R.C.P.

General Surgery
Mr R. Wood Power, B.A., M.B., Ch.B., B.A.O., D.P.H., F.R.C.S.I.
Mr B.G. Scholefield, M.A., D.M., M.Ch., F.R.C.S.
Mr Geoffrey M. Housden, M.B., B.Ch., L.R.C.P., F.R.C.S.
Prof. S.G. Barlings, M.S., M.B., B.S., M.Ch., F.R.C.S., M.R.C.S., L.R.C.P. (Birm.)

Radiology
Dr Malcolm M. Melrose, M.R.C.S., L.R.C.P.

Radiotherapy
Dr John F. Bromley, M.B., Ch.B., M.R.C.P., F.F.A., D.M.R.E. (Birm.)

Thoracic Surgery
Mr Wynne Edwards, M.B., B.Ch., F.R.C.S. (Birm.)
Mr A.L. d'Abreu Ch.M., F.R.C.S. (Birm.)

Neuro-Surgery
Mr Wylie McKissock, M.B., B.S., M.R.C.S., L.R.C.P., F.R.C.S., M.S. (Birm.)

E.N.T. Surgery
Mr W. Ogilvie Reid, M.A., B.Sc., M.B., Ch.B., F.R.C.S
Mr G.G. Airley, M.R.C.S., L.R.C.P. (Ledbury)
Mr Ian W. MacGregor, M.B., Ch.B.

Psychiatry
Dr T. Burrows, B.A., M.R.C.S., L.R.C.P., D.P.M.

Opthalmology
Mr A.H. Richardson, M.R.C.S., L.R.C.P., D.O.M.S.

Paediatrics
Sir Leonard Parsons, F.R.S., M.D., M.B., B.S., F.R.C.P., F.R.C.O.G. (Birm.)

Orthopaedics
Mr G.P. Mills, M.B., B.S., M.R.C.S., L.R.C.P., F.R.C.S. (Worcester)
Mr F.B. Thomas, B.A., M.B., B.S., M.R.C.S., L.R.C.P.

Pathology
Dr William H.J. Baker, M.B., B.S., M.R.C.S., L.R.C.P.

Table 21 Part time appointments of visiting staff, 1945-48

Nevertheless, the County Hospital had turned into a general hospital with over 300 beds and was well equipped to join the General Hospital in providing Herefordshire with its future hospital services.

CHAPTER 13

One Family 1948 - 1959

The surviving voluntary hospitals—the Herefordshire General Hospital, the four cottage hospitals, and the Victoria Eye Hospital—together with the eight municipal hospitals—the Hereford County and City Mental Hospital, Holme Lacy Hospital, the five isolation hospitals and the Hereford County Hospital—were nationalised on 5th July 1948. They then came under the authority of the Herefordshire Hospital Management Committee, (H.H.M.C.), itself responsible to the Birmingham Regional Hospital Board. In addition the P.A.I.s in Bromyard and Ross were nationalised and came under the H.H.M.C.

The hospitals were divided into six groups, each with a House Committee, which had little authority, but reported to the H.H.M.C. One of the groups oversaw the three acute hospitals in Hereford City and another the two Psychiatric Hospitals. Four of the House Committees covered the cottage hospitals in the market towns. The Leominster House Committee were responsible for the P.A.I. at Bromyard and the Ross House Committee was also responsible for the P.A.I. at Ross. An example of the house committees' impotence was when the Ross House Committee required the permission of the H.H.M.C. to purchase an extra long bed in their cottage hospital for a patient who was 6 foot 7 inches tall. The P.A.Is at Kingswood Hall, Kington, the Priory, Leominster and Belle Orchard, Ledbury remained with the county council to largely provide social welfare services, though the H.H.M.C. had access to beds at Kingswood Hall and the Priory for the chronically sick.

The Birmingham Regional Hospital Board laid down the general policies to be followed, appointed the senior medical staff and had to be consulted on any significant new expense or building project. Major changes in facilities and their use required the additional approval of the Ministry of Health. The

237

Mr Dennis Edmunds

H.H.M.C. itself consisted of 21 members appointed by the Board and drawn from Hereford, Kington, Ledbury, Leominster and Ross, five of whom were doctors, three consultants and two general practitioners who had hospital appointments. They were appointed for their expertise and not as representatives, and all were unpaid 'volunteers'. The Chairman was Capt. Lionel Green, the previous Chairman of the County Hospital Management Committee, and the secretary Mr Dennis Edmunds, previously an assistant secretary at the Board in Birmingham.

The tasks of the H.H.M.C. included supervising the running of all the hospitals, rationalising the services provided by the previously independent hospitals, and planning and providing the future services required by the district, all within the Board's guidelines.

The central administration was initially housed at the County in Hut 4, and within four years had expanded to 58 people of all grades. In 1956 it was transferred to Victoria House, adjacent to the Victoria Eye Hospital, which had previously been the house occupied by the honorary ophthalmic surgeon.

Early in 1949 the H.H.M.C. obtained the approval of the Board to designate a certain number of beds as amenity or private beds but this was only approved by the Ministry in 1950 and was modified again two years later. Amenity beds allowed a patient to pay a little extra for a single or double room, yet get the rest of the treatment free, whilst the full maintenance fee was charged for a private bed in a single room. In 1949 plans were agreed to upgrade the public health laboratories at the County. Four years later mass radiography was established in Herefordshire mainly to diagnose tuberculosis of the lungs at an early stage. At this time an animal house was approved mainly to help in the diagnosis of tuberculosis—some specimens from patients suspected of being infected with tuberculosis required to be cultured by injecting them into guinea pigs which were killed some weeks later and examined for tuberculosis lesions.

Maternity facilities remained scattered. Of the 63 lying in beds, 48 were at the County, eight at the General and seven in old P.A.I.s in Bromyard, Leominster and Ross. By 1951 all this provision was finally brought together at the County, leaving just the General Practitioners' Maternity Unit at the General.

The H.H.M.C. also found itself were several non-hospital facilities. There were farms at the Mental Hospital, Burghill and Holme Lacy which they either rented out or continued to run. Piggeries had proved very popular as the pigs could be fattened on hospital swill and later slaughtered to improve the hospital diet. The piggery at Burghill ran to 120 sows and was allowed to continue while the others gradually closed as swill became less available and hygiene more important. All the hospitals had gardens. There were six gardeners at the Mental Hospital, 11 at Holme Lacy and three at the County. In 1954 a gardening competition between 13 hospitals was held. The section for hospitals with full-time gardeners was won by Holme Lacy and that for part-time gardeners by Leominster Hospital. A cricket pitch was preserved at Burghill for the use of the staff of the district.

The total expenditure for the Group in the year to March 1951 was £459,000. Prices kept increasing by 10 to 15 per cent a year, as salaries subject to central negotiations moved upwards, most services expanded and new ones appeared. By the year to March 1959 total expenditure reached £784,925, an increase of 71 per cent over nine years. Annual income from amenity beds brought in around £6,000 and private beds around £5,000 and remained relatively static.

When the N.H.S. came into being, all general endowments and the majority of the existing funds of voluntary hospitals across the country were transferred to an N.H.S. fund which reached £20,000,000. The income from this fund was then redistributed and the H.H.M.C.'s share was around £2,000 p.a. Trust Funds given for specific purposes had been retained by individual hospitals, and in Herefordshire included funds relating to the General Hospital, the Lunatic Aid Fund, the Bull Convalescent Fund, the Venn Fund in Aid of Incurables and the Samaritan Fund. Likewise income from the Stanley Holloway Fund continued to be available for Leominster District Hospital, the Victoria Eye Hospital and the General Hospital. In addition, new legacies for a hospital could be retained by the hospital concerned.

Consultants and senior hospital medical officers (S.H.M.O.s) were appointed by the Board to the Group and not to individual hospitals, whilst the H.H.M.C. appointed junior staff and general practitioners to relevant hospitals. Chaplains from the Church of England, the Roman Catholic and Free Churches were appointed to cover all the hospitals at a cost of £773, £45 and £130p.a. respectively.

In 1952 the numbers of nurses employed throughout the group was 348 which had risen to 534 by December 1958. In 1958 nurse's hours were reduced to an 88 hour fortnight except for female mental nurses where there was an acute shortage of applicants. It was only in 1958 that the first qualified social worker in the county was appointed and began to replace almoners.

After several years of discussion between the Board and Herefordshire County Council a plan was agreed upon to handle major accidents that involved large numbers of casualties. There were several exercises with fake casualties, but to everyone's relief no real disasters materialised.

In the year to March 1950 a total of 45,506 treatments were given across Herefordshire to 2,882 patients. There were 1,518 beds available with an average bed occupancy of 1,289. Inpatient operations totalled 3,898. The number of outpatients seen was 22,282 of whom 2,503 were operated on. More concern was being shown for patients' welfare resulting in appointment systems being introduced to avoid excessive waiting times. Staff were also encouraged to explain a patient's illness and treatment with them, while the comfort of inpatients was given more attention. All hospital wards were provided with radio and television.

County (general)	163
County (midwifery)	18
General	93
Stretton Sugwas	12
Tupsley	10
Victoria Eye	10
Ledbury Cottage	10
Leominster District	11
Kington Cottage	8
Ross Cottage	6
Bromyard (chronic)	17
Alton Street, Ross (learning disability)	54
Burghill Mental	104
Holme Lacy	18
TOTAL:	**534**

Table 22 Nursing establishment at 31st December 1958

The Central Hospitals
The necessity for rationalising the service was greatest in the hospitals run by the Central House Committee. The isolation hospitals were duplicated and being used less and less—no cases of smallpox had been isolated since 1930, diphtheria was being controlled by inoculation and scarlet fever was fast disappearing. It was therefore agreed that Stretton Sugwas Hospital would accept any cases of infectious disease, other than smallpox, requiring isolation. With the numbers of infectious cases still dropping the hospital increasingly accepted convalescent cases and later a few chronic sick.

Tupsley Infectious Disease Hospital stopped admitting infectious disease cases in 1951. Instead, with Board approval, it admitted patients with tuberculosis of the lungs, plus other lung conditions and some chronic sick.

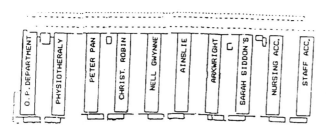

Plan of the hutted wards in 1956-9 showing the huts with their names

In May 1948 the Ministry planned to close Nieuport Sanatorium. Treatment of tuberculosis by antibiotics had resulted in a reduction of the disease and most cases could be treated as outpatients. But some capacity was still needed and as the new sanatorium, St Wulstans at Malvern, was not yet ready to accept cases, Nieuport Sanatorium was temporarily run by the N.H.S. till it closed in 1952. Most of its patients were then transferred to St Wulstan's with some going to Tupsley Hospital.

The smallpox hospitals at Tupsley and Bromyard were closed in 1949. The fabric of Tupsley Hospital was kept in repair up to 1960 to allow it to reopen if required but this was never necessary.

In 1951 the hutted wards at the County were upgraded and converted. Hut 1 continued to be the outpatient department while Hut 2 was occupied by the physiotherapy department. Huts 5 and 6 were temporarily used for orthopaedics while Huts 7 and 8 were used for chronic sick. Huts 9 and 10 accommodated nurses and some domestic staff. The corridor between the huts was gradually enclosed during the 1950s as money became available, but it was not until the late 1950s that the Board provided funds for a covered way between the corridor and the main hospital. Up to 1956 the individual huts were heated by different systems including overhead gas heating, electricity or combustion stoves. In that year a comprehensive central heating system for the whole hospital was installed with new boilers, sited opposite Huts 1 and 2.

The County, General and Victoria Eye Hospitals were to form the future District Hospital but it was in the first two that services were duplicated and needed rationalising. But full integration of the two hospitals' services was delayed until a single united nursing school was established in 1957, as each had felt that their recognition as nursing schools depended on having a full range of medical services in their own hospital. The combined school, called The Herefordshire Nurses Training School, soon had 47 nurses in training. The school allowed for general nurses to attend a short course in mental nursing at Burghill Mental Hospital.

In late 1956, with a unified nursing school imminent, a more rational arrangement of the specialties at the County and General hospitals became possible. The antenatal clinic was transferred to the outpatient department in Hut 1, allowing the dental department to move into the vacated space on the ground floor of the 1930 block. Christopher Robin Ward was transferred to Hut 4, after it had been evacuated by the administration, and used to accommodate babies and young children. Its old ward was occupied by the General Practitioners Midwifery Unit, transferred from the General, thus concentrating all maternity at the County. Hut 3 was named Peter Pan, after J.M. Barrie's mythical character, and accommodated older children. The children in Victoria Ward at the General were transferred to these two wards, thus forming the paediatric unit at the County.

In June 1957 it was decided to name four more of the hutted wards. The Central House Committee wanted to name them after the surrounding counties, but the H.H.M.C. decided to name them

General Medicine
Dr Charles Walker
Dr Freddie Strange
Dr John Wells
Dr Basil Miles, M.A., M.D., M.R.C.P., M.B., Ch.B.

General Surgery
Mr Richard Wood Power
Mr Bernard Scholefield
Mr W. Moir Brown
Mr Geoffrey M. Housden
Mr Peter Devlin, M.B., M.Ch., B.A.O., L.M.
  (in 1950 he became an obstetrician & gynaecologist)

Obstetrics & Gynaecology
Mr Patrick Brown, M.R.C.S., L.R.C.P., M.N.S.A.
Mr W. Ainslie
Mr Peter Devlin

Orthopaedics
Mr Brian Thomas

E.N.T.
Mr Ian MacGregor
Mr J.B. Cavenagh
Mr T.S. Stewart, M.D., Ch.B., F.R.C.S.

Paediatrics
Sir Leonard Parsons (Birmingham)
Dr H.J.W. Fisher, M.B., B.S., M.R.C.S.,
  M.R.C.P., D.C.H.

Psychiatry
Dr T.E. Burrows
Dr John D. Richardson, M.B., B.S., M.R.C.S.,
  L.R.C.P., D.P.M.
Dr William A. Shepley, M.B., Ch.B., M.D., D.P.M.
Dr G.A. Betts, M.R.C.S., L.R.C.P.
Dr William E. McIlroy, M.B., B.Ch., B.A.O., D.P.H.

Table 23 (and opposite)
Herefordshire Hospital Group
specialist appointments 1948-58

Opthalmology
Mr Woodward Barnes
Mr A.H.S. Richardson
Mr T.S.B. Kelly, F.R.C.S., D.O.M.S.
Mr H.F.T. MacFetridge, D.S.O., M.A., Ch.B.,
    D.O.M.S.

Anaesthetics
Dr Thomas F. Heavey, M.B., B.Ch.,
    B.A.O., D.A.
Dr M.E. Potter
Dr H.S. Perrot
Dr A.H. Zair
Dr H.W.D. Lawson

Radiology
Dr M.M. Melrose
Dr Philip Cliff, M.B., Ch.B., D.M.R.D.

Pathology
Dr. W.H.J. Baker
Dr Valteris, L.M.S.S.A.

Tuberculosis and Chest Physician
Dr V.R. Philip, M.B., Ch.B., D.P.H.
Dr K. Murray, M.B., Ch.B. (Nieuport Sanatorium)
Dr M. Boveri, M.D., L.R.C.P., L.R.C.S.

Dental Surgery
Mr F.S. Machin
Col. S.H. Woods, C.B.E., F.D.S.R.C.S.

Dermatology
Dr Ann Lawton M.A., M.D., B.Ch.

Infectious Diseases
Dr Raymond Townsend, M.R.C.S., L.R.C.P.,
    M.R.C.G.P. (Stretton Sugwas Hospital)
Dr J.R. Bulman (Tupsley Hospital)

Chronic Sick
Dr Samuel W. Russell, M.A., M.B., B.Ch.,
    B.A.O. (Bromyard Hospital)

after personalities associated with Hereford. Ward 5 was named Nell Gwynne, after the actress and King Charles II's mistress. Traditionally she is thought to have been born in Pipewell Lane, now Gwynne Street, Hereford. Ward 6 was named Ainslie Ward. There is some controversy whether it was named after Mr William Ainslie, the surgeon who had worked in both hospitals and who had been Chief Steward of the City or his wife Mrs Janet Ainslie who served for seven years on the city council before becoming mayor in 1955. A letter was sent to both of them asking their permission, which they both gave, suggesting that the ward was in fact named after them both. Dr Ainslie died in 1959 aged 83.

Hut 7 was named Arkwright Ward after the distinguished Sir John Arkwright, 1872-1954, who lived in Kinsham Court, Presteigne. His grandfather, Sir Richard invented the Spinning Frame or Jenny and he himself, whilst an army captain in the First World War, wrote the famous poem 'Supreme Sacrifice' which was set to music and is often sung at Remembrance Services. Hut 8 was named after Sarah Siddons, a descendent of St John Kemble's family, who was born in Brecon. She acted with David Garrick and was later known as a great tragic actress.

In 1953 the X-ray department was transferred from the new block to the ground floor of the old P.A.I. The pharmacy expanded to fill the space.

Initially the use of the wards at the General varied with surgical, gynaeco-logical and E.N.T. patients accommodated in Davey Ward and Upper Hinton Wards. With the unification of the nursing schools a more permanent and rational use of the wards emerged. In order to concentrate orthopaedics at the General two wards were required. Victoria Ward, once the children had been moved to the County, was one of those used for orthopaedic cases. In March 1959 a cedarwood clad prefabricated ward with a glass veranda facing south, accommodating 24 orthopaedic beds, was opened as the second ward, opposite the Hewat Pavilion which became a clinic. The cost of this new ward was

Mr H.F.T. MacFetridge, known as 'Mac', was appointed as a second part time consultant opthalmologist in 1955

£16,595 and the H.H.M.C. intended to contribute £13,000 of monies it still controlled, notably from a bequest of £9,581 left by Mrs Harriette Davies of Wye Terrace, Hereford to the General Hospital. She also left legacies to the Victoria Eye Hospital and the Hereford Dispensary as well as to five hospitals and nine charities elsewhere. The ward was duly named Harriette Davies after her. But once completed the Board unexpectedly paid the total cost so the bequest was used to furnish the ward and the remainder used for other purposes. Later a hearing aid unit was established.

The Victoria Eye Hospital established peripheral clinics at the four market towns with cottage hospitals as well as at Llandrindod Wells, Knighton and Clyro. From 1952 an Orthoptic Department was

Medical wards General: County:	Total beds 98 Davey (M) 17, Talbot (F) 21 Nell Gwynne (F) 30, Ainslie (M) 30
Surgical wards: General: County:	Total beds 103 Hawkins (F) 20, Oxford (M) 30, Kings (M) 10 David Garrick (F) 25, John Masefield (M) 18
Maternity wards: County:	Total beds 48 Queen Mary, St Ethelbert, Kemble and G.P.s maternity Unit
Gynaecology ward: Paediatric wards:	Maples 22 beds Total beds 50 Peter Pan 20, Christopher Robin 30
T.B. & Isolation:	Nightingale 12 beds
Orthopaedics wards:	Total beds 44 Victoria (F) 20, Harriette Davies (M, F) 24
E.N.T. ward:	12 beds (previous maternity unit)

Table 24   Beds available in the General and County hospitals 1956-59
(M = Male, F = Female)

available in the hospital and within two years a second part time Orthoptist was appointed. Orthoptics or 'straight eyes' is concerned with obtaining equal vision in both eyes and the comfortable use of those eyes together.

In 1948 the senior staff were designated consultants if they held recognised higher degrees and had adequate training and experience in their specialty. Otherwise they were appointed as S.H.M.O.s. When a doctor accepted one of these senior appointments they had to relinquish any partnership in general practice. Each appointment carried a certain number of sessions, each notion-ally of three hours or a half day. The total number available in the week was 11 for a full time consultant while a part-time consultant who wished to carry out private hospital practice could not have more than nine sessions. Many of the highly specialised services did not merit a full time consultant and were served by visiting specialists. Most held regular clinics in Hereford, others were avail-able when required.

Dr Basil Elystan Miles was appointed Consultant Physician to Herefordshire's Hospitals (or the Group as they were commonly called) in 1954. His academic interests were to Hereford's advantage and he rapidly expanded postgraduate teaching and reorganised the hospital records. He was instrumental in getting funds to establish a medical library with new books and periodicals. His talents were recognised when the Board made him an area director of postgraduate education. A dedicated naturalist he also developed a special interest in wildlife including moths, fungi, plant galls and fossils.

Dr Basil Miles

In the first 12 years of the N.H.S. there was a constant request for more junior staff, but the establishment was only slowly increased and even then there was difficulty in getting candidates and financing them. In 1950 there were four registrars, junior specialists in training, at the County, one each in surgery, medicine, paediatrics and gynaecology and a surgical one at the General. There was a house physician and house surgeon at both hospitals. Soon orthopaedic and ophthalmology registrars were appointed. A year later it was agreed by the doctors and administrators that consultant work should not be carried out by junior officers. This subsequently proved difficult to define and the responsibility allowed juniors often depended not only on their experience, but on the availability of consultants and unsocial hours—they obtained plenty of experience during the night.

It was not until 1958 that married quarters for junior staff were provided in Wolseley Villa in Nelson Street and on the ground floor of the old nurses' home. A new nurses' home at the County had been planned since 1949, located beyond the huts. It was eventually opened in 1954 by Capt. Lionel Green and named the Lionel Green Nurses Home. It was a three storey, centrally heated building providing 76 single bedrooms each with a wash basin plus four flats

Venereal Disease
Mr Arthur S. Wigfield, M.A., B.Ch., M.R.C.S., L.R.C.P., M.D. (Worcester)

Radiotherapy
Mr John H. Bromley (Birmingham)
Mr Robert Morrison, M.B., Ch.B., F.R.C.S., D.M.R. (Birmingham)

Neuro-surgery
Mr Wylie McKissock (Birmingham)
Mr Rainer Connolly, M.R.C.S., L.R.C.P., F.R.C.S.,

Neurology
Dr Edwin Bickerstaff, M.B., Ch., F.R.C.P., M.D.,

Thoracic Surgery
Mr A.L. D'Abreau (Birmingham)

Plastic Surgery
Mr J.F. North, M.A., M.B., Ch.B., B.Ch., F.R.C.S.

Table 25   Herefordshire Hospital Group visiting specialists in 1958

for senior sisters and four flats for administrative staff. The old home was used for student nurses and pre-nursing cadets taken on as school leavers till they could start nurse training when 18 years of age.

An attempt to name the old nursing home Harding House after Mr Gilbert Harding who was born in the workhouse in 1907 and became a famous personality for his broadcasting on radio and television in series such as 'What's My Line?', failed as Mr Harding objected. It was subsequently named the Gwyndra Downs Home after the much respected sister tutor who had served in both hospitals and continued to teach into the 1960s. The General provided 46 single rooms for nurses as well as accommodation in nearby villas.

It was not until 1959 that Miss Ker-Ramsey was appointed matron of the three central hospitals with an assistant matron in each of the County and General hospitals, so creating a single nursing service. The paramedical and support staff numbered 216 people in the 1950s giving some idea as to how large the organisation had become.

By the mid-1950s the hospitals were becoming more patient friendly and a booklet was issued to patients, their relatives and friends, stating the availability of hospital chaplains, visiting hours, meal times, a trolley shop service,

Left: Sister Gwyndra Downs after whom the nurses' home was named.
Right: Miss E.M. Ker-Ramsey, appointed matron of the three hospitals

a library and information about making claims for sickness benefit. Meanwhile, the new appointment systems had temporarily eliminated waiting times.

The Psychiatric Hospitals

The function of the Burghill Mental Hospital continued relatively unchanged. Many patients were still accommodated in large wards with four rows of beds, though additional amenities such as a shop and canteen had improved life somewhat. By coming under the same authority as all the other hospitals the psychiatric services were no longer hidden from sight and in due course they were to 'come in from the cold'. Dr Burrows continued as medical superintendent until 1961 having served the hospital for 27 years.

In May 1951 the wards, which up to that time had simply been given the tag 'Male' or 'Female' followed by a number were renamed using the names of trees and flowers. It was not until 1962 that the name of the hospital itself was changed to St Mary's Hospital after the local parish church.

After 1948 Holme Lacy Hospital admitted non private psychiatric female patients and some male patients were accommodated on the ground floor. With increasingly senile and confused elderly patients it became a hospital for the mental health of the elderly, or psychogeriatrics.

The Cottage Hospitals and P.A. Institutes

In 1950 a national policy on the function of cottage hospitals was agreed. They were to be used as local hospitals for the use of general practitioners, to admit and treat patients for conditions within the practitioners' scope which could not be treated at home. During the following years the restrictions on surgery increased resulting in a steady decrease in intermediate and major operations but an increase in other services such as speciality clinics and physiotherapy. Some general practitioners were paid for sessions to provide a surgical or anaesthetic service for their local hospital. New practitioners were usually appointed to their local hospital as general practitioners in attendance, which did not attract any paid sessions.

In 1950 physiotherapy services to some of the smaller hospitals was provided by a mobile van run by the Red Cross. Two years later physiotherapy and ophthalmology clinics were established at the cottage or district hospitals of Ledbury, Leominster and Ross, while an ophthalmic clinic was provided at Kington Cottage Hospital. The numbers of beds did not significantly change. A League of Friends was formed to provide voluntary support for each of Kington, Ledbury and Ross Cottage Hospitals.

Kington got a new outpatient and casualty department built in 1954 partly paid for by monies retained at the time that the N.H.S. was established. The additional accommodation allowed physiotherapy and speech clinics to be opened. The physiotherapy clinic served both Kington and Presteigne.

Ledbury Cottage Hospital also had a new outpatient department which opened in 1957, costing £2,465 including a donation of £500 from the Friends of Ledbury Hospital. The hospital contained 13 beds and provided facilities for E.N.T. operations, mainly tonsillectomies referred from the school medical service. A gynaecological clinic was run once a fortnight.

Leominster District Hospital provided facilities for several local authority clinics, including one for tuberculosis. Improvements were carried out to the outpatient and casualty departments in 1959. At Ross Cottage Hospital ante-natal and postnatal clinics were started in 1954.

Bromyard Hospital, the old P.A.I. on the Worcester Road, was developed into a hospital for the chronic sick. In 1951 it was upgraded at a cost of £17,000 and four years later some 40 chronic sick patients were transferred from Alton Street Hospital, Ross. By 1958 nearly 100 patients were accommodated and 17 nurses were employed. Alton Street Hospital, Ross was to become the centre for mentally handicapped patients in the district and most of the chronic sick were transferred elsewhere. Improvements to the buildings were carried out in 1952 which also increased the accommodation. The piggery was closed as it was too near to the buildings. By 1959 167 patients were accommodated, including 65 male and 62 female adult patients with a mental handicap plus a chronic sick unit of 17 male and 23 female patients from the south of Herefordshire.

CHAPTER 14

Epilogue 1960-99

The administration of the county's hospitals was reorganised four times in the next 40 years. In 1974, Hereford and Worcester Area Health Authority was established, under the overall control of the Birmingham Regional Health Authority, to match the geographical area of the new county. Under the Area Authority, Herefordshire was administered by the District Management Team (D.M.T.) consisting of six members—the district administrator, the treasurer, a community physician, a consultant, a general practitioner and a nurse. Their decisions were reached by consensus.

In 1982, Herefordshire Health Authority was established to manage Herefordshire alone. Initially management continued under the D.M.T., but three years later a further administrative reorganisation resulted in the appointment of a District General Manager with executive powers responsible to the Health Authority. Two units were formed—a District General Hospital Unit containing the central hospitals, and a Community Unit which included the cottage hospitals and Burghill Mental Hospital (renamed as St. Mary's Hospital), each unit having its own manager.

In the early 1990s, Herefordshire Health Authority was reorganised and given a budget to purchase services from within Herefordshire as well as from further afield. In response to this, in 1992 Herefordshire Community Health NHS Trust was established out of the previous Community Unit and two years later the Hereford Hospitals NHS Trust was formed from the D.G.H. Unit.

At the General Hospital, the isolation block was converted into the Department of Aged Care in the mid-1960s. New Physiotherapy and Occupational Therapy Departments were opened in 1969. The following year the Hewat pavilion, which had become an orthopaedic clinic, was replaced by the Dennis Edmunds pavilion, which provided an orthopaedic and a fracture clinic.

In 1974 an Aged Care Day Hospital was built at the front of the hospital adjacent to Victoria Ward. Three years later a day ward extension was built onto Davey Ward. In 1982 the nurses' home was altered to provide a Department for the Mental Health of the Elderly and renamed Cantilupe Wing. In 1995 this department was transferred to the Stonebow Unit at the County Hospital. The Cantilupe Wing was then renamed Riverside Wing and subsequently provided accommodation for a rheumatology clinic on the ground floor, whilst the Department of Aged Care with its outpatient clinic transferred from the old isolation ward. In addition a day ward was created on the first floor and a stroke discharge team and clinical audit on the second floor.

At the County Hospital in 1968 a new Physiotherapy Department was built behind the old Public Assistance Institute and a Postgraduate Centre was built with private funds behind the Lionel Green Nurses Home. The same year a twin theatre was opened opposite Huts 9 and 10 which became surgical wards Elgar and Coningsby. Shortly after this Huts 7 & 8 also became surgical wards being renamed Ainslie & Nell Gwynne, while Huts 5 & 6 were renamed Arkwright and Sarah Siddons wards. In 1974 new laboratories were built behind the old P.A.I. adjacent to the Physiotherapy Department, followed by a new mortuary across Stonebow Road.

In 1977 John Birch Ward was opened next to the twin theatres to provide accommodation for Intensive Therapy and Coronary Care units. The same year a residential block behind the Lionel Green Home provided 54 single rooms and 18 flats mainly for medical staff. In 1984 a prefabricated theatre was placed next to John Birch Ward to allow the twin theatre to close for rewiring. Subsequently it became an Endoscopy unit.

In 1985 an acute psychiatric block, called the Stonebow unit, with 46 beds was built between the Gwyndra Downs Home and Stonebow Road. Three years later a building to house the nursing school was erected between the residential block and the Lionel Green Home. The following year the school was combined into Hereford and Worcestershire College of Nursing, but initial nurse training continued in Hereford till 1995 when it was transferred to the University College of Worcester.

A new gynaecological theatre was opened on the upper floor of the 1930 block in April 1988, the old theatre becoming a chapel in 1993 and the original chapel used to house a scanner for diagnostic radiology. In 1996 a unit to oversee the management of malignant disease was installed in the ground floor of the Lionel Green Home and named the Charles Renton Unit.

The Victoria Eye Hospital had a new extension built onto the east end in 1966 to provide a casualty room, treatment room and pharmacy. In 1971 Henry Wiggin Ltd financed a lift. Two years later a new Orthoptic Department was opened and in 1979 a modern theatre was constructed.

The District General Hospital Unit had an allocation to treat up to 11 private inpatients at any one time in designated beds spread between the three hospitals, although most were located in private rooms adjacent to Talbot Ward, at the General. In 1974 a private hospital, the Wye Valley Nuffield Hospital was opened in Venns Lane with 18 single rooms. Over subsequent years it was regularly upgraded to provide all the facilities expected of a small modern hospital.

The cottage hospitals changed their name to community hospitals. In 1973, on the centenary of the cottage hospital in Ledbury, a new Casualty Department was built; at Kington, a new ward and day room was provided; a new community hospital was built at Bromyard in 1989; in 1991 Leominster Community Hospital was extensively rebuilt providing inpatient beds, a day unit and a centre for community services; and in 1997 the Ross Community Hospital was closed after a new 32 bed community hospital had been built on the site of the old Alton Road Hospital.

Holme lacy Hospital closed in 1981. St Mary's Hospital continued to function with reducing numbers of patients till it finally closed in 1994. Most of the remaining patients were accommodated in homes in the community.

Stretton Sugwas Hospital latterly accommodated mainly preconvalescent cases and some general practitioner beds with one bed designated for infectious diseases. When it closed in 1983 the unit was transferred to St Mary's Hospital. Tupsley Hospital increasingly admitted preconvalescent medical patients and some geriatric ones, finally closing in 1983.

Bromyard Geriatric Hospital closed in 1989, transferring patients to the new Bromyard Community Hospital or private residential homes. Alton Street Hospital in Ross was renamed Dean Hill Hospital in 1962 and accommodated mainly patients with a mental handicap. It closed in 1993, after the patients had been accommodated in a mix of supported accommodation in the community, residential and nursing homes, some of the latter created out of old nurses' homes, some purpose built and spread around the county.

In April 1999 a contract, costing £65 million, was signed between the Hereford Hospitals NHS Trust and Mercia Healthcare Ltd, a private consortium, to build and maintain for 30 years a new District General Hospital on the County Hospital site to replace the General, County and Victoria Eye Hospitals. A new chapter had opened.

APPENDIX

Medical and Dental Degrees, Diplomas & Qualifications

Basic Qualifications
Ch.B., B.Ch., B.S. or B.C.   Bachelor of Surgery from different universities
L.F.P.S.   Licentiate of the Faculty of Physicians and Surgeons of Glasgow (The
            Faculty only obtained its Royal titles in 1908)
L.M.S.S.A. Licentiate in Medicine & Surgery of the Society of Apothecaries of
            London
L.R.C.P.   Licentiate of the Royal College of Physicians
L.R.C.S.   Licentiate of the Royal College of Surgeons
L.R.F.P.S. Licentiate of the Royal Faculty of Physicians and Surgeons of Glasgow
L.S.A.   Licentiate of the Society of Apothecaries
M.B.   Bachelor in Medicine
M.R.C.S.   Member of the Royal College of Surgeons

Higher Degrees in Medicine, Surgery and Obstetrics
C.M., M.Ch., M.Chir.   Master of Surgery from different universities involving
            a thesis and an examination
F.R.C.S.   Fellow of the Royal College of Surgeons
F.R.F.P.S. Fellow of the Royal Faculty of Physicians & Surgeons of Glasgow
M.D.   Doctor of Medicine, a university higher degree obtained by thesis and
            examination
M.R.C.P.   Member of the Royal College of Physicians. A member could be elected
            a Fellow, F.R.C.P., for distinguished service

Specialist Qualifications
B.A.O.   Batchelor in the art of Obstetrics
D.A.   Diploma in Anaesthetics
D.C.H.   Diploma of Child Health
D.L.O.   Diploma in Laryngology and Otology
D.M.R.   Diploma of Medical Radiotherapy
D.M.R.D.   Diploma in Medical Radio Diagnosis
D.M.R.E.   Diploma in Medical Radiology and Electrolysis
D.O.M.S.   Diploma in Ophthalmic Medicine and Surgery
D.P.H.   Diploma in Public Health
D.P.M.   Diploma in Psychological Medicine
F.D.S.R.C.S. Fellow of Dental Surgery Royal College of Surgeons
F.F.A.   Fellow of the Faculty of Anaesthetists
F.R.C.O.G. Fellow of the Royal College of Obstetricians and Gynaecologists
L.D.S.   Licentiate in Dental Surgery
L.D.S.R.C.S. Licentiate in Dental Surgery from the Royal College of Surgeons
L.M.   Licentiate in Midwifery awarded by the Rotunda Hospital
M.D.S.   Master in Dental Surgery
M.M.S.A.   Master of Midwifery of the Society of Apothecaries
M.R.C.G.P. Member of the Royal College of General Practitioners

Index

Abergavenny Asylum 186
    Committee of Visitors 186, 187
Acts of Parliament
    Act for Regulating Private Madhouses
        1774 183
    Education Act 1907 60
    Kington Improvement Act 137
    Local Government Act 1929 219
    Lunacy Act 1890 191
    Medical Act 1858 13
    Medical Treatment Act 1930 194
    Midwives Act 1902 15
    National Insurance Act 1911 18
    Ross Improvement Act 109
accident planning 240
Adams, Dr George 216, 217
Aged Care Day Hospital 252
Ainslie, William 29, 64, 65, 79, 81, 88, 90,
    141, 145, 217, 229, 242, 252
Ainslie Ward 241, 243
Airey, G.G. 127
Airley, Mr G.G. 235
almoners 86, 231
almshouses 1
Alton Court Brewery Co. 116
Alton Street Hospital 249-50, 253
anaesthetics 9, 37, 54, 56, 65, 83
Anderson, David Irving 112
antiseptic surgery 56
apothecary 2, 8, 13, 14
apprentices 13, 36
Arkwright, John Hungerford 101
    Mr George 101
    Ward 243, 252
Armitage, Miss Maud 216
Arundel, Shirley Woolmer 141
asylums 183-198
Austen, Miss Feodora 142, 145-6

Bacon, Miss H. 31, 142
bacteriology 64, 83
Bailey, Sir J.R. 171
    Lady 171
Baker, Dr W.H.J. 65, 235, 243
Ballanger, Mr 96, 97
Bamber, Miss 130, 132
Bambino Guild 77
Bamhall, Dr 116
Banks, Dorothy 144
    Mrs 147

Barker, E.H. Lingen 170
Barker, Miss M. 97
Barlings, S.G. 235
Barneby, Edmund 103
    William H. 101, 103, 108,
Barneby-Letley, Mr. J.H. 101
Barnes, H. Woodward 65, 85, 177, 181, 243
Barrell, William 136
Barton, W.G. 48
Barton, Miss 160, 166
Bateman, Miss Mary Helen 142
Bateman, Viscount 6, 111
Bauser, Miss 86
Baxter, Mr 88
Bayley, F.E. 181
    J.J. 181
    W.T. 181
Baynam, Sister 168
Beck, Edward Ashton Anthony 107
Beddoe, H.C. 202
Beddoes, Mr 60
Beedie, Miss Alice M. 142
Bell, Annie C. 31
Bellars, John 4
Benn, Mr C.A. 181
Benson, Rev. Edward G. 190, 198
Bentley, R.M. 48
Bentley-Taylor, Mr R. 181, 182
Best, Mr G.D. 181
Betts, Dr G.A. 242
Bevan, Aneurin 20
Bickam, Spenser 131
Bickerstaff, Dr Edwin 247
Biddulph, Lord 11
    Lady Elizabeth 129, 131, 131, 132
    John Michael 128
    Michael 26, 66, 111, 125, 126, 128,
    Miss Violet 68
Billiald, Richard 137, 141
biochemistry 84
Bird, Miss 86, 88
Birmingham & Midlands Eye Hospital 180
Birmingham Regional Health Authority 251
    Regional Hospital Board 20, 237, 238,
        244, 246
Birtley 207
Bishops Frome Oddfellows 106
Blackfield, Mr 30
bladder stones 9-10, 142
Blake, P.A. 31, 51

Blake, Miss Thomas 109, 110, 113
Bleek Lye, John 13, 28, 49
Blount, Thomas 28
Board of Commissioners 186
Bodenham-Lubienski, Count L. 48
Bounds, Miss Eleanor 142
Boveri, Dr M. 243
Bower, Dr 208
Bowers, Mr 11
Bowers, Messrs. S.W. & Co. 220
Bradley, Mr 88
Braithwaite, Francis 29
Bramhall, Sykes 112
Bramwell, Miss 132
Brennan, Mrs A.C. 213
Bridge, Sidney 164
Bridger, Mrs 108
Bright, Richard 155, 157, 158
Bristol Royal Infirmary 1
Bristowe, Dr 39
British Hospital Assn. 18, 19
        Nurses Assn. 15
        Medical Assn. 18, 19
Bromley, F.S. 141
Bromley, Dr John F. 235, 247
Bromyard Cottage Hospital 7, 101-8, 249,
        253
        building work 104-5
        finance 107-8
        honorary medical staff 103
        management 103
        rules 101-2, 103, 106
Bromyard Isolation Hospital 204-6
Budinger, Miss C. 203
Bulmer, Rev. C. 178, 190, 191
        Frederick 59, 177, 178
        Mary 178
        Percy 59, 178
Bulmer's Cider 179, 182
Brown, Margaret 31
        Patrick 229, 242
Browne, Conrad 97
Buckell, John William 127
Bull, Henry Graves 28, 37, 46, 49-50
Bull Convalescent Fund 47, 239
Bullock, Miss Dora 132, 135
Bulman, J. R. 28, 100, 214, 243
Burdett, Sir Henry 63, 120
Burghill Hospital (see Hereford County and
        City Asylum, and St Mary's Hopsital)
Burley 205
Burr, Higford 54

Burrows, Thomas 65, 87, 190, 193, 235, 242,
        248
Butler, William B. 29, 76, 83, 88

Cam, John 27, 28
        Thomas 21, 27, 28, 29
        jnr 28, 29, 36, 44, 48
        Samuel 9, 28, 29
        Walter Holcroft 112
        William 27, 29
Cameron, Anabel 31, 76
Camp Meadow Isolation Hospital, Ross
        210-1
Campbell, Francis 27, 28, 184
        Dr 121
Cantilupe Wing 252
Capel, Major Amphlett 177, 181
cardiovascular 85
Carless, Joseph 48
cataracts 2
Cavenagh, John B. 65, 242
Cawley, Sir Frederick 158
Central Hospitals, the 240-8
chaplains (see also County and General
        hospitals) 239
Chapman, Paul M. 11, 15, 28, 50, 53, 54, 55,
        81
Chapman, Dr T. Algernon 189, 190
Charles, Rev Edward 154
Charles Renton Unit 252
Chartered Society of Massage & Medical
        Gymnasts 17
Charteris, Rev. Thomas O. 190
Chave, Mr 94
Chesterfield, Countess of 170
children's services (see also paediatrics) 44,
        244
cholera 199
Christopher Robin ward 227, 241, 242
Chubb, Capt 77
Chute, James 141
Clansey, Horace 229
Clarke, Miss Miriam I. 132
Clay, Miss 142, 143
Cliff, Dr Philip 243
Clive, Rev. Archer 187, 190
        Col Edward 113
        George 109, 113
        Lt Col Winser 99
Clowes, Mrs 165
coal miners 176
Cocks, Cambridge Cary 109, 110, 112, 113,

115, 117
Coghlan, James G. 127
Collard, George 153, 154
Commissioners in Lunacy 187, 189
Community Unit 251
Company of Barber Surgeons 2
Coningsby, Lady Frances 26
Coningsby Hospital 1
      Ward 252
Connolly, Mr Rainer 247
contributory schemes 11, 12, 13
Cooper, Frederick 111, 117, 119, 122
      Percival 119
Cope, Capt. C. 181
Cordery, E. M. 31, 98
Cornewall, Sir Geoffrey 48
      Sir George 6
Coronary Care 252
Corry, S.L. 64
Cotes, Rev. Digby 28
      Thomas 28, 29, 30, 36
cottage hospitals (see also by name) 10, 11,
      13, 237, 249-50, 251, 253
Cotterell, Sir John 26
couching 2
County Hospital 95, 97, 216, 219-36, 222,
      237, 238, 241, 246, 247, 252
      chaplains 231
      hutted wards 221, 223, 231, 233, 241
      mortuary 227, 252
County Smallpox Hospital 17
Cox, Lt Col Richard 139
Cragg, Miss A.E. 132
Craigie, Miss 147
Crawford, Miss C.M. 118, 132
Crawley, Lord 162
Crawshaw, Miss Helen 108
Cresswell, George 10, 11, 103, 175
      Penny Fund 10, 11-2, 13, 107, 132,
      135, 144, 147, 158, 163
Cressy, George J. 159
Croft, Sir H. Archer 11, 48
      Sir Herbert 111
      Major Owen 48, 73
Crosbie, Miss L.M. 142, 148, 149
Currie, Henry 170
Cutfield, Arthur 112, 120
Cuthbert, William Hawkins 137, 141

d'Abreu, Mr A.L. 235, 247
Dash, Nurse 146
Davenport, Rev. George H. 190

David Garrick Ward 225, 233
Davidson, Richard Holden 159
Davies, David 184
      E.G. 155
      Harriette 244
      Susan 31, 36
      Miss 108
Davey, Major George 72, 73
      Ward 71, 74, 244, 251
Dawson, Squ. Leader R.F. 93
Deacon, Ernest 147
Dean Hill Hospital 253
Debenham, Horace K. 141
Dennis Edmunds Pavilion 252
Devereux, The Honourable R.C. 48, 161,
      181
Devlin, Mr Peter 234, 242
diabetes 89
Dicey & Co, Messrs. 2
Dighton, Charles Allen Adair 112
diphtheria 199, 202, 204, 205, 206, 210, 211,
      212, 214, 215, 217, 240
District General Hospital Unit 251
      General Manager 251
      Management Team 251
Dodderidge, Rev. Sidney 106
Doig, Alexander Driver, A.H. 112
Domestic Physician or Guardian of Health 2
domestic staff 14
Dore Ward 214
Douney, Miss Sibyl 118
Dowding, John Benjamin 153, 155, 161
Downes, Sister Gwyndra 248
      Mrs H.H. 181
Driver, A.H. 159
drugs 2, 9, 216, 218
Drury, Miss Florence 142
Drybrook Hospital 210-1
Dryland, Gilbert Winter 141, 145, 148, 151
      Dorothy 145, 148
DuBuisson, Edward 15, 29, 82, 88
Duckworth, H.L. D'Olier 112
Duncan, Sir Andrew 94
      Cllr Andrew 155
Dumughn, Horace Banfield 159
Dunlop, John Leeper 112
Durham, Mr 16
dysentery 204

E.N.T. 86, 97
Eady, George F. 159
Ear & Eye Hospital 7

Ebnal 206
Edmondson, Miss 142
Edmunds, Dennis 238
Edwards, Harford 159
Edwards, Jean 93
    Martha 176
Edwards, Octavius 159, 206
Edwards, Mr Wynne 235
Elder, Rev. 166
Elgar Ward 252
Elphick, Miss K. 31, 52
Emergency Medical Service 221
Ennis, Mrs 111, 118
Ethelbert Ward 252
Etheridge, G. Ernest Frederick 107
Evans, Mr S. 79
Everitt, T.F. 159, 165
eye treatment *(see also Ear and Eye
    Hospital; Victoria Eye Hospital)* 51,
    85

farms (hospital) 187, 191, 194, 217, 228
Fern, Nurse 146
Findlay, Miss E.G. 118
Fisher, H.J.W. 242
Fitsimons, Dr 202
Flatau-Berwin, Mrs 84
Flemming, G.W. 65, 87, 190, 193
Florence Nightingale Chapel 76
Foley, Thomas 6
Folly House 204, 214
Forbes, Miss 142
Foresters, the 153
Foster, Mrs Alice 115-6, 119, 121, 122
    Arthur 119, 120
    Cedric 121
    Miss 142
Freeth, Miss Ivy 142

Garrick Theatre 61, 62
General Infirmary/Hospital 5-6, 7-8, 11, 13,
    16, 18, 21-100, 183, 186, 201,
    217, 219, 221, 222, 225, 226,
    227-8, 233, 234, 237, 239, 241,
    244, 246, 247, 251
    apothecary 25, 31
    building work 38-45, 62, 68-76
    chaplains 30, 37, 48, 53
    domestic staff 89, 98
    drugs 25
    electricity 62
    finance 27, 32, 35, 47, 48, 59-60, 61,
        77-9, 97, 100

heating 45
honorary medical staff 25, 31, 47, 49-
    54, 79-87, 90, 202, 232
isolation block 44, 75, 183
management 25, 47, 60, 78, 79, 91
matrons 30, 31, 36, 51, 66, 76, 87, 90
nurses 30, 36, 52, 53, 66, 87, 89, 85,
    97, 98
nurses' accommodation 68, 69, 70, 71,
    74
physicians 25, 26, 27, 28, 80
porter's lodge 34, 39
Rules 27, 30, 33, 34, 47, 61, 74, 80
servants 30, 53, 98
surgeons 25, 26, 27, 28, 80
superintendent 59
mortuary 42
operating theatre 69-71
water supply 45
General Medical Council 13
    Nursing Council 16, 230
George, John Winnell 110, 112
Giles, Mr 51
Gillam, Thomas Henry 107
Gillies, Miss 108
Gilliland, John 185
    William L. 28, 35, 185, 186
Girvin, Mrs 143
    Ward 143
Goddard-Fenwick, Rev. William H. 190
Goldie, Edward Alexander Marie Joachim
    127
Goodburn, Miss 132
Goodridge, Sister 66
Gore, Miss M.J. 132
Gosling, Mr H. 190
Gough, J.E. 35
Graham Lodge Sanatorium 215
Graham-Lynn, Miss 160, 166
Graves, Dr Thomas Chivers 190, 191
Green, Arthur Llewellyn Baldwin 112, 121
    Arthur R. 127
    Capt. Lionel 19, 73, 152, 221, 238,
        246
    Rev. Maddison 129
    Richard 139, 140
Greenly, Edward 139
Greenway, Mrs 210-1
Gretton, Rev. 37
Gregory, Mr 165
'Grey Lady', the 99-100
Griffin, William 127
Griffiths snr, John 29, 35

jnr, John 29
Groves, John Nixon 127
Guild of the Brave Young Things 62
Gummer, Sister 84
Gurney, Alfred 202
Gwatkin, Ann 31
Gwilt, Miss Margaret Daisy 174, 181, 182
Gwyndra Downs Nurses Home 247
gynaecology 252

Hacking, Miss 215
Haddon Bros, Messrs 113
haematology 84
Haines, Nurse Beatrice 211
Hall, Mr G.A. 181
Hallum, Mrs 31
Hampton Court Convalescent Hospital 167
Harding, Gilbert 247
        Richard 141, 145
Hardwicke, Richard 27, 28, 29
Harley, Edward, Earl of Oxford 22
Harrington, Miss Ellen 157, 160
Harris, Miss Elsie 160, 166
        Dr George 26
Harris Wards 26, 85
Harrison, James McKean 127
Hart-Smith, C. 155, 156, 158, 159
Hartford, Mary 31, 36
Hastings, Sir Charles 18
Hatton, George 129-30
Hawkins, Francis 43, 48
        Francis jnr 177
        Thomas J. 190
        Ward 43, 74, 75
hearing aid centre 97
Heavey, Dr Thomas F. 234, 243
Henry, Dr William 125, 126
Herbert, John Maurice 109
        Mr S. C. 181
Hereford County and City Asylum 17,
        187-98, 239, 241, 247-8
                Committee of Visitors 187
                patients 194, 197
                Rules 188
        Hospitals NHS Trust 251
        Sir James 26
        Lady 163, 180, 181
        Nurses Training School 241
        RDC 206, 207, 208, 210, 211, 214
        & Worcestershire Area Health
                Authority 251
        & Worcestershire College of Nursing
                252

Herefordshire County Council 215, 219
        Farmers Hospital League 77
        General Hospital Contributory Scheme
                12
        Health Authority 251
        Hospitals Management Committee
                20, 237, 238, 239, 242, 244
        Medical Assn 14
        Militia 61
Heriot, Miss 108
Hewat, Col. 48, 61, 69
        Mrs 63, 68, 71
        Pavilion 71, 72, 86, 92, 251
Hewett, Mr John E.S. 109
Higginson, Edmund 101, 103
High Lane Foresters 106
Hill, George 128, 133
        Miss Maria 118
        Miss Rudland 87
        Thomas 127
        T.H. 133
        William 110
Hinings, John William 107
Hinton wards 45, 90, 244
histology 64
Holdbrook, Miss 108
Holford, Miss 132
Holland, Edward Stanley 164
        E.S. Estate 178
        Miss 157
        Ward 165
Holme Lacy Hospital 195, 239, 248, 253
        House 17
honorary staff 13
Hooper, Ernest Arthur Gwynne 141
Hopkins, Lt.-Gen. Sir Edward 48
Horton, Dr 104, 107
Hospital Assn. 15
hospital food 57
Hospital Sunday 35, 105, 131, 134, 140, 154,
        158
Housden, Charles 159
Housden, Geoffrey McIvor 159, 165, 167,
        235, 242
Howey, Edward Werge 107
Hudson, Alfred George 159
Hughes, Squ. Leader J. 93
        Samuel 26
Hulbert, Miss Annie E. 142, 146
        Arthur 44
Humble Bee Cottage 205
Humfrys, W.A. 59
        W.J. 50

Humphrys, W. 202
Hunter, Miss Francis 174
Hursey, Ken 93
Hutchinson, James 48
Hutton jnr., John 159
Hyde, Mr 94
  Mrs 212, 213

Incorporated Society of Trained Masseuses
  17
Industrious Aid Society 61
infectious diseases 17, 199-218
  hospitals 199-218, 240
Institute of Massage & Medical Gymnasts 17
Ivy Cottage 209

Jack, W. Logan 85, 141, 148, 149, 150, 151
Jackson Almshouses 101
James, G.H. 64, 159, 167
  Meyrick 11, 63, 64, 65
Jobson, Richard 141
John Birch ward 252
John Masefield Ward 226, 233
Johnson, Miss L.A. Worley 230
  Dr Samuel 5
  Miss 132, 142
Johnson's Hospital 219
Johnston, Henry Wallace 159, 165
Jones, Herbert 64, 65
  Dr Herbert 212
Jones, Miss Mary 174
  R.E. 65
  Thomas 112
  Thomas Arthur 127
  Mrs 30, 31
Jones-Roberts, William Arthur Derek 112
Jubilee Ward 113, 122
Julian, Mr F.L. 123

Kelly, Mr T.S.B. 243
Kemble Ward 226, 233, 241
Kempson, Mr 104
Ker-Ramsey, Miss E.M. 247, 248
Keys-Wells, Constance 31, 88
Killgow, Rev. 99
King Edward VII Memorial Hospital 215
Kingdon, William Edward 159
Kinglake, Capt. 143
Kings Ward 45, 74
Kington Isolation Hospital 208-10
Knapp, Edward Michael Molineaux 112
Knight, Mr 183
Kyrle Wing 115

LMS Railway Fund 179, 229
ladies linen leagues 110
Lamb, Harold Victor 159, 162
Langdale-Smith 127
Langdon, Sister 31, 87
Lara, Miss 66
Latham, Helen 53
Lawson, Dr H.W.D. 243
Lawton, Dr Ann 243
Lazenby, Mr 141
  Mrs Margaret 142
League of Mercy 77
le Grand, Aga 119
Ledbury Cottage Hospital 7, 13, 125-36,
  249, 253
  fundraising 131, 134
  honorary medical staff 127, 130
  operating table 134
  Rules 125, 127, 134
  surgery 130
Leominster Borough Isolation Hospital
  206-7
  & Wigmore RD Isolation Hospital
  207-8
Leominster Cottage Hospital 7, 153-68, 239,
  249, 253
  fundraising 158, 164
  honorary medical staff 158, 159, 165
  mortuary 163
  Rules 156, 158, 165
Levason, Arthur 47, 141, 142
  Joseph 37
  Peyton 29, 141, 142
Levis, Miss 142
Lewis, James King 107
Lewis, Philip I. 159
  Philip King 107
  Miss S.C. 174
Lilley, James H. 15, 28
Lindsay, Eric 11, 85
  Mr Francis 85, 169, 174, 176, 177
Lingdon, Alfred Thomas Lock 159
Lingen, Charles 29, 37
Lionel Green Nurses' Home 246
Lister, Lord 56
Little Cowarne 205
Llanwarne, Alderman 202
Lloyd, E. Jean McQ. 112
  G. Marner 112
local authorities 13, 17, 18, 185, 188, 199,
  200, 217, 219, 220
Local Government Board 210, 204
London County Council 217

Lucas, Miss 120
Lunatic Aid Fund 239
lunatics 17, 35
Lutley, Col. John 108
Lynch, Mrs 98
Lysaght, Squ. Leader A.C. 93

MacFetridge, Mr H.F.T. 243, 244
MacGregor, Ian W. 65, 87, 203, 214, 235, 242
Machin, Frank S. 29, 243
Mackay, John 170, 171, 174
Maclaverty, Alexander 110, 11, 112
Maillard, John & Beatrice 201
Maitland, Miss E.G. 118
Malcomson, Madeline 64
Malkin, G.R. 64
Maples, E.W. 227
       Ward 227, 233
Marfell, Miss Eva 142
Markham, E.J. 31, 51
Marley, Richard 107
Marshall, Nurse 149
Martin, John 125
       Rev. William 103, 104, 107
Masefield, Charles 135, 136
       George Edward 126
Mason, Henry 112
masseuses 17-8, 66, 86, 96
Matthews, Thomas 117-8
       Dr 50
matrons 14
Maule, W.G. 64
May Fair Hour 62
McAdam, George 29
McCall, H.D 159
McIlroy, Dr William E. 242
McKean, George Bartley 127
McKissock, Mr Wylie 235, 247
McLaren, Donald James 159
Measures, Marion 31
Melrose, Dr M.M. 65, 84, 235, 243
meningitis 199, 204, 232
mental health 183-98, 252
Meredith, Mrs Fanny 174
Meredith, Miss S. (later Mrs West) 142, 148
midwifery 8, 15, 90, 166, 168, 219, 225, 226, 232, 233, 239, 242
Miles, Dr Basil 242, 246
Millechap, Mr 106
Mills, Mr G.P. 235
Milner, Ernest A. 141

Mines, Mr 91
Minett, Henry 111
Mitchell, Brian Raymond 141
       James 202
Moir Brown, William 29, 64, 82, 93, 96, 98, 242
Moore, Diana 30, 31
       Miss 96
Morgan, Rev. H.C. 113
Morris, Edgar G.F. 29, 201, 213
       John Freeman 29
       John 34-5
       Margaret 143
       Mrs 118
       Wards 35
Morrison, Dr C.S. 190, 191
Morrison, Mr Robert 247
Murray, Mrs Alan 108
Murray, Dr K. 243

Nash, John 183
       Miss 120
National Health Service 19, 20, 100, 239
Nell Gwynne Ward 241, 243, 252
1 Nelson Street 92
2 Nelson Street 98
Niblick, William James 159
Nicol, Miss 63
Nicholson, Mr J.H.T. 181
Nieuport Sanatorium 18, 215-8, 241
Nightingale Ward 226, 233
Norman, John William 112
North, Mr J.F. 247
nurse training 15-6, 36, 52, 97, 230, 241, 252
nurses 14, 15, 240
Nuttall, Mr H.A. 122

occupational therapy 230, 251
Ocle Pychard 205
Oddfellows, Lord Hill Lodge 153
Old Nuffield Lungs, the 232
ophthalmology 83, 246, 249
Orde, Mr 78
Ormathwaite, Lady 138, 139
orthopaedics 86, 234, 244, 246
Orthopaedic Hospital, Oswestry 217, 234
orthoptics 244-5, 253
Owen, Charles Langley 64, 93, 112
       Mr W.A. 147
       John 107
Oxford Ward 39

paediatrics 242
Page, George 153, 155
      James 153
Painter Bros., Messrs 178
Palin, Dr 119
Parker, William 23
Parsons, Sir Leonard 235, 242
Pasteur, Louis 56
Pateshall, Col. H.E.P. 48, 73
      John 184, 185
pathology 45, 84
Patterson, Dr 28, 88, 89
Paulson, William 112, 121
paupers 8
Pechell, Mrs 113
Pencombe 205
Perch, Miss S.M. 132
Perkins, Miss 118
      Mr 30
Perrin, Joseph 6, 183
Perrot, H.S. 64, 243
Peterchurch Asylum 186
Peters Pan Ward 241, 242
Peters, Alfred 97
Petrie, Miss 118
Philip, Dr V.R. 217, 243
Phillips, Miss R 231
Philp, C.H.G. 64
Philpin, Bernard 143
Phipps, Mr 104
physicians 13
physiotherapy 96, 230, 249, 252, 252
Picton, Dr. H.A. 127, 132
Picketts, Arthur Augustus 141
      Francis Lionel 141
Pierce, Arthur 60
Pike, Norman H. 65, 85
Pillans, Anne 64, 112
      George Lynn 112
Poor Laws 1, 18, 33, 185, 232
Pope, Henry 141
Postgraduate Centre 252
Potter, Dr M.E. 64, 243
Potts, James Ashford 112, 119
Pound Days 77
Powell, J.H. 112, 117
      Richard 45
      William 106, 107
Power, Capt. Kingsmill 109, 111
Prendergrass, Capt. 33
Prescott, Mrs 103
Price, William Elliott 112, 118
Pritchard, J.A. 64

Elizabeth 31
private patients 13, 60, 90, 94, 95, 253
probationers 14, 15, 16
psychiatry 252
psychology 86
Public Assistance Institutes 18, 91, 167, 207,
      219, 223-4, 237, 249-50, 252
Public Health laboratory 233
pupils 13, 36, 51
Purchase, Keynes 139
Pye, Miss Jane 118

Queen Alexandra's Rose Day 61, 178
Queen Mary 220
      Mary's Ward 226

Radcliffe's, Dr's elixir 2
radiotherapy 96
Railway Inn, Ledbury 126
Rankin, Lady Annie 156
      Sir James 157, 158
Reade, Rev. Compton 190
Red Cross 67, 68, 86, 91, 93, 96, 122, 145,
      162, 182
Redhill Hostel 196
Reed, Dr W.O. 222, 229, 235
Rees, Miss Charlotte M. 160, 166
rheumatology 252
restraint 189
Richardo, Osman 125, 126
Richards, Berkeley K. 112, 117
Richardson, Mr. A.H. 159, 235, 243
      Dr John D. 242
      Miss M.E. 132
      Miss 160, 166
Riddell, Rev. G.D.E. 181
Riley, John 131
Riverside Walk 46
      Ward 45
      Wing 252
Robey, Dr Odie 235
Robinson, Charles A. 159
      Stephen 137, 139
      Major Stewart 177
Robinson, Miss Mary 142
Rogers, Henry 202
Ross Dispensary 109
      Cottage Hospital 7, 109-24, 237, 249,
            253
      fundraising 123
      Honorary Medical Staff 112,
            116, 120
      Jubilee Ward 115, 122

Kyrle Wing 115
League of Friends 120
operating theatre 115-6
Rules 110, 122
visitors 113
Railwaymen's Union 122
Trades Labour Council 122
& Ledbury Working Men's Assn 129
Rotherwas Munitions Factory 67, 93, 221
Royal College of Physicians 2
College of Surgeons 2
Salop Infirmary 1
Rules, hospital 7, 13, 21
Rundle, Lt Col C. 67
Rushcliffe Report 16
Russell, Eleanor 64, 112
Russell, Dr Samuel W. 243
Mrs 129
William Kerr 112

St Bartholomew's 1
St James's Vicarage 98
St Mary's Hospital (*see also Hereford County and City Asylum*) 251, 253
St Thomas's 1
Samaritan Fund 61, 239
Sarah Siddons Ward 241, 244, 252
Sarum House 98
scabies 204
Scales, Martin 159, 165
scarification 9
scarlet fever 199, 202, 203, 204, 205, 206, 209, 210, 212, 214, 215
Scholefield, Bernard 29, 80, 141, 159, 229, 235, 242
Sciven, Me R.L.G. 181
Scobie Mr/Col 12, 169, 173, 175, 177
Scudamore, John 6
Seaton, Rev. Douglas 110
Sellars, Miss 89
servants 16
Sessarrego, Mr 198
Shepley, Dr William A. 242
Shanks, Sister 217
Sharpe, A.A. 51
Miss 160, 166
Shelton, John Brown 107
Shepherd, Thomas Scott 112, 118
Shepperson, Sir Ernest, M.P. 99
Siddall, Joseph Bower 112, 117
Simpson, Albert 64
Skuse, Mr 224
Slater, Mrs 211

Sleeman, Col 12, 13, 77, 177
smallpox 203, 205, 206, 207, 208, 212, 240
Smith, Alfred Rickards 28
Miss Alice Lee 132
Mrs Elizabeth 45
Dr John Grimmond 190, 192, 193
Misses N. & C. 132
Mr W. 106
Soars, Mrs. E. 108
social workers 240
Society for Aiding the Industrious 48, 50, 178
of Trained Masseuses 17, 109
Southall, Henry 111
Mr John T. 190
Southgate Villas 162
Stallard, Blanche E. Walter 29, 63, 64, 79, 82, 88, 90
Stanhope, Rev. B.L.S. 190
Stanley Holloway Fund 239
Stanton, Miss 132
Stanways, Mr 143
Steadman, William 127
Steed, John 28
Steel, Gerald 159
Steers, Miss M. 31
Stephen & Bairstow, Messrs 170
Stephenson, Rev. Nash 101, 103
Stewart, Mr T.S. 242
W. 65
Dr W. 83
Still, Miss 132
Stonebow Unit 252
Strange, Dr Frederick O.T. 28, 80, 97, 242
Stretton Sugwas Hospital 17, 207, 108, 210, 211-5, 240, 253
Stubbs, Mrs 113
Studt, Henry 131-2, 140, 154
surgeons 2, 13
surgery 9
Symmons, George Stratton 127, 131
Symonds, George H.H. 28, 88, 89

Talbot, Rev. Dr Thomas 4, 5, 23
W.W. 127
Ward 39, 74, 253
Talgarth 196
Tanner, Robert 127
Taylor, Rev. Charles H. 190
Temple, Anthony 138, 139, 143
Templeton, Miss Margaret 160
Tew, Miss Ethel Frances 160, 166
Thomas, Brian 65, 96, 233, 235, 242

Thomas, Mr F.W. 224
    Gordon Wilson 159
    Jim 203
Thomason, Richard 29
Thompson, Robert Gordon Ffolliott 159, 167
Thomson, Charles Edward 111
throat treatment (see also E.N.T.) 54
Thynne, G.A.C. 48
Tidman, Miss E. 31
Titterington, George Mills 159
Toll House, Bromyard 103
Tolley, Miss Mary 126, 132
Townsend, Dr Raymond 243
treatment 9, 31-2, 54-8, 69-72, 95-101, 238, 249
Tredegar Medical Aid Society 178
Trotter, Leslie B.C. 127
    Miss 167
    Mrs 133
tuberculosis 199, 211, 215-8, 220, 226, 232, 240
Tullis, George Donaldson Edie 141
Tupsley Hospital 17, 200-2, 240, 241
Turner, Alderman A.P 190
    Mrs M.T. 182
    Thomas 15, 29, 44, 56, 202
typhoid 199, 203, 212

Valteris, Dr 243
Vaughan, Douglas Cyril 159
Venn, Rev. John 48, 169
    Fund in Aid of Incurables 239
    Memorial Fund 48
Vevers, Henry 29, 50
Victoria Cottage Hospital, Kington 7, 13, 16, 137-52, 249, 253
    contributory scheme 147, 150
    drugs 151
    fundraising 140, 147, 151
    Girvin Ward 143
    Rules 138, 142
Victoria Eye (& Ear) Hospital 169-82, 237, 239, 241, 244, 253
    fundraising 174, 178
    operating theatre 180
    Rules 173
    visitors 175
Victoria House 238
Victoria Ward 44, 62, 63, 86, 99-100, 242, 244
Vilmet-Scott, Miss Maud 142
Visiting Committee of Justices 185

Waddington, Miss 107, 108
Wallis, A. 176, 179
Walker, Dr Charles 28, 64, 85, 235, 242
Walker, Ronald R. 141
Walrond, Maineswete 28, 35
Warner, Rev. Preb. C.E. 231
Waterfield, The Very Rev. R. 48
Watkins, John 156
    Miss 147
Webb, Mrs Ann 118
    Edward J. 126
Wells, Dr John 28, 80, 242
Weobley 223
    District Council 211, 212
West, Mrs 147
Westminster Hospital 1
Wheeler, Miss Catherine 230
Whitchurch Asylum 186
Whitecroft, Dr 88
Wigfield, Mr Arthur S. 247
Wigmore Isolation Hospital (see Leominster & Wigmore)
Williams, Miss B.M. 132
    H.T. 202
    Huw Owen 159
Wilson, J.W. 112
    Miss 118
Wishlade, Henry 139
Witts, C. 202
Wolseley Villa 68, 92, 246
Wood, Helen 64
    J. Arthur 29
    John Henry 127
    Miles Astman 125, 127
    Miles Astman jnr. 127
Wood Power, Richard 29, 65, 80, 86, 141, 159, 230, 235, 242
Woods, Col. S.H. 243
    Miss 156
Wooler, Henry 117
Woolhope Naturalists Field Club 50
Worcester Royal Infirmary 1
workhouses 1, 101, 109, 117, 191, 219
World War I 121
World War II 91, 92-5, 168, 221-33
Wye Valley Nuffield Hospital 253

X rays 55, 56, 64, 65, 82, 83, 84, 95

Zair, A.H. 64, 159, 243